Evolution
and Genetics

THE

MODERN

THEORY

OF

EVOLUTION

Evolution
and Genetics

DAVID J. MERRELL

UNIVERSITY OF MINNESOTA

With illustrations by

OLIVIA JENSEN INGERSOLL

HOLT, RINEHART AND WINSTON
New York

LIBRARY OF CONGRESS CATALOG CARD NUMBER: 62-8420

2109502

PRINTED IN THE UNITED STATES OF AMERICA

Preface

The human species, in a remarkable manner, has become the dominant species on the earth. Man's range has expanded explosively out of the tropics, and as he has gained mastery over his competitors, his parasites, and his environment, human numbers have increased at an accelerating pace. These biological facts are of primary significance in the world of today. To understand them requires an understanding of the evolutionary forces that have been at work in the past and continue to work at present.

The study of evolution received its major impetus just over a century ago with the publication of Darwin's *Origin of Species* in 1859. Since then, great progress has been made in biology. Knowledge has accumulated so rapidly that the field has splintered into a number of subdisciplines. As specialization has increased, the need for a unifying principle in biology has grown. The most notable success in tying together the many threads of biological thought has been achieved by a return to the study of evolution. It is a return because, after the original impetus from Darwin's work had dwindled, a rather strong reaction against Darwinism developed early in this century. The validity of the theory of evolution was generally accepted by biologists, but the discoveries of the early geneticists seemed to cast considerable doubt on his theory of natural selection.

A reflection of the appraisal of Darwin at that time can be found in Nordenskiöld's *History of Biology* (1927). "To raise the theory of selection, as has often been done, to the rank of a 'natural law' comparable in value with the law of gravity established by Newton is, of course, quite irrational, as time has already shown: Darwin's theory of the origin of species was long ago abandoned. Other facts established by Darwin are all of second-rate value. But if we measure him by his influence on the general cultural development of humanity, then the proximity of his grave to Newton's is fully justified." However, further progress, particularly in the fields of genetics, systematics, and paleontology, has led to an increased understanding not only of evolution but of the mechanism by which it takes place.

The expanded theory of evolution that has been recently developed is sometimes known as neo-Darwinism, or as "the modern synthesis," and the theory of natural selection has proven to be more resilient than Darwin's critics supposed. Furthermore, the study of evolution has come to be a unifying force in biology, drawing together information from many disciplines into a comprehensive and comprehensible whole. At the present time, more research on evolutionary problems is being conducted than at any time since 1859.

It has become routine for biologists to preface their remarks about evolution with the statement, "Everyone now accepts the *fact* of evolution." However, my experience has been, in talking with a variety of audiences, that not everyone does accept evolution as a fact, even though they may have been exposed to the concept. Furthermore, since there are millions of people in many parts of the world who have never even heard of the theory of evolution, the supposition that everyone accepts it obviously needs some qualification. Because all mankind is caught up in the same evolutionary skein, it seems highly desirable that all of us should be made aware of this fact. If man continues to pursue his evolutionary future blindly, without awareness or regard for the forces at work, that future may be bedeviled by unnecessary hazards and hardships.

Doubts about the validity of evolution by intelligent and supposedly educated people are due in many cases to the fact that they have never really heard the evidence in its favor. The extent of this ignorance was most forcibly impressed on me during a recent talk with a group of high school biology teachers. As the discussion progressed, it became clear that at least half of this select group of teachers did not themselves believe in evolution, and thus it was a real problem for them to decide how to handle the subject in class. Their reactions made clear the need to continue presenting the case for evolution to new generations of students. For unless students, at some stage in their training, are given the opportunity to become acquainted with the nature, variety, and weight of the data concerning evolution, they are required to accept evolution on faith. It is, therefore, perhaps not surprising that people never exposed to the evidence may find other explanations more emotionally satisfying. Only after the facts have been reviewed and understood does the theory of evolution become inescapable. I have no particular desire to convert anyone to a belief in evolution, but at the same time I feel that even those who are unconvinced about evolution should be familiar with the evidence. At least then their beliefs will not be based on ignorance, and they will know exactly what it is that they do not believe.

For these reasons the first part of the book has been devoted to a consideration of the nature of the evidence for evolution. No more than a sampling of the wealth of material, of course, can be presented. It is hoped that for the great majority of readers this presentation will be sufficiently convincing. For those who remain in doubt as to the reality of evolution, the references open a number of paths from which any who follow them with an open mind can scarcely return unconvinced that evolution has occurred. The supplementary reading suggested at the end of each chapter can thus serve the dual purpose of documenting statements in the text and also of giving additional information to the student desirous of learning more about a particular topic. I have referred freely to the writings and opinions of many authors without citing or documenting the actual sources in the text. Since literature citations and footnotes can be a major source of distraction to the weak-willed reader, it seemed desirable to keep such diversions to a minimum so that the reader will be better able to follow the argument being presented. To those not cited, and thereby slighted, my apologies. The references, though not complete, should be a sufficient guide into any area in which further information or documentation is desired.

This book has been written primarily for those who wish to know more about the theory of evolution and the operation of evolutionary forces. The problem of discussing evolution is complicated by the fact that it must be taken up a piece at a time and fitted together like a jig-saw puzzle. Only when all of the pieces are together can the whole picture be fully appreciated. The discussion ranges over a wide variety of subjects, but an effort has been made to develop each topic in such a way that the reader can follow the argument with only a minimum of background. One of the major hurdles for the student of biology is the number of new terms that constantly appear. If he does not learn the vocabulary so that he can handle the biologists' jargon, he remains biologically illiterate. As an aid over this hurdle, terms are generally explained when first introduced, but a glossary is also included at the end for quick reference.

The modern theory of the mechanism of evolution is a genetic theory. Since without some understanding of genetics the modern theory of evolution is incomprehensible, it is essential to devote a section of the book to the fundamental principles of genetics. From the text the reader should be able to gain an understanding of the basic genetic principles, but if he becomes interested in pursuing the subject further, he should refer to the numerous excellent books in the field. Evolution is a population phenomenon and is best understood in terms of the genetics of populations. Population genetics requires the use of some mathematics, which, unfortunately, causes consternation for some students. However, only rather simple examples have been included, requiring at most a knowledge of elementary algebra. A dash of common sense and a little persistence in dealing with this material will be well rewarded in terms of the insight gained.

A biological approach has been used throughout the book, and no attempt has been made to explore the philosophical or religious implications of the theory of evolution. This approach is sometimes disturbing to students. However, just among the various Christian denominations, attitudes range from unqualified acceptance to complete rejection of evolution. Because of the diversity of opinion and belief, generalizations are virtually meaningless, and it seems wisest to encourage each student to reconcile his knowledge of evolution with his personal beliefs, if this is necessary.

I wish to acknowledge the inspiration of Dr. Dwight E. Minnich, who first encouraged me to undertake teaching a course in evolution, and of the many students whose interest has made this particular course such a pleasure to teach. The comments and suggestions of my colleagues at the University of Minnesota, James C. Underhill, Joseph G. Gall, John W. Hall, and Frank G. Nordlie, have been most helpful, but I, of course, am solely responsible for the final form of the book. In a work of this sort, covering as it does subjects ranging from the origin of life to cultural anthropology, choices must be made in matters of emphasis and interpretation. It is hoped that the net result is a reasonably balanced account of current thought on evolution.

My collaboration with Mrs. Olivia Jensen Ingersoll, whose imaginative drawings illustrate the book, of necessity was carried on at long range since her home is in Ohio. However, her competence, both as an illustrator and as a zoologist, greatly eased the problems involved. Finally, I wish to acknowledge the devoted assistance of my wife, Jessie, who assumed the onerous task of typing the manuscript.

D. J. M.

Minneapolis, Minnesota
January, 1962

Credits

The following illustrations are used with the kind permission of the authors and publishers listed below.

Fig. 1-2. Cott, H. B., 1940, *Adaptive coloration in animals,* Methuen and Co., Ltd.

Fig. 4-2. Simpson, G. G., 1951, *Horses,* Oxford University Press.

Fig. 8-1. The quail were very kindly made available by Dr. Dwain Warner, Curator of Birds, University of Minnesota Museum of Natural History.

Fig. 12-1. Baldwin, E., 1949, *An introduction to comparative biochemistry,* Cambridge University Press. (Redrawn)

Fig. 13-2. Lemche, H., 1957. "A new living deep-sea mollusc of the Cambro-Devonian class Monoplacophora," *Nature* 179(1):415.

Fig. 13-4. Ralph Buchsbaum.

Fig. 14-2. Fuller, H. B., and O. Tippo, 1949, *College botany,* Holt, Rinehart and Winston, Inc.

Fig. 17-1. Snyder, L. H., and P. R. David, 1957, *The principles of heredity,* 5th ed., D. C. Heath and Company.

Fig. 17-2. Srb, A., and R. D. Owen, 1952, *General genetics,* W. H. Freeman and Company.

Fig. 18-3. Wilson, C. L., and W. E. Loomis, 1957, *Botany,* rev. ed., Holt, Rinehart and Winston, Inc.

Fig. 21-1. Edmund Bert Gerard, Cinematographer, Great Neck, N. Y.

Fig. 23-2. Clausen, J., and W. M. Hiesey, 1958, *Experimental studies on the nature of species,* IV, Carnegie Institution of Washington.

Fig. 23-3. Müntzing, A., 1930, "Über Chromosomen-vermehrung in *Galeopsis*—Kreuzungen und ihre phylogenetische Bedeutung," *Hereditas* 14:155.

Fig. 25-1. Snyder, L. H., and P. R. David, 1957, *The principles of heredity,* 5th ed., D. C. Heath and Company. (Pictures from *The Cattleman*)

Fig. 28-1. Clausen, J., D. D. Keck, and W. M. Hiesey, 1947, "Heredity of geographically and ecologically isolated races," *Am. Naturalist* 81:114-123.

Fig. 28-2. Moore, J. A., 1949, "Patterns of evolution in the genus *Rana.*" In *Genetics, paleontology, and evolution,* Jepsen, G. L., E. Mayr, and G. G. Simpson, eds., Princeton University Press.

Fig. 29-2. Anderson, E., 1949, *Introgressive hybridization,* John Wiley and Sons.

Fig. 29-3. Manton, I., 1934, "The problem of *Biscutella laevigata,*" L. *Zeitschr. f. ind. Abst. n. Vererbungsl.* 67, Springer-Verlag, Heidelberg.

Fig. 31-4. Lack, D., 1947, *Darwin's finches,* Cambridge University Press.

Fig. 32-1. Begg, C. M. M., 1959, *Introduction to genetics,* The Macmillan Company.

Fig. 32-2. Stern, C., 1954, "Two or three bristles," *Am. Sci.* 42:284.

Fig. 32-3. Snyder, L. H., and P. R. David, 1957, *The principles of heredity,* 5th ed., D. C. Heath and Company. (Photograph by Dr. L. V. Domm)

Fig. 33-1. a, d, and e, Zoological Society of London. b, Walker, E. P., 1954, *The monkey book,* The Macmillan Company. c, Chicago Zoological Park, Brookfield, Ill.

Fig. 33-2. a and b, Walker, E. P., 1954, *The monkey book,* The Macmillan Company. c, National Zoological Park, Smithsonian Institution, Washington, D. C.

Figs. 33-6 and 33-8. Washburn, S. L., 1960, "Tools and human evolution," *Sci. American* 203(3) September 1960.

Fig. 33-7. a-e, Peabody Museum, Harvard University.

Fig. 34-1. Begg, C. M. M., 1959, *Introduction to genetics,* The Macmillan Company.

Fig. 34-2. Sax, K., 1950. "The effects of x-rays on chromosome structure," *J. Cell. Comp. Physiol.* 35, Suppl. 1.

Fig. 35-1. Sax, K., 1955, *Standing room only,* Beacon Press.

Fig. 35-2. *World population and resources,* 1955, P. E. P. 16, Queen Anne's Gate, London.

Fig. 35-3. Van Loon, H. W., 1932, *Van Loon's geography,* Simon and Schuster, Inc.

Contents

PART *IV*

Evolution and Man

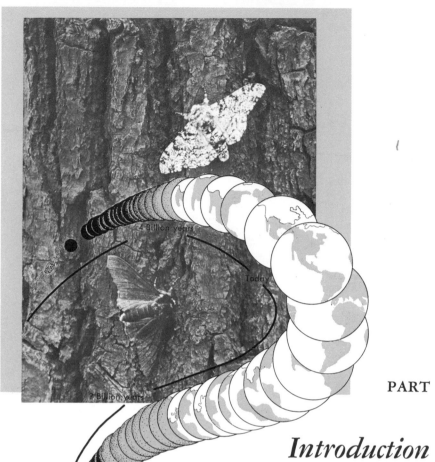

PART *I*

Introduction

CHAPTER 1

Adaptation

In this world are many strange and wondrous sights, but the one that most easily arouses a sense of the ludicrous nature of things is the slightly balding, slightly paunchy, slightly middle-aged father bouncing on his knee a baldish, pot-bellied infant, a replica of himself not only in general but in many particulars. This is the joke he has played on encroaching old age, and around the process by which it has come to pass has always hung an aura of mystery, myth, taboo, superstition, and mirth. Despite the intense interest man has always shown in his own self-duplication, only in the last century has any real progress been made toward an understanding of the process. The sight of doting parents and their offspring raises still broader questions, however. How far back into the mists of antiquity does this living chain extend? What was its beginning? And how far into the future will it persist? Here, too, knowledge has accumulated at an accelerating pace during the past century. In many ways, our knowledge and understanding of heredity and evolution have developed hand in hand, for the physical basis of heredity is also the physical basis of evolution. But man is only one species. He lives on a ball of matter spinning in space and populated by billions of individuals belonging to millions of different species, as diverse in nature as bacteria and orchids, honey bees and humans. This situation seems very improbable, for a living organism appears to contradict, even to defy, the ordinary laws of chemistry, physics, and thermodynamics. The question is, What is the origin, the history, and the future of this great variety of individualized protoplasm? We cannot hope at present to know all of the answers, but our knowledge has increased to the point where we now know something of what has happened in the past and of the mechanisms responsible for the changes that have occurred.

The physical evidence for the study of this question consists of the species of animals and plants now living and of the fossils, which are the remnants or traces of organisms that have lived in the past. For the moment, let us consider the living species. One feature common to the great variety of living things is that they are adapted for life in the environment in which they are found. Obviously, if they were not adapted to their environment, they would not be found there; they simply could not survive. However, each species is adapted to a somewhat different set of environmental conditions from every other species. Not only are fish found in water, monkeys in trees, and antelope on the prairie, but each different species of fish tends to have its own habitat, as any good fisherman (or ichthyologist, for that matter) will testify. Adaptation is so universal and so self-evident that we tend to overlook or to ignore it, but it is a basic biological fact. Each living organism has a particular set of adaptations peculiarly suited to its mode of life. In fact, the adaptations are so precise in so many cases that they appear exactly suited to the needs of the organism in its environment. A fish, for example, in order to move about in the water in which it lives, obviously needs appendages such as the fins. To speak of the "needs" of the organism, however, is to run the risk of being teleological. Such usage, which often is a reflection of a way of thinking, has considerably hampered the study of adaptation. Just because an organism is constructed in a certain way or behaves in a certain way is no indication that it necessarily has any recognition of its needs or that any conscious purpose or plan governs it. On the other hand, lack of recognition of its needs by the organism does not indicate a lack of functional significance in its structure or behavior. A fin *is* for swimming, and a wing for flying, entirely aside from the question of needs or cognition.

Types of Adaptation

Two general types of adaptation may be distinguished. One type might be called *individual adaptation,* by which an organism, through suitable modifications in its physiology, adjusts to environmental stresses. Fair-skinned people, for example, when exposed to sunlight, typically become "tanned." Even though this change is an individual response to a particular stimulus, it is ultimately under the control of that person's hereditary make-up or genotype, for not all people have the ability to form melanin in response to exposure to sunlight. Albinos and people with very light complexions may continue to sunburn despite continued exposure to the sun; the ability to tan is simply beyond the capacity of their genotypes. The discomfort of such people could be considered sufficient evidence of the adaptive value of the ability to tan, but it would be desirable to know more about the process. On the other hand, some human populations are much more heavily pigmented than others, the pigment developing even though the individuals may not be exposed to the sun. In the dark-skinned races, pigment is formed under the control of the genotype also, but no external stimulus is needed. In these races, *population adaptation* may be said to exist, for the whole population routinely has darkly pigmented skin. There seems little reason to doubt that the skin pigment of the dark-skinned races has adaptive value just as it does in the case of individual adaptation, but the exact nature of this adaptive value at present remains a matter of speculation. The two types of adaptation, individual and population, are rather different although both are under hereditary control. One of the more intriguing questions in evolutionary research is how individual adaptation may be transformed into population adaptation. It may seem to verge on the question of the inheritance of acquired characteristics but is nonetheless quite distinct from it.

Although each species is unique in its adaptations to its own particular physical and biological environment, nevertheless all species face essentially the same basic problems. The variety of different kinds of adaptations represent different solutions to these problems. For example, oxygen is required in the metabolism of fish and mammals (and most other species); the fish extract oxygen from the water through their gills, but the mammals use quite different structures—the lungs—to obtain oxygen from air. The basic problems confronting every species, if it is to continue to exist, are very simple: it must survive, and it must reproduce. In order to survive, an organism must obtain an adequate supply of food; it must have some measure of protection from other organisms, whether predators, competitors, or parasites; and it must make suitable adjustments to the existing physical conditions. Survival alone is not enough, however. If, at a given time, all the members of one species survived through maturity to old age without reproducing, that species would become extinct with that generation.

No adaptation is perfect. With the variety of functions required of the organism, the adaptations achieved must be, perforce, a compromise among all these functions. The organism is a complex bundle of adjustments to its neighbors of all degree and to its physical environment.

The Environment

The nature of the environment is worthy of comment, for it will emphasize the variety of adaptations required for survival and reproduction. The physical environment consists of some sort of substrate; this may be fresh or salt water, or land, or air, or, for the parasites, another organism. Fresh water alone represents a variety of substrates requiring somewhat different adaptations for survival—in lakes, rivers, streams, ponds, swamps, and so on—whereas each different species represents a different substrate for the parasites. Another limiting physical factor is temperature. Different species may have somewhat different ranges of temperature tolerance, but the actual range at which any life as we know it is possible is really rather narrow. Strangely enough, this range happens to coincide with existing temperatures on the earth. Other forces such as pressure and gravity are a constant part of the environment. Furthermore, sound waves, light waves, and chemical particles are constantly impinging upon the organism.

The biotic environment of an organism consists, first, of other members of the same species, which interact with each other in various ways. In relation to reproduction there may be courtship and care of the young. There may also be various group activities—colony formation or migration, for example—requiring some degree of cooperation. Competition between members of the same species may develop in the quest for food or in the establishment of nesting territories. Many adaptations appear to be related to these functions. Furthermore, the relations between different species may be as diverse as predation, parasitism, competition, and cooperation.

Adaptation in the Frog

Thus far, our discussion has been rather general, and it may be helpful to consider briefly the problems of adaptation as they have been solved by one species. The leopard frog, *Rana pipiens,* has been widely used in zoological laboratories in the United States. Because it is so familiar, the frog is especially suitable for reappraisal here in terms of its adaptations rather than of its organ systems. In so doing, we may seem to belabor the obvious.

To survive, the frog is confronted with the problem of finding and securing an adequate supply of food. To move about in this search, the frog has legs, which are adapted for swimming in water and for jumping on land. The webbed feet are obvious adaptations for swimming. However, since the legs function for locomotion in or on two media, they represent an adaptive compromise, and it is quite clear that the frog is not very efficient at moving about in either. His search for food is guided by the major sense organs of sight, hearing, smell, and taste, which serve as receptors of more or less distant stimuli. It is a rather remarkable fact, though you may not at first so consider it, that all of these major sense organs are localized in the head, which is at the front end of his bilaterally symmetrical body. (Bilateral symmetry—that is, an arrangement of the body into anterior and posterior ends, and dorsal and ventral surfaces—is an adaptation to an active life. Sessile species are generally radially symmetrical; that is, their body parts are arranged about a central axis.) It would seem quite a coincidence that these sense organs are so strategically placed at the anterior end, which is constantly probing into new parts of the environment. Imagine how much less useful these structures would be if arranged on the frog's posterior.

Once the food has been located, the mouth assumes the problem of securing it. The tongue, unlike man's, is attached at the front of the mouth cavity and is flicked out with speed and precision to pick off unwary insects that come within reach. The vomerine teeth, in the roof of the mouth, crush the insects before they pass into the digestive tract. In the digestive system, the food is broken down into molecules that can be absorbed through the walls of the intestine and transported by the circulatory system to the immediate vicinity of the individual living cells. The respiratory system is also tied in with the circulatory system so that the oxygen essential for the utilization of the food molecules during the metabolic activity of the cells is made available to them. The waste products of cellular metabolism are in turn removed by the circulatory system, carbon dioxide (CO_2) being eliminated primarily from the lungs and nitrogenous wastes by the kidneys. The frog's digestive system, respiratory system, circulatory system, and excretory system are fundamental adaptations for supplying the necessary metabolic raw materials to the living cells and removing the waste products after the cells have extracted energy and essential compounds from them. Without adaptations of this sort, multicellular life would not be at all possible.

Furthermore, the organism acts as an integrated whole, not merely as a collection of cells, tissues, and organs. This integration is due to chemical coordinating systems, mainly hormonal, and to the nervous system. As a result, the individual cells become interacting and interdependent parts of a well-integrated unit. These chemical and nervous mechanisms operate in such a way that even under stress a balanced internal environment is maintained. Maintenance of an internal dynamic equilibrium is called *homeostasis*.

There are several ways in which the frog secures some degree of protection from other organisms. The sense organs and the locomotor system obviously serve a dual purpose, in securing food and escaping predators. The dorsal placement of the eyes and nostrils is adaptive in that the frog can remain almost completely submerged in water, and yet it can breathe and see above the surface. Placement of the eyes in the skull is an adaptive feature, as can be easily observed by comparing the angles of vision in a carnivore like the cat and an herbivore such as the rabbit.

The coloration of the leopard frog has considerable protective value. The basic color is a cryptic green or greenish brown, matching the tall grass or weeded bank that is the frequent habitat of this species. By its ability to regulate the degree of dispersion of the pigment granules in its chromatophores, the frog is capable of considerable change in shade to match its background. Moreover, the outline of the body is broken up by the numerous spots on the skin. This so-called disruptive pattern destroys the visual impression that would otherwise be gained of the frog's size and shape, and it is especially effective when observed (or not observed) in the pattern of light and shadow created in a grassy meadow on a sunny morning. Even to details, the disruptive effect is much in evidence; the eye is masked to some extent by a dark line that seems to run through it, and the matching up of the spots on the upper and lower parts of the hind legs creates a series of dark bands running at right angles to the length of the long bones, disrupting the outline of these otherwise quite prominent appendages. It should be noted that all of this coloration is found only on the dorsal surfaces of the body; the ventral surfaces are creamy white. This pattern of dark above and light below is known as countershading, and its adaptive significance lies in the fact that the frog when seen from below in the water will be very light, matching the sky. (For a most interesting and authoritative account on the functional significance of animal coloration, see Cott's *Adaptive Coloration in Animals*.) In addition to its concealing function, the skin serves as a more or less effective barrier to infection by a variety of parasites and as a respiratory organ.

The frog is a rather stupid animal with quite stereotyped behavior. It escapes the notice of its predators by remaining motionless; if alarmed sufficiently, it gives a series of explosive leaps and then once again freezes. If it jumps into the water, it burrows into the mud or debris for concealment. These behavior patterns, though simple, are clearly adaptive for the protection of the frog from predators. However, leopard frogs appear to have a rather complex pattern of migratory behavior. In the spring they migrate to the breeding ponds, and then, after breeding, apparently move on to summer feeding territories. In the fall, as colder weather ensues, large-scale migrations to over-wintering sites in lakes and streams take place. These migratory patterns are clearly adaptive.

In winter, the air temperature drops below the range at which the frogs can remain active, and to survive, they burrow into the debris at the bottom of ponds and streams. Other controlling physical factors in the life of the frog include moisture. Though leopard frogs seem less closely tied to damp areas than most other amphibian species, it is clear that this species too may be subject to dehydration rather quickly. Certainly they are much less in evidence in open meadows on sunny, dry, and windy days than on cloudy and humid days.

Perhaps the most remarkable adaptations of all are those related to reproduction. Reproduction in the leopard frog occurs in the spring in rather shallow pools. The calling males congregate in large numbers at the breeding site. The females are attracted to the site, deposit their eggs while clasped in amplexus by the males, and depart. The physical and biological factors that initiate and control this elaborate series of events are in most instances matters of conjecture; for example, we do not know what determines the selection of the breeding site, which must not dry up before the tadpoles metamorphose. The obvious differences between males and females are not great, the nuptial pads and the song of the males during the breeding season being the most noticeable.

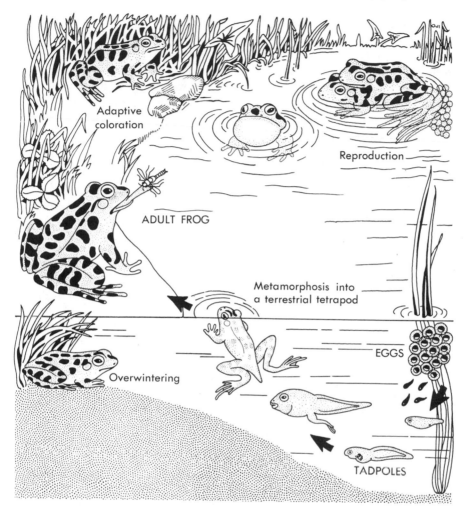

Fig. 1-1. Life cycle of the leopard frog, *Rana pipiens.*

At every stage in the life cycle (Fig. 1-1), adaptations appear. The egg mass of *pipiens* from the warm southern parts of the United States is rather flattened, whereas that of females from the northern states is globular; there is an obvious relation to the lower oxygen concentration in warm water as compared to cold. The eggs are countershaded. The larva that emerges is an aquatic animal, swimming with fins and respiring with gills. Unlike the adult, it is an herbivore, with its digestive tract correspondingly adapted for handling this different type of food. The remarkable series of changes known as metamorphosis then occurs, with the adult frog, a terrestrial tetrapod, the result.

These, then, are some of the adaptations in the frog; for the most part they are not particularly striking or unusual. The frog was chosen as an example to illustrate the fact that even the most familiar species is quite precisely adapted to its ecological niche. As species go, the leopard frog must be regarded as sort of a fringe dweller, firmly established neither in water nor on land. Yet in this marginal environment, which is its normal habitat, the frog has been quite successful by the only criterion we have for measuring biological success—that is, survival as a species. Mere survival may not seem at first glance to be a very lofty criterion by which to judge success, but at least it is objective. Certainly this evolutionary line has outlasted some more impressive and dominant species that have lived in the past, such as the mammoth, the saber-toothed tiger, and all of the dinosaurs.

Protective Coloration

The discussion of adaptation sometimes tends to dwell on the more spectacular types of adaptive changes, some of which—among them, protective coloration—are extremely fascinating. The adaptive value of animal colors has sometimes been doubted. For example, when the Nile catfish was found to show reversed countershading—that is, the dorsal surface light and the ventral surface dark—the whole theory of countershading was brought under suspicion. However, the concept was doubly strengthened when it was discovered that this fish characteristically swims upside down.

Not only are colors frequently adapted for concealment of the organism, but the animal may enhance the protective value of its coloration by its behavior. Certain moths are cryptically colored to match the bark on which they ordinarily rest, and in addition they hold their wings flat against the bark, which eliminates the shadow, and position their bodies in such a manner that their pattern best matches the pattern of the bark (Fig. 1-2).

The coloration of some animals is adapted not so much for concealment by blending in with the background of its habitat as it is for disguise, by which they resemble some other object in their environment. A number of species—for example, butterflies and other insects, fish, and frogs—resemble leaves; still others resemble twigs or lichens. A most peculiar group are the geometrid moths that resemble bird droppings, especially startling when they fly away. There is much in common between the desert lizard, which lures unwary insects to their deaths because the corner of its mouth when opened resembles a small red desert flower, and the anglerfish, which has a dorsal spine modified into a lure that dangles before its gaping mouth.

In some species the so-called aposematic colors serve as advertisements rather than as disguise or concealment. The skunk, with his striking black and white colors, is not easily missed nor is he easily mistaken for any other species. The white flag of the Virginia white-tailed deer appears to serve as a warning

Fig. 1-2. Willow beauty moth *(Boarmia gemmaria)* resting on bark. Concealment is achieved by the similarity between the wing pattern and the bark, and is further enhanced by the horizontal positioning of the body and the elimination of shadows from the wings. (Courtesy of Cott.)

signal. In birds, the same colors used by the male as a part of the courtship display may also be used in a threat display toward other males invading his territory.

The insects with stings, such as bees, wasps, and hornets, are usually strikingly colored black and yellow and tend to some extent to resemble each other. This type of mimicry, in which a number of dangerous or unpalatable species resemble one another, is known as Müllerian mimicry. This is distinct from Batesian mimicry, in which the harmless species resemble the harmful or nauseous types. A classical example of mimicry is the resemblance of the Viceroy butterfly (*Limenitis archippus*) to the Monarch (*Danaus plexippus*). The Viceroy is colored orange and black like the Monarch and is quite different from the other members of its own genus, which are black with white spots. Originally thought to be a case of Batesian mimicry, this example may not fit either classical pattern, for recent evidence has shown that the Viceroy, though more palatable to birds than the Monarch, is eaten somewhat less often than other butterflies. The whole subject of mimicry is of extreme interest, and much work remains to be done to clarify many of the questions in this field.

Examples of remarkable adaptations could be cited almost endlessly, but only one more will be mentioned. A certain shrike in Ceylon (*Hemipus picatus*) builds its nest on the bare limbs of trees. The n· .t is so constructed that it resembles a knot, and is cunningly camouflaged with its of bark and lichen to heighten the effect. The young birds are cryptically col· ·ed so that they blend with the nest. Most remarkable of all, however, is the fact that the birds sit facing each other with their eyes partially closed and their beaks pointing upward and almost touching. The total effect of the cooperative efforts of parents and young is that of a knot on a dead branch with just a small stub of a broken branch protruding from the knot. To visualize how these complex behavior patterns became incorporated into the hereditary make-up of this species, as they clearly must be, is to stretch the imagination.

Adaptation in Man

Although we tend to think of man as having mastered his environment, actually he is adapted to rather specific environmental conditions, and his mastery is due to his skill in modifying the environment to approximate his needs rather than in broadening his environmental tolerances. Man is a terrestrial animal, and was undoubtedly confined to the tropics and subtropics until his relatively recent discovery of the use of fire and clothing. His erect bipedal locomotion is adapted to life in relatively open country rather than to heavily forested or mountainous regions. His lungs enable him to extract oxygen from the air, and he requires an adequate daily supply of fresh drinking water. Though an omnivore, he is ultimately dependent on green plants for all of his food. This analysis could be extended, but it should suffice to demonstrate that man, too, makes well-defined demands on his environment.

SUGGESTED READING

Carpenter, G. D. H., and E. B. Ford, 1933. *Mimicry*. London: Methuen.
Caspari, E., 1951. "On the biological basis of adaptedness," *Am. Scientist, 39*:441-451.

Cott, H. B., 1940. *Adaptive coloration in animals.* New York: Oxford University Press.

Emerson, A. E., 1960. "The evolution of adaptation in population systems," *Evolution after Darwin,* Vol. I, *The evolution of life,* S. Tax, ed. Chicago: University of Chicago Press.

Huxley, J. S., 1943. *Evolution. The modern synthesis.* New York: Harper.

Muller, H. J., 1950. "Evidence of the precision of genetic adaptation," *Harvey Lectures, 43:165-229.*

Portmann, A., 1959. *Animal camouflage,* A. J. Pomerans, tr. Ann Arbor: University of Michigan Press.

Simpson, G. G., 1953. *The major features of evolution.* New York: Columbia University Press.

Stephenson, E. M., and C. Stewart, 1955. *Animal camouflage,* 2d ed. London: Black.

Waddington, C. H., 1960. "Evolutionary adaptation," *Evolution after Darwin,* Vol. I, *The evolution of life,* S. Tax, ed. Chicago: University of Chicago Press.

CHAPTER 2

Evolutionary Thought before Darwin

Although thought on the origin of species has apparently preoccupied men of almost every culture, much of the speculation has been of such a nature that it must be regarded as based largely on myth, superstition, or vague philosophical ideas rather than on careful observation and the accumulation of facts. Furthermore, the modern reader may read into the statements of earlier writers things they did not intend to say. In this short review we obviously cannot hope to trace the complete history of the development of the evolution concept. Instead a sampling of the ideas advanced at different periods will be presented in an effort to convey some of the flavor of the thinking of different ages.

Greek Thought

Among the Greeks, Anaximander, who lived in the sixth century B.C. (611-547 B.C.) merits attention, for he attempted to explain the origin of the universe on a rational basis rather than by myths or legends. He visualized all things as having come from a primordial fluid or slime to which they ultimately return. Living things, both plant and animal, were formed as this mud dried. This concept appears to be one of the earliest known theories of spontaneous generation. Man himself was first shaped like a fish and lived in the water. Later, when he became capable of terrestrial life, he burst forth from his fishlike capsule

14

like a butterfly from its chrysalis and assumed human form and a life on land. This theory was crude, yet the implication of evolution is clear.

Xenophanes (576?-480 B.C.), believed to have been a pupil of Anaximander, is the first person known to have recognized that fossils were the remnants of once-living organisms and that marine fossils on land indicated that the sea formerly covered the earth.

Empedocles in the fifth century B.C. (495-435 B.C.) stated that the four elements were air, earth, fire, and water, and that these elements were acted upon by two forces, love and hate, which caused their union or separation. He also suggested that plants had arisen first, and that animals were later formed from them. The germ of the idea of natural selection was contained in his belief that the parts of animals were formed separately and then united at random by the triumph of love over hate. Most would then be monsters and unviable, but a few could survive. He and many others, both before him and for centuries afterward, believed in the possibility of spontaneous generation of life from nonliving materials, and thus settled, in rather simple fashion, the question of the origin of life.

Aristotle (384-322 B.C.), whose ideas dominated biological thought for well over a thousand years, was the greatest of the Greek men of science. He was a vitalist, believing that living things were animated by a vital force or guiding intelligence quite different from anything to be found in nonliving matter. In this idea he was preceded by Anaxagoras (500-428 B.C.), but to Aristotle this internal force became a perfecting principle, operating constantly to improve or perfect the living world. Growing out of this concept was his ladder of nature ("Scala naturae") or chain of being in which he arranged living things on a scale of perfection. The succession ranged from inanimate matter through the lower plants to the higher animals on a single scale with man, at the top, being the most nearly perfect. Aristotle apparently never interpreted the chain as possibly suggesting that each group had evolved from the one below it. He believed in spontaneous generation not only for smaller animals but for larger ones such as frogs and snakes. He thought that the inheritance of mutilations was rather common, but rejected the idea of the inherited effects of use and disuse. Adaptation to him was the result neither of the survival of accidental fitness, as it was for Empedocles, nor of functional modifications but rather of the action of the perfecting principle. Thus Aristotle did not add in any direct way to the development of modern evolutionary thought despite his many contributions to biology. Since he remained the most authoritative source of biological information for so long a period, it could be argued that some of his theories actually hampered the development of the theory of evolution. The difficulties, however, lay less with Aristotle than with the nature of the times that followed him.

For centuries after Aristotle little progress was made toward a better understanding of evolution, for the spirit of inquiry that characterized the Greeks gradually withered away and died. Epicurus (341-270 B.C.) is worth mentioning, not because he added significantly to evolutionary thought but because he attempted to explain the world and the universe as natural phenomena governed by natural causes. As a materialist or mechanist, he tried to combat the superstitious beliefs in supernatural forces ruling the universe. In this effort he opposed the Aristotelian argument of teleology, or the grand design or purposefulness of events, which was widely accepted at the time. As a part of his philosophy he adopted the atomic theory of Democritus (460?-362? B.C.).

The Decline of Science

The Roman poet Lucretius (99-55 B.C.) was a follower of Epicurus, and in his famous work, *On the Nature of Things (De Rerum Natura),* summed up most of the Greek non-Aristotelian thought. Lucretius is significant, not for any particular advance in evolutionary thought, but because he marked the end of a period of thought, and through his work preserved the atomic theory during the Dark and Middle Ages and gave a forceful restatement of the mechanistic position. In his rejection of Aristotle's teleology, he also rejected much of the rest of Aristotle's work, and thus did not achieve a complete synthesis of the best of Greek thought.

The Roman Pliny (A.D. 23-79) compiled a tremendous store of information and misinformation in his *Natural History,* which served as man's primary source of knowledge about natural history for nearly 1500 years. He was not primarily an investigator, however, and his uncritical recitation of the work of others added nothing new. Galen (A.D. 130-200), the last important biologist of antiquity and the personal physician of Marcus Aurelius, made investigations in anatomy and physiology that were accepted as authoritative for centuries, but he, too, made no direct contribution to evolutionary theory. Thus, at the close of the classical period some few ideas that had a bearing on evolution had been expressed, but the concept was far from its modern form.

Although the decline of ancient science has at times been attributed to the rise of Christianity, this seems hardly to have been the case. The decline set in long before the birth of Christ and even at the time of Galen's death, in A.D. 200, the Christians were only a small group without influence. Preoccupation with spiritual matters did little to advance science, and active conflicts did develop later, but no one church can claim any monopoly on this sort of opposition. For centuries the churches were the primary centers of learning. Such leaders among the early Christians as St. Augustine (354-430) and much later St. Thomas Aquinas (1225-1275), who has remained an authority of the Church, rejected a literal interpretation of the story of special creation in Genesis and suggested instead an allegorical naturalistic interpretation patterned after Aristotle. However, throughout the Dark Ages no progress was made in the development of the theory of evolution. The rise of Scholasticism in the thirteenth century led to the study of the writings of the ancients on nature but to little study of nature itself. Much of this material was obtained from translations of works in Arabic, many of which had in turn been derived from the Greek. In the reaction by the Church in 1209 against Arabian science and philosophy, the study of Aristotle was also banned, but this interdiction was later relaxed. This period marked the beginning of the trend toward a literal interpretation of the seven days of creation, a trend that predominated for centuries. The Spanish Jesuit Suarez (1548-1617) was among those who argued strongly in favor of a literal interpretation of Genesis and refuted Augustine and Thomas Aquinas. The result was that for three centuries, from the sixteenth to the middle of the nineteenth, Special Creation was official Church doctrine even though it was a departure from the beliefs of some of the earlier leaders of Christianity. Diversity of opinion was denounced as heresy, and free discussion of the concept of evolution carried with it the risk of reprimand or excommunication by the Church even up to the time of Buffon in the late eighteenth century. Whether this attitude aided or hindered the development of the theory of evolution is hard to say, but it did play a significant part in the history of the concept.

The Renaissance

The revival of the classical art and learning of the Greeks and Romans, which was known as the Renaissance, took place during the fourteenth, fifteenth, and sixteenth centuries. This development, in turn, led to a rebirth in the spirit of inquiry; the Renaissance was not, however, marked by any notable progress on the question of the origin of species. Leonardo da Vinci (1452-1519) realized that the fossil marine shells that he found in the Apennine mountains indicated that they must once have been covered by the sea, but he did not develop the idea in relation to biological evolution. Similarly, Cesalpino (1519-1603) suggested that flower petals were modified leaves, another concept that could have led to the theory of evolution. Most of the naturalists of the time were Encyclopedists who made every effort to collect all the known facts about living things. The discovery by Harvey (1578-1657) of the circulation of the blood in a sense marks the transition from the biology of the ancients to modern experimental biology.

The Natural Philosophers

In the seventeenth and eighteenth centuries a number of men now known as the natural philosophers tried to develop unified systems of thought by which they could interpret the universe. Since life is a part of the universe, biological matters were included in their schemes of things. Although their interests were not always primarily biological, they did make some advances in evolutionary thought. We will mention here just some of the biological insights of a few of these men. Francis Bacon (1561-1626) called upon men to seek knowledge by observation, experiment, and inductive reasoning, and to free themselves from both Scholasticism and Aristotelean philosophy. He strongly urged that the variations in nature should be studied and their causes determined. Furthermore, he pointed out that artificial selection among these variations could be used to cause species to change and that transitional forms exist in nature. Although his examples were somewhat farfetched—he suggested, for example, that flying fishes were intermediate between fishes and birds, and bats between birds and quadrupeds—the fact remains that even at the opening of the seventeenth century the question of the fixity of species was being raised.

Bacon proposed methods by which the nature of the universe could be determined, but Descartes (1596-1650) was the pioneer among the systematic philosophers who speculated on the nature of the system itself. Guarded in his expression, he postulated that the universe could be explained on physical principles. This mechanistic approach had a great impact on biology, especially since it came just after Harvey's success in explaining the circulation of the blood in physical terms. Descartes was circumspect in presenting his ideas out of fear of offending the Church, and his writings on physiology, which became the foundations of modern physiology, were withheld from publication until after his death. Since he spoke in terms of the evolution of the universe, and life was a part of this system, the evolution of life was more or less indirectly included.

Leibnitz (1646-1716) had a better scientific background than his predecessors, for he understood the nature and origin of fossils, had extensive knowledge of plant and animal classification and of comparative anatomy, and was familiar with the wonders revealed by the recently discovered microscope. His doctrine of continuity applied to life was still another revival of the Aristotelean chain of being, but it did not necessarily lead him to the concept of evolution. He did, however, speculate on the relationship between the fossil ammonites and the living nautilus and even suggested that major changes of habitat might cause changes in animal species. He stated that his doctrine of continuity led to the idea that intermediate species should exist, but he shied away from the thought of species intermediate between man and the apes, saying that if they existed, it must be in another world. Kant (1724-1804), who has often been cited as a predecessor of Darwin, was undoubtedly familiar with the suggestion that species change but he apparently never embraced the idea of evolution completely.

Biological Research and Writings

Just as the natural philosophers influenced the thought and direction of research of the biologists of their day, they, in turn, were influenced by the advances being made. One such advance was the development of a system of classification for plants and animals. The foremost predecessor of Linnaeus (1707-1778), who is universally regarded as the father of the modern binomial system of nomenclature, was John Ray (1627-1705), an English naturalist. Ray wrote a number of systematic works, primarily on plants but also on animals, that represented major advances toward the "natural system" of classification, which takes into account all known similarities and differences. It was Ray who first clearly defined the species concept as being related to community of descent and inter-fertility rather than to fixity of type, but he did not extend this idea in the direction of evolution. Linnaeus himself in the tenth edition (1758) of his *Systema Naturae* established the foundation on which taxonomy has since been built. His scheme was a branching one, rather than a chain or ladder form, and living things were named according to genus and species—man, for example, being *Homo sapiens*. Althought he developed a branching system, Linnaeus at first believed in the fixity of species; as his experience broadened, however, he came in later editions to accept the possibility of evolution, at least within the genus, due either to hybridization or the effects of environment.

The work of de Maupertius (1698-1759) has recently been rescued from an undeserved obscurity. Eminent in his own day, he aroused the wrath of Voltaire, whose bitter mockery has undoubtedly colored the opinions of posterity. His arguments against the preformation doctrine in embryology preceded those of Wolff by fifteen years. Moreover, he developed a particulate theory of heredity based on experiments in animal breeding and investigations of human heredity, applying probability theory to his findings a century before Mendel. In addition to foreshadowing nearly all aspects of Mendelian genetics, he developed a theory of evolution based on mutation, selection, and geographic isolation. In this work he was so far ahead of his time that it is perhaps not surprising that his theories were not understood or appreciated.

The evolutionary writings of Buffon (1707-1788), one of the most influential biologists of the eighteenth century, have been variously interpreted—perhaps because they were so widely scattered among his extensive works. There can be little doubt that Buffon influenced the thinking of his successors about evolution, but it is not entirely clear whether he himself ever developed a consistent theory of evolution in which he believed wholeheartedly. One factor was his concern not to arouse the displeasure of the ecclesiastical authorities. However, he did state parts of the theory of organic evolution in considerable detail, and his writings thus served as the starting point for much of the subsequent work. Among his contributions were several of significance. He anticipated Malthus, concerning the relation between population and food supply. He called attention to the fundamental similarities between animals of quite different species, thus giving impetus to the study of comparative anatomy, now a cornerstone in the evidence for evolution. His recognition of variation within species and of the possibility of gradual change within species giving rise to new varieties seems very modern. The similarities between apes and men, the horse and the ass, made him raise the question of their relations to one another. His suggestion that the apes and the ass were degenerate types led to the idea of a common ancestry. He understood the significance of fossils and believed that the time scale needed to be greatly extended beyond the commonly accepted scale of his day. These and many other portions of his works indicate the modern lines along which his thinking was progressing. On the other hand, many passages could be cited to indicate that he believed in the immutability of species, a belief that grew from his use of hybrid sterility as the criterion for delimiting the species. Within the species, he thought change was possible, but, not visualizing a mechanism by which sterility might arise during evolution, he was more or less forced to argue against large-scale evolution. Buffon's writings contain contradictions, but they nevertheless were most influential in their impact on subsequent generations.

Going back in time, we find a number of speculative authors dealing with evolution, of whom we shall mention just one. De Maillet (1656-1738) in *Telliamed* drew together from the science of his day many threads to weave his theories. His unorthodox views were attributed to an Indian philosopher, "Telliamed" (De Maillet spelled backward). Perhaps his major contribution was his clear statement on the nature and origin of fossils, about which varied opinions were still held. In his view, the gradual drying up of the seas over long periods of time was responsible for marine fossils in the mountains and could also explain the similarities between aquatic and terrestrial forms, terrestrial species having been transformed from marine animals trapped in marshes. Many species undoubtedly failed to make the transition, he thought, but from the successful ones the land animals and birds arose. When he cited specific cases, however, he was not so cogent, for he derived birds from flying fish, and men and women from mermen and mermaids. Thus, he entangled facts with myths and legends, and his real contributions in the interpretation of fossils and rock stratification came under suspicion.

The uniformitarianism of James Hutton (1726-1797) postulated that the ordinary forces of wind, water, heat, cold, and so forth, that we observe today are the same forces that worked to reshape and restructure the earth's surface in the past, and hence no mysterious or supernatural phenomena were involved in these changes. If this were the case, Hutton reasoned, the earth's age must be much greater than previously imagined and the various catastrophic theories must be wrong. William Smith (1769-1839) was primarily responsible for recognizing that each of the different layers or strata of rock has its own characteristic types of fossils and that the lower the strata, the less the fossils resemble living forms. Charles Lyell (1797-1875) in his *Principles of Geology* established the science of geology in its modern form. This work, published at the time of Darwin's voyage on the *Beagle*, was of great importance to the development of Darwin's ideas. One of the major effects of the development of geology on the theory of evolution was that it showed the existence of a vast span of time during which evolution could have taken place.

Erasmus Darwin (1731-1802), the grandfather of Charles, is noteworthy not only for that fact but also because in *Zoonomia* he gave the first clear statement of the theory of the inheritance of acquired characteristics, according to which the effects wrought by the environment on the organism are thought to be transmissible to the offspring. This theory was more completely developed by Lamarck (1744-1829), with whose name it is usually associated (Fig. 2-1).

Fig. 2-1. Lamarck.

Lamarck's early years were spent in military service until ill health forced him to resign. An interest in botany, acquired while stationed in Monaco, led him to study medicine, of which botany was then an important part. A book on the flora of France established his reputation, won him the friendship of Buffon and other biologists, and eventually gained him a post as botanist at the Jardin du Roi. The reforms touched off by the French Revolution included the ouster of men who had previously been leaders in biology, and when two new chairs in zoology were created, the two most suitable candidates were Lamarck, a botanist nearing fifty, and St. Hilaire, a mineralogist. They apparently decided to split the animal kingdom between them, Lamarck taking the invertebrates and St. Hilaire the vertebrates. The most remarkable aspect of this story is that both men went on to distinguished careers in their new fields.

In *Philosophie Zoologique* (1809) Lamarck wrote more extensively about the evidence for evolution than had anyone prior to that time. His suggested mechanism for evolution was the inheritance of acquired characteristics. He believed that the activity of an animal enhanced the development of the more frequently used structures, producing modifications that were inherited; lack of use led to degenerative changes, which were also inherited. St. Hilaire, in supporting Lamarck, stressed the direct effects of the environment as causes of hereditary change, but Lamarck accepted this theory only in plants. An animal's need for a structure might also lead to its development—the long neck of a giraffe, for example, being the result of constant stretching over many generations. Thus, use and disuse, need, and the direct effects of the environment have come to be considered as basic concepts in the theory of the inheritance of acquired characteristics.

Unfortunately, despite its many appealing features, no critical evidence has ever been produced in favor of Lamarckianism. Nevertheless, this theory has been made the official theory of heredity in the Soviet Union under the name of Michurinism. The rise to power of Lysenko, which began in the early 1930s and became complete in 1948 with the abolition of teaching and research in Mendelian genetics, is a most unusual story. The attack was basically political, and the geneticists as well as their science were made to suffer. Despite its political success, Lamarck's theory of the inheritance of acquired characteristics still remains to be demonstrated experimentally, for Lysenko's experiments lack adequate controls, do not involve strains of known ancestry, and are not treated statistically at all.

Lamarck's ideas on evolution were subjected to forceful criticism by Cuvier (1769-1832), who was virtually a scientific dictator in France with unparalleled political and scientific influence. Cuvier is generally considered to be the father of two sciences, paleontology and comparative anatomy. However, even though these two fields now furnish some of the most impressive evidence available on the course of evolution, Cuvier's work led him to believe in the fixity of species and to deny that evolution gave a satisfactory interpretation of his findings. He recognized that different rock strata contained different types of fossils, but attributed the gaps in the record to a series of catastrophes, following which immigration of different species from other areas repopulated the devastated regions. He believed the last such catastrophe to have been the flood recorded in Genesis. His followers carried his ideas one step further and postulated that successive creations were responsible for the new kinds of species found after each catastrophe. Although his active opposition to Lamarck and St. Hilaire certainly hampered the development and acceptance of the theory of evolution, nevertheless in one respect Cuvier was of great significance to subsequent work. St. Hilaire supported the concept of the unity of type among all animal species—the old idea of the scale of being or ladder of nature that can be traced all the way back to Aristotle. In particular, he compared the cephalopod mollusks, such as the squid, with the vertebrates. In the controversy that broke into the open between St. Hilaire and Cuvier in 1830, Cuvier conclusively demonstrated that no such unity existed and thus cleared the ground for the branching system of divergent evolution. Whereas St. Hilaire (and Lamarck) were right in principle about evolution and wrong in detail, Cuvier was wrong in principle but right in detail about the data drawn from comparative anatomy. Since his views prevailed on both subjects, the evolution theory undeniably suffered.

Thus the idea of evolution—that species change—was clearly not entirely original with Charles Darwin. Nor, as Darwin recorded in an introductory historical sketch to the *Origin of Species,* was he the first to propose the theory of natural selection as the mechanism of evolution. Several of his predecessors deserve mention. An expatriate royalist American physician, William Wells (1757-1817), appears to have been the first to enunciate the principle of natural selection in a reasonably modern form, in a paper entitled "An account of a white female, part of whose skin resembles that of a Negro" read in 1813 but generally ignored at the time. Another of Darwin's predecessors whom he also apparently overlooked was Patrick Matthew. In this case, Darwin could probably be excused, for Matthew's views on natural selection were published in the appendix of a work entitled *Naval Timber and Arboriculture.* Yet Matthew, in his quest for recognition, called attention to his priority over Darwin in the title pages of his subsequent works. Recently, still another candidate for the honor of discovering natural selection has been unearthed in the person of Edward Blyth (1810-1873). It has been suggested that Darwin was less than completely candid in disclosing the extent of his debt to his predecessors, although to what extent this criticism is valid may be very difficult to determine. Even though it may be established that Darwin had read the papers of such men as Blyth and Matthew, it would be difficult if not impossible to learn whether he consciously drew on them at the time he achieved his great synthesis. Certainly his conduct toward Alfred Russell Wallace was always both proper and generous.

The book *The Vestiges of the Natural History of Creation* was anonymously published by Robert Chambers (1802-1871) in 1844 and went through ten editions in nine years. Since Chambers was an amateur scientist, his book was filled with errors, and scientists generally attacked it bitterly, an attack in which they were joined by the clergy. Their vehemence seemed to stimulate interest in the book rather than to kill it, however. The book showed that Chambers was familiar with the works of geologists such as Hutton and Smith and of such biologists as Buffon, Erasmus Darwin, Lamarck, St. Hilaire, and Cuvier. From them he drew his arguments in favor of cosmic and biological evolution as opposed to special creation. The book was not significant for originality but rather for the controversy and interest it aroused in the subject of evolution. Much of the ire that might have broken over Darwin's head had already been spent on Chambers. That the idea of evolution did not lack influential support even in the 1850s just prior to publication of the *Origin of Species* is indicated by the 1852 essay of Herbert Spencer (1820-1903) called "The Development Hypothesis." In it for the first time the word "evolution" was used in the general sense in which it is used today. Thus it should be clear that the theories of Darwin and Wallace that struck with such impact in 1859 had a long period of development prior to the synthesis set forth in the *Origin of Species*.

SUGGESTED READING

Barlow, N., ed., 1958. *The autobiography of Charles Darwin 1809-1882*. London: Collins.

Carter, G. S., 1957. *A hundred years of evolution*. London: Sidgwick and Jackson.

Darwin, C., 1839. *The voyage of the Beagle*. New York: Bantam Books (1958).

———, 1872. *On the origin of species*. New York: Mentor Books (1958).

———, and A. R. Wallace, 1958. *Evolution by natural selection*. New York: Cambridge University Press.

Eiseley, L., 1958. *Darwin's century*. Garden City, New York: Doubleday.

———, 1959. Charles Darwin, Edward Blyth, and the theory of natural selection. Proc. Amer. Philos. Soc. *103:*94-158.

Glass, B., O. Temkin, and W. Straus, Jr., eds., 1959. *Forerunners of Darwin. 1745-1859*. Baltimore: Johns Hopkins University Press.

Grant, V., 1956. "The development of a theory of heredity," *Am. Scientist*, 44:158-179.

Greene, J. C., 1960. *The death of Adam*. Ames: Iowa State College Press.

Huxley, J. S., 1949. *Soviet genetics and world science*. London: Chatto and Windus.

Irvine, W., 1955. *Apes, angels, and Victorians*. New York: McGraw-Hill.

Lovejoy, H. O., 1953. *The great chain of being*. Cambridge, Massachusetts: Harvard University Press.

Moore, R., 1953. *Man, time, and fossils*. New York: Knopf.

Nordenskiöld, E., 1928. *The history of biology*, L. B. Eyre, tr. New York: Knopf.

Osborn, H. F., 1929. *From the Greeks to Darwin*, 2d ed. New York: Scribner's.

Singer, C., 1959. *A history of biology*, 3d ed. New York: Abelard-Schuman.

CHAPTER 3

Darwin and
after Darwin

On February 12, 1809, two of the greatest figures of the nineteenth century were born, Abraham Lincoln and Charles Darwin. The circumstances surrounding the events could hardly have been less similar. Lincoln's start came in a backwoods log cabin, whereas Darwin was the son of a successful, well-to-do physician, Robert Darwin, who had married a girl of the famed Wedgewood pottery family. Thus, his family was doubly well off financially, and Charles later further insured his financial status by marrying his first cousin, another Wedgewood. As he put it in his autobiography, "I have had ample leisure from not having to earn my own bread." This, then, is one route to making great scientific discoveries, but it should be noted that the names of many others as well off financially as Darwin are now lost in obscurity.

Darwin was quite a normal boy. He liked to fish and hunt, to collect almost anything, but not to attend school. His training at Dr. Butler's school consisted of classics exclusively, and he was considered by both his teachers and his father as a little below average in intelligence. His liking for mathematics and chemistry, and his interests in collecting insects and minerals were not satisfied in school. It seemed logical that he should follow in the footsteps of his father and grandfather before him and study medicine. For this purpose, he went to Edinburgh, but soon dropped this course of study. A major reason was his revulsion at some of the more gory and hideous scenes a medical man was expected to endure in those days before anesthesia. During his stay in Edinburgh he became acquainted with people who were interested in geology and natural history, and his own interests were aroused to the point where he took courses at the University in these subjects. Unfortunately, as too often happens, formal instruction quickly killed this interest.

His father, apparently fearing that his son was never going to amount to anything and seeking some sort of respectable career for him, then suggested that he go to Cambridge to study for the clergy. Charles was quite amenable to this suggestion, and went to Cambridge where, in due course, he received his degree, having achieved no particular distinction and having made no great efforts in his studies. In fact, most of his energies were devoted elsewhere, for he was an ardent hunter and horseman, and in the evenings, in a gentlemanly way, he sowed his wild oats, drinking and playing cards. Small wonder that his father thought that the cloak of respectability of a clergyman might help to keep his son from becoming a well-to-do ne'er-do-well.

At this time his scientific inclinations were slightly manifest in his attendance at lectures in botany by Henslow, in his beetle collecting (he once was confronted by three unusual specimens and freed a hand to try for the third by tossing one into his mouth), and in his friendship with distinguished scientists such as Henslow and the geologist Sedgwick. This last aspect of his behavior was perhaps the most unusual. It is rather rare for a young college student to seek friendship among the professors, and it is perhaps even more rare to find the professors accepting as a friend one who had so far shown no particular promise. It is to their credit that the professors apparently saw something in him. Out of his friendship with the botanist Henslow came the event that changed and shaped the entire subsequent course of Darwin's life, for Henslow recommended him for the position of naturalist without pay on the *Beagle* (Fig. 3-1), a ship that was to make a long cruise around the world, charting many little-known areas (Fig. 3-2). After some discussion with his family, Charles accepted, and his career in the clergy was never again seriously considered.

The voyage lasted five years, for the *Beagle* made many long stops, and much of the time was spent in South American waters. Darwin's account of his adventures, *The Voyage of the Beagle,* is a most fascinating and readable book, much more so than the closely argued *Origin of Species.* It is obvious that his experiences on this trip started the chain of thought that ultimately led to his theories of evolution. The course of his work gave him his first insight into the relations between species. He observed at first hand how species changed as one traveled from north to south in South America; he observed the character of island faunas; and he saw the relations between the fossils he discovered and the existing species in the same areas. He not only observed, but he made extensive and systematic collections of living and fossil materials. The facts of species

Fig. 3-1. The *Beagle,* the vessel in which Charles Darwin sailed around the world.

variation, of geographic distribution, and of the fossil record were almost forced to his attention.

Unfortunately, the weak stomach that had contributed to the ending of his medical studies still plagued him, and he was seasick a good part of this five-year period. In fact, through the rest of his life, he was unable to stand any sort of excitement, for it almost inevitably led to digestive disturbances. Even having friends for dinner and a quiet talk afterward was enough to lead to discomfort and sleeplessness. A modern diagnosis would probably suggest that his troubles were psychosomatic, but nevertheless they were severe and sometimes incapacitated him for months at a time in later life.

Upon his return to England in 1836, Darwin started to work on his collections and to write up the results of his travels. At the same time he began to collect all kinds of data bearing on the question of the transmutation of species. He carefully recorded all of the arguments both for and against, being especially careful to put down quickly those against, for he found that he could very conveniently forget them. In October 1838 he read for the first time Malthus' "Essay on Population," an excerpt from which is found in Ap-

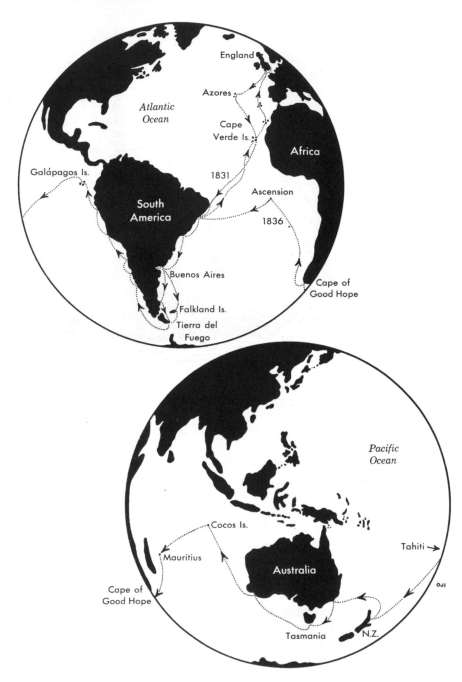

Fig. 3-2. The voyage of the *Beagle* (1831-1836).

pendix B. Here was a clue as to the mechanism by which species change. In Malthus' discussion of the reproductive potential of man being greater than the power of the earth to produce subsistence Darwin saw the essence of the struggle for existence that led to the theory of natural selection.

He first wrote out his ideas on the origin of species in rough form in 1842 and a more complete draft was drawn up in 1844, but he continued to assemble facts until 1856. Then, urged on by Lyell, he started to write up his

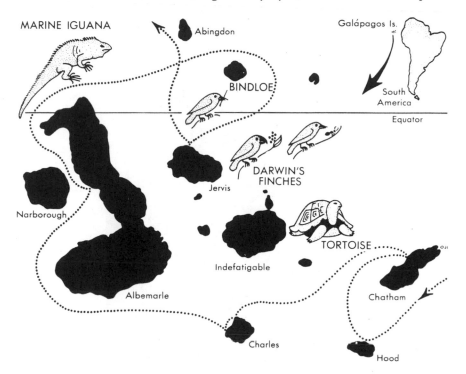

MARINE IGUANA Abingdon Galápagos Is.
BINDLOE South America Equator
DARWIN'S FINCHES Jervis
Narborough
TORTOISE
Indefatigable Chatham
Albemarle
Charles Hood

Fig. 3-3. The Galápagos Islands and route of the *Beagle*.

material in a work that he expected to fill four volumes. This undertaking was nowhere near completion when he received a manuscript from Alfred Russel Wallace, then in the Malay Archipelago, who asked him to read it and, if he thought well of it, to send it on to Lyell for his opinion. The paper contained, in complete detail, the theory of natural selection.

The subsequent events tend to restore one's faith in human nature. Jealousy over priority among scientists is fairly common, yet the attitudes of Darwin and Wallace at this time and for the rest of their lives were exceedingly generous. Darwin sent the paper on with praise and the recommendation that it be published at once. Lyell and the botanist Hooker, aware of the long years

Darwin had spent in developing the theory, insisted that Wallace's paper and an extract of Darwin's manuscript and one of his letters written to the American botanist, Asa Gray of Harvard, should be published simultaneously. This was done, with the papers appearing in 1858. The projected four-volume work was abandoned by Darwin, who condensed his material into a single volume, the famed *Origin of Species,* which appeared the following year. This work was an immediate success and had terrific impact not only on the scientific world but on the world at large, in contrast to the reception of the original papers.

Fig. 3-4. Charles Darwin in 1840, two years prior to his first draft of the theory of evolution by natural selection. (From a water color by George Richmond.)

The circumstances under which Wallace arrived at the theory of natural selection were rather similar to those that initiated Darwin's trend of thought. Wallace was a naturalist whose travels among the islands of the East Indies impressed on him the differences between species as well as their obvious relationships to each other, and led him to evolution and natural selection as the explanation for his observations. It seems as if biological knowledge had reached the point where an adequate training and extensive field work led almost inevitably to the major synthesis that Darwin and Wallace achieved independently.

In his book Darwin actually presented evidence bearing on two distinct subjects: the theory of evolution, and a theory of the mechanism of evolution—

that is, natural selection. Darwin proposed on the one hand that evolution had occurred, that existing species are descended from similar but somewhat different species that lived in the past. The evidence he presented came from his study of variation under domestication and in nature, from taxonomy, from comparative anatomy and embryology, from the geographical distribution of species, and from the geological record. His presentation is still one of the finest arguments for evolution. He also proposed natural selection as the mechanism making evolution possible. It should be noted that evolution could still be valid even if, as now seems very unlikely, the theory of natural selection were shown to be false.

The theory of natural selection is based upon a few, simple, easily verified observations and the conclusions to be drawn from them. It can readily be observed that the reproductive potential of all species is far greater than is required to replace the existing population, the possible rate of increase forming a geometrical progression. Even elephants, presumably the slowest breeders of all, were shown by Darwin to have this great potential. He estimated that from one pair, breeding from age 30 to 90 and having only six young in this span, there would be descended a living population of 19,000,000 after 750 years. The spread of the English sparrow and the starling after their introduction into the United States in small numbers less than a century ago is further evidence of the tremendous reproductive capacity of all species, which is only realized under the most favorable conditions.

Despite this reproductive potential, however, it can easily be verified that the population size of any species in a given area is relatively constant. Fluctuations occur from year to year, but ordinarily there is no continuous increase.

The obvious conclusion from these two observations is that not all of the progeny produced by any generation reach maturity, but that many die during the early stages of the life cycle.

The third observation by Darwin was that variation is a universal phenomenon, that no two individuals are ever exactly alike.

Darwin's final conclusion, then, was that, since individuals differ from each other, some will inevitably be better adapted to survive under the existing conditions than others. Since a large proportion of each generation dies before reaching maturity, the better adapted individuals will tend to survive while the less well adapted will die. Even though most of the deaths occur at random, if this differential affects the survival of the remainder, it will still be significant although more difficult to detect. Finally, if the adaptive traits are hereditary, the survivors, who become the progenitors of the next generation, will tend to transmit their favorable traits to their offspring. Therefore, the next generation will have a higher proportion of well-adapted individuals than the previous one. Hence, in time, this natural selective process will change the average characteristics of a species, and evolution will occur.

The *Origin of Species* was widely read and discussed as soon as it appeared. Controversies arose over the validity of the theories of evolution and natural selection. Powerful forces in the church, the most eminent being Bishop Wilberforce, attacked the book, but there were also eminent scientists such as the anatomist Richard Owen and the Swiss American zoologist Louis Agassiz who did not accept its conclusions. The distinguished German embryologist von Baer accepted evolution but rejected natural selection, for he did not accept the idea of a completely materialistic system. The strongest advocate of Darwin's views, since his health limited his participation in the public discussions stimulated by his book, was Thomas Henry Huxley. In lectures, articles, and debates Huxley educated the world on the significance of these theories. The acceptance of Darwin's views came quite rapidly among the scientists, but somewhat more slowly by the general public. Owen rather weakened his case in opposition when it was discovered that anonymous articles, attacking Darwinism and citing the eminent authority, Dr. Richard Owen, had actually been written by Owen himself. The position of the church was modified, in part at least, as the result of the famous debate between Bishop Wilberforce and Huxley in which Huxley won a decisive victory. When Bishop Wilberforce "begged to know, was it through his grandfather or his grandmother that he claimed his descent from a monkey?" Huxley replied that he would not be ashamed to have a monkey for an ancestor, but he would be "ashamed to be connected with a man who used great gifts to obscure the truth," and with this stirring statement, he won the day. A rather similar debate took place at Harvard between Asa Gray and Louis Agassiz. With the support of such distinguished advocates as Lyell, Huxley, and Hooker in England, Asa Gray in America, and Haeckel, an embryologist, and Gegenbauer, a comparative anatomist in Germany, Darwin's theories within a very few years gained a strong foothold in the world of ideas.

The effects of Darwin's theories on biology were far reaching. Systematics received a great stimulus, for now the rationale behind classification was the actual relationship among the different species. Systematics became the study of evolution. Similarly, comparative embryology and comparative anatomy underwent rapid growth as their value in the working out of phylogenies became apparent. Paleontology, of course, as the main source of information about the past history of living things, also received a great impetus. Other fields were influenced to greater or lesser degrees, but none remained untouched.

In the years just after the book was published, the major advances were made in disentangling the phylogenetic threads. The theory of natural selection was accepted by the adherents of Darwinism and condemned by its opponents, both without much evidence. The major weakness in the theory of natural selection was the lack of understanding of variation and its mode of transmission from one generation to the next. Darwin recognized this weakness better perhaps than most of his adherents. The basic principles of heredity were known, but they were understood apparently only by their discoverer, Mendel; others who knew of his work either failed to understand it or else failed to appreciate its significance. Darwin, who might have been the one person capable of appreciating Mendel's work, never became cognizant of it. It is interesting to speculate what the course of events might have been if Mendel had written to Darwin of his results. But it never happened, and Mendel's work lay neglected from 1865 to 1900.

However, progress was being made in still another area of biology, the study of the cell, particularly by Strasburger and Flemming. The details of the structure and behavior of the various parts of the cell were worked out in the closing years of the nineteenth century. In particular, the chromosomes were identified, and the details of their behavior during cell division and gametogenesis were scrutinized. Cytology became a separate branch of biology. A synthesis of much of this work was undertaken by Weismann, who realized that the hereditary material must reside in the nucleus on the chromosomes, and who also originated the "germ line" theory. This theory pointed out that the germ cells are set aside very early in development and are uninfluenced by the rest of the cells in the body, the somatic cells. Under this theory, the inheritance of acquired characteristics would be impossible. Furthermore, the suggested mechanism for such inheritance, Darwin's theory of pangenesis, was outmoded. The pangenes had been visualized as being formed in all parts of the body and, bearing the traits exhibited there, coming together to form the gametes. There is no evidence for this theory proposed by Darwin.

In 1900, Correns, de Vries, and von Tschermak independently discovered Mendel's paper, after essentially reaching Mendel's results, and the new science of genetics finally was born. Mendel's laws were a major step forward in the understanding of variation. They showed that variations were inherited in a particulate fashion, and that blending inheritance, visualized by Darwin, did not occur. Hence, variability is not lost in crossing, but rather, as Hardy and Weinberg independently suggested in 1908, tends to remain constant in a population. Furthermore, Mendel's work led to an understanding of the way in which the recombination of characters could occur with the consequent new variations.

The rise of genetics, despite its contributions to the understanding of variation, was followed by a general eclipse of the theory of natural selection as the mechanism of evolution. Its place was taken by the mutation theory of de Vries, proposed in 1902. In his work with the evening primrose, *Oenothera,* de Vries occasionally found sports—that is, distinctly different types of plants, now known by the more pedestrian term "mutations." He therefore proposed that evolution was not due to the gradual accumulation of numerous small changes by natural selection, but instead occurred as the result of large jumps made possible by mutations of the type he was discovering. This theory won wide support among early geneticists, for the variations familiar to them in their work were of this type, and did not conform at all to Darwin's concept. Thus, such eminent geneticists as William Bateson and Thomas Hunt Morgan led the way in the early years of the century in rejecting natural selection, and many others concurred. Ironically, most of de Vries' mutations were later demonstrated to be due to chromosomal changes rather than to changes in the genes themselves, and hence were not mutations in the usual restricted sense at all.

Still further reason to doubt Darwin's theory came with Johannsen's demonstration, in 1910, that selection was effective only in genetically heterogeneous populations and was completely without effect on environmental variations. Darwin's failure to distinguish clearly between hereditary and environmental variation and his acceptance of Lamarckianism were thus shown decisively to be in error.

Not all biologists followed the lead of the geneticists. Many felt, as the paleontologist Simpson puts it, "that a geneticist was a person who shut himself in a room, pulled down the shades, watched small flies disporting themselves in milk bottles, and thought that he was studying nature." The studies of the fossil record revealed, where the evidence was complete, that evolutionary changes had been gradual rather than abrupt. Taxonomists, in their work with living species, found that the different species and subspecies differed from each other in numerous minor quantitative traits rather than in a few major characteristics. Furthermore, a group of students of heredity who worked with continuously varying traits rather than the alternative traits so commonly studied by Mendelian methods obtained results more in keeping with Darwin's ideas than those of the new Mendelian genetics. This group had its origin with Galton, Darwin's first cousin, well before 1900, and was responsible for the development of the science of biometry. Karl Pearson was the biometrician who came most directly into conflict with the early Mendelians, led in England by Bateson. Neither side recognized any merit in the work of the other group. Feelings ran so high that Bateson, in order to get his experimental results into print, had to start his own journal. However, people such as the paleontologists, taxonomists, and biometricians who continued to believe in natural selection were frequently regarded as out-of-date die-hards.

A major advance was made when it was shown that continuous variation had a Mendelian basis. Thus a reconciliation was possible between the Mendelians and the followers of Pearson. Since then, there has come about a synthesis leading to an evolutionary theory that is now generally accepted among paleontologists, systematists, geneticists, and most other biologists. Underlying this new synthesis is the increased knowledge and understanding of variation. Morgan and his co-workers conclusively demonstrated that the Mendelian factors or genes were located on the chromosomes, and thus established not only the physical basis of heredity but of evolution. Our understanding of the nature of mutation and of the mutation process has greatly increased, notable advances being Muller's induction of mutations with x-rays in 1927, and the more recent success of chemical mutagens, first demonstrated by Auerbach. The direct application of genetic knowledge to evolutionary problems was made possible by the theoretical development by Fisher, Haldane, Tchetverikov, and Wright of population genetics. As a result of their efforts, evolutionary change has come to be recognized as the result of the combined effects of several forces on the frequencies of the genes in breeding populations. One of these forces is natural selection, which remains as a cornerstone to an expanded and strengthened theory of the mechanism of evolution. The modern synthesis or Neo-Darwinism, as it is often called, has been largely responsible for the renewed interest in evolutionary problems.

SUGGESTED READING

See references at the end of Chapter 2.

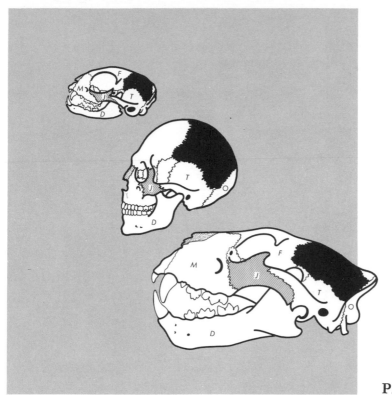

PART *II*

The Evidence
for Evolution

CHAPTER 4

The Fossil Record

Living species, by their very existence, pose the questions that the theory of evolution attempts to answer, but the fossil record is another material source from which information and insight can be derived. Few people have ever tried to deny the existence of living species, but many interpretations have been made of the fossils that have been found all over the world. These interpretations now have passed into the realm of myths, and fossils are generally accepted for what they are, the remains or traces of previously existing animals and plants preserved in the earth's crust. The fossil record, unfortunately, is incomplete, but the reasons for the gaps in the record will become clear from a knowledge of the nature of fossils and the conditions necessary for their formation. The two conditions under which a fossil is generally formed from a living organism are that it have some hard parts, and that it be buried quickly in some protecting medium. Quick burial tends to retard or prevent the decomposition of the organisms by solution or oxidation or bacterial action. Fossils have been formed in such places as the floors of caves, in tarpits and oil seeps, in bogs and quicksand, and under volcanic ash or windblown sands, but the great majority have been covered over by water-borne sediments.

A fossil may be anything from an intact woolly mammoth frozen in the Siberian tundra to the footprint of a dinosaur. Complete organisms, however, are very rare, and even unchanged hard parts, such as bone, shell, or woody tissue, are uncommon. Usually the fossil has undergone some change, with the original hard parts having gradually been replaced by some mineral substance such as calcium carbonate, silica, or iron pyrite. This particle-by-particle replacement is so slow that the microscopic structure of the hard parts is preserved, and the cell walls of wood, for example, can still be studied even though the organic matter is completely gone. In some cases, however, especially in plants, the more volatile elements may be distilled off, leaving behind them a carbon residue. If the original hard parts are dissolved, a "mold" of the shape may then be left in the surrounding rock. If the mold is subsequently filled by a foreign mineral substance, such as quartz, a "cast" is formed. The cast, of course, retains no indications of the original microscopic structure.

The normal habitat of many species has undoubtedly precluded their appearance in the fossil record simply because conditions were unsuitable for fossil formation, as in the deep seas or high uplands, for example. Even if buried, the organism needs hard parts, for otherwise the chances of preservation are very slight. Whole groups of species may be virtually absent from the fossil record because they did not meet these requirements. The fossil record is therefore by no means a random sample of all previously existing species, but a specially selected group. From the nature of the record, it is obvious that it will never be complete, although subsequent finds will tend always to narrow the gaps and to supply the "missing links."

In addition to the information about life in the past, fossils reveal still other facts about past conditions. The discovery of the fossil remains of marine organisms like corals and sea urchins far inland in Indiana or 20,000 feet up in the Himalayas has far-reaching geological implications, for at one time Indiana must have been covered by the ocean, as were the Himalayas, which were subsequently thrust up to their present towering heights. Fossil palms and alligators in the Dakotas and musk oxen in Arkansas are indicative of wide fluctuations in past climatic conditions.

Reconstructing the Past

Perhaps the greatest accomplishment of the paleontologists has been their reconstruction of the sequence of past events. Water-borne sediments are deposited in layers or strata that are then, through pressure, converted to rock. Undisturbed deposition over a long period of time has thus given rise to an accumulation of sediments many feet thick, with the oldest deposits at the bottom and the most recent at the top. The fossils in the bottom layers must, therefore, represent the oldest species. If it were possible to find a place where deposition of sediments had been continuous since the formation of the earth in its present structure, the strata would form a complete geological column, and the included fossils would furnish a fairly good record of the forms of life that had existed during this period. Although some deposits are thousands of feet thick, no such complete geological column is known. Such thicknesses, built up very gradually, give some appreciation of the vastness of geological time, yet they represent only small fractions of the total. In a given bed of sedimentary rock, the fossils in different strata are different from one another, but the fossils in adjacent layers are more alike than those further removed. The more recently formed fossils show greater similarity to existing species than those in the lower strata. The presence of the same types of fossils in deposits in different parts of the world has been assumed, as seems reasonable, to indicate that these sediments were laid down at approximately the same time. On this basis, it has been possible to correlate the deposits all over the world into one chronological series, and a geological column has been constructed through these correlations. Thus has the earth's history been reconstructed. New finds can be fitted into the rest of the record, but the dating is relative rather than absolute. The absolute age, which is obtained from studies of radioactive minerals, has been estimated as about 4.5 billion years. Though rocks apparently bearing fossils of algae, protozoans, and fungus spores have been estimated to be as old as 3.3 billion years, the record was very fragmentary up until about 500 million years ago. Some of the major subdivisions of geological time are shown in Table 4-1. Though the major phyla have been represented in the fossil record ever since the Paleozoic, the species representing each phylum have changed considerably with the passage of time.

TABLE 4-1
The Geological Time Scale (After Kulp)

Era	Period	Epoch	Time estimated in millions of years	
			Since Beginning	Duration
Cenozoic (Age of Mammals)	Quaternary	Recent	.011	.011
		Pleistocene	1	1
	Tertiary	Pliocene	13	12
		Miocene	25	12
		Oligocene	36	11
		Eocene	58	22
		Paleocene	63	5
Mesozoic (Age of Reptiles)	Cretaceous		135	72
	Jurassic		181	46
	Triassic		230	49
Paleozoic (Age of Fishes)	Permian		280	50
	Pennsylvanian		310	30
	Mississippian		345	35
	Devonian		405	60
	Silurian		425	20
	Ordovician		500	75
	Cambrian		600	100
Precambrian			5,000±	4,400±

The Paleozoic, for example, is known as the Age of Fishes, the Mesozoic as the Age of Reptiles, and the Cenozoic as the Age of Mammals; the mammals first appeared in the fossil record during the late Mesozoic but reached their climax only during the Cenozoic.

Even as recently as the Mesozoic era, practically no living species existed. Many species have appeared in the fossil record, persisted in it for varying periods, and then disappeared. Where the record is fairly complete, gradual changes within a given group can be followed from the older to the more recent strata. The evidence shows that distinct new species have appeared in all parts of the world throughout geological time. There is no time or place, apparently, at which new species could not have originated. The most reasonable and complete explanation for the evidence from the rocks—physical evidence that can hardly be ignored—is the theory of evolution; that is, living species, through a series of gradual changes, have descended from somewhat different species living in the past. Today, in fact, we think of the fossil record in terms of evolution to such a degree that it is hard to separate the record from its interpretation. Yet Cuvier, in Lamarck's time, and Louis Agassiz in Darwin's, probably the leading paleontologists of their day, both opposed the theory of evolution, using the paleontological materials to support their arguments. Since then, however, our vastly increased knowledge about paleontology, due in large part to the stimulus of Darwin's theories, has made it one of the bulwarks of proof that evolution has actually occurred.

Extinction and Evolution

Practically all of the species recognized from fossils no longer exist. There are two routes to extinction—one leading to complete extinction; the other, through evolutionary change, to new species. The evolution of new species may take place in two ways. One is a transformation in time, species A evolving into B, B into C, and so on as time passes. The other is a multiplication of species in space, two species, B and C, originating simultaneously from a single species, A. Because of this latter process (now usually referred to as speciation, in a restricted sense of the word), the number of coexisting species has tended to increase as more and more of the available ecological niches have been occupied. For example, invasion of the land did not occur until plant and animal species adapted to life on land had evolved from the ancient aquatic types. A whole new range of possibilities then opened up, and adaptive radiation of species from these first successful invaders of the land into a variety of diverse habitats occurred. Because the process of adaptive radiation through speciation has continued through geological time, the number of living species is probably greater today than it has been at any time in the past.

Evolutionary changes are gradual, with no positive evidence for the formation of species by a cataclysmic process or saltation existing in the fossil record, but all evolutionary rates are not the same. Different groups may have different average rates of evolution; the mammals, for example, appear to have evolved much more rapidly than the ammonites. Even within a single group, the rate of evolution may change from one time to another. Though evolution goes on between generations rather than within generations, nevertheless generation length seems to have no relation to evolutionary rates, for the mammals, with a very long generation length, have had an extremely rapid rate of evolution.

Frequently, the slow, steady evolution within a particular evolutionary line shows a series of changes in a single direction or a trend, a type of evolution known as "orthogenesis." Because such trends are so common, it has been suggested that evolution may have a sort of momentum, which causes it, once under way, to continue to move in the same direction, even when the changes are no longer adaptive. It has been suggested, for example, that the Irish elk became extinct when its massive antlers became so heavy that the animals could no longer hold up their heads or else snagged them in the brush and thus starved to death. The saber-toothed tiger was supposed to have met a similar fate when his fearsome fangs became so long that he could no longer get any food past them. However, more thorough study has shown that the trends are due to constant selection pressure in a given direction, and that the changes are adaptive; hence the term "orthoselection" would be more descriptive than orthogenesis. Whatever the causes of extinction for the Irish elk and the saber-toothed tiger, they were not carried off by runaway evolution.

One implication of orthogenesis, divorced as it is from adaptation, is that there is a vital force or *élan vital* animating all living things. In addition, the prevalence of evolutionary trends has led to speculation that evolution is directed toward some ultimate goal, a concept known as "finalism." There is no reason or need, however, to invoke either vitalism or finalism to account for the evidence.

Major adaptive shifts, giving rise to new and distinctive groups, represent changes in the direction of evolution and usually a change in rate as well. The gaps in the fossil record usually seem to occur at the crucial stages where, if evolution is a gradual process, transitional forms connecting major groups ought to be found. Failure to find many transitional fossils has led many authorities to postulate a different evolutionary mechanism for the origin of higher taxonomic groups, but our subsequent discussion will show that no special mechanism is demanded by the evidence.

In discussions of trends in evolution, the terms "generalized" and "specialized" are frequently used, often with the corollary that "specialization is the prelude to extinction." Such a generalization is unwarranted. The terms "generalized" and "specialized" have meaning only in a relative and rather limited sense, though they can be useful. To raise a specific question, were the early mammals specialized or generalized? Had a zoologist of the day (if such existed) compared them with their contemporaries, the dominant reptilian group, they might well have been considered a small, specialized, and rather aberrant group of reptiles, destined therefore to rapid extinction. In this instance specialization was a prelude to new evolutionary opportunities. Compared with recent mammals, however, these early mammals must be considered quite generalized. A rather similar verbal pitfall is found in the use of the terms "primitive" and "modern" species. The shark and the frog, for instance, are often cited as examples of primitive vertebrates, with the mammals held up as the modern type. Since sharks, frogs, and mammals are all living today, one group is just as old as the other, and the ancestry of one can be traced back just as far as that of another, though a greater variety of ancestors may appear in one lineage. The fallacy would be even clearer if, through some quirk of fate, all mammals became extinct. If used with reference to time of origin, however, the terms can be useful and not especially confusing.

Vertebrate Evolution

In order to give some appreciation of the type of information available in the fossil record, the history of the vertebrates or backboned animals (the subphylum Vertebrata of the phylum Chordata) will be outlined (see Fig. 4-1). The first vertebrate fossils appeared in the Ordovician period of the Paleozoic era, which began about 425 million years ago. These fishlike animals were small, armored, bottom dwellers, but lacked both jaws and paired fins. Known as ostracoderms, they belonged to the class Agnatha, which today is represented by just a few surviving species, the most familiar being the lampreys. The Agnatha remained common throughout the Silurian and Devonian periods. The first vertebrates to have jaws and paired appendages appeared among the late Silurian fossils, were very common in the Devonian (325 million years ago), and had virtually disappeared from the Mississippian record. This class of early fishes, the Placodermi, is now extinct. The Chondrichthyes, a group to which the present-day sharks and rays belong, first appeared in the middle and late Devonian, became abundant in the Mississippian and Pennsylvanian, and have remained common up to the present day. At about the same time the bony fishes (Osteichthyes) appeared in the fossil record and have flourished ever since. Unlike the sharks, they had a specialized spiracle, an added (hyoid) support for the jaws, and an air bladder or lungs. They include two major groups, the Choanichthyes, including the lobe-finned fishes or crossopterygians and the living lung fishes or Dipnoi, and the Actinopterygii, or ray-finned fishes, to which belong more than 90 percent of the existing species of fish.

The first land vertebrates, with legs and lungs, did not appear as fossils until the late Devonian. These first tetrapods were amphibians, a group that had

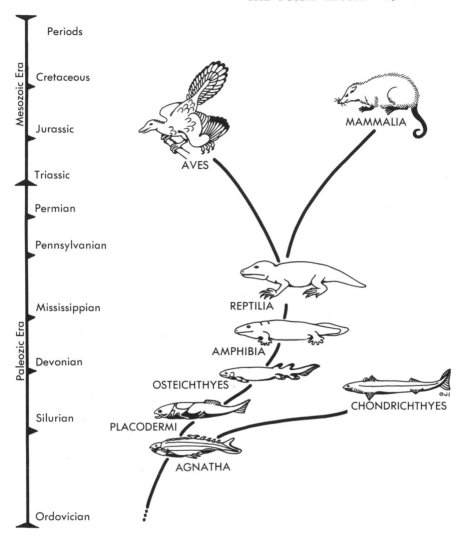

Fig. 4-1. The phylogeny of the vertebrates. (After Romer).

its heyday during the Mississippian and Pennsylvanian periods and has since been a subordinate part of the land vertebrate fauna, represented today by the frogs, toads, and salamanders. The first known reptiles were found in rocks of Pennsylvanian origin. Though it is a relatively simple matter to distinguish between recent amphibians and reptiles, the criteria tend to break down for the ancient species. One reason for this difficulty is that the most significant difference between the amphibians and reptiles lies in their modes of reproduction and development. The reptiles were completely freed from dependence on an aquatic environment at any stage of their life cycle because their shelled eggs could develop on land. The amphibian egg, with little yolk, must be laid in the water, and the young tadpoles, a larval stage, soon emerge. The developing embryo of the reptilian egg is bathed in fluid, too, but the fluid is contained in a sac, the amnion, which encloses the embryo. Another membranous sac, the allantois, serves as a respiratory structure for gaseous exchange and also as a storage place for excretory wastes. Because of the large yolk supply, the young reptiles develop much further than the amphibians before they hatch from the egg. The reptiles increased in numbers during the Permian and were the dominant land vertebrates throughout the Mesozoic era. Many of the reptilian groups then prominent, such as the dinosaurs, ichthyosaurs, mosasaurs, and plesiosaurs, are now extinct, and the reptiles today are represented by such groups as the snakes, turtles, alligators, and lizards.

The first birds (Aves) appeared in the fossil record in the Jurassic period of the Mesozoic, but unlike modern birds, which did not appear until the Cenozoic, they had teeth and a tail composed of vertebrae, and were difficult to distinguish from reptiles. Even today birds seem much like glorified reptiles.

Though mammallike reptiles (Therapsids) existed in the late Paleozoic, the first true mammals did not appear as fossils until the Triassic and they did not form an important part of the fauna until the Cenozoic. The mammals are characterized by the presence of mammary glands, hair, warm blood, and a relatively large brain, which is probably in large measure responsible for their current dominance. Though most mammals bear living young, which have undergone development in the uterus of the mother while nourished via the placenta, some living mammals, such as the duck-billed platypus, lay shelled eggs. This group, the monotremes or Protheria, is apparently quite distantly related to the mammalian lines of descent that gave rise to the marsupials (Metatheria) and the placental mammals (Eutheria). The first fossils that show clearly human affinities appeared in the fossil record less than two million years ago.

Evolution of the Horse

Horses have left behind the most complete sequence of fossils yet discovered. Their history has therefore been worked out in greater detail than that of any other group (see Fig. 4-2). Man and the horse have been closely associated for centuries, but whereas the human fossil record has been traced back to something less than two million years, fossil horses first make an appearance in the early Eocene some sixty million years ago. Although no direct links with animals living in the Paleocene are known, the indications are that the horses, or Equidae, are descended from the order Condylarthra, an order of five-toed hoofed mammals or ungulates that is now extinct. Horses belong to the order of odd-toed ungulates, the Perissodactyla, and number among their relatives the

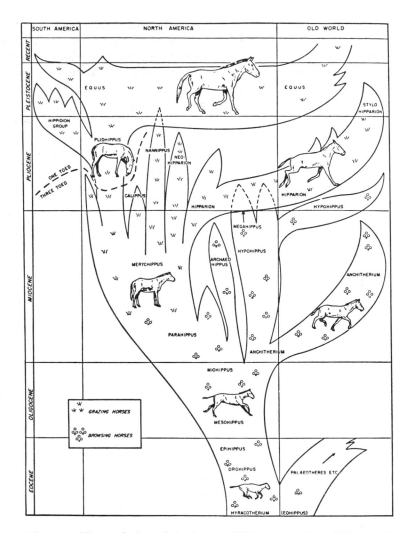

Fig. 4-2. The evolution of the horse. (With permission of Simpson.)

living rhinoceroses and tapirs and the extinct chalicotheres with clawed feet and the enormous "horned" brontotheres.

The primary center for horse evolution was in North America, especially in the Great Plains region, for the most abundant and continuous fossil record has been found there. From time to time some of the species spread to the Old World, but not until a land connection was again established at the end of the Pliocene were they able to reach South America. Consequently the fossil record of the horses on that continent is confined to Pleistocene deposits.

The earliest Eocene equines were so unlike the modern horses that they were called *Hyracotherium* because of their rodentlike appearance. They later became known as eohippus, the dawn horse. Eohippus, from which all subsequent horse evolution proceeded, was a small, browsing animal the size of a fox terrier and standing only ten to twenty inches tall at the shoulder. His back was arched, and his hind legs and tail were relatively long. His front feet each had four toes, the hind feet only three, and even though tiny hoofs were present, most of the weight was born by pads.

Miohippus from the Oligocene was the first horse with three toes on all feet, but the lateral toes were still functional. About the size of a sheep, this browsing horse was apparently more intelligent and fleet of foot than its predecessors.

The fossils of *Merychippus* come primarily from the Miocene. This group of horses had high-crowned teeth, adapted for grazing on the relatively harsh grasses of an open prairie habitat, rather than the low-crowned teeth of its predecessors, which were adapted to browsing on succulent shoots and leaves. Furthermore, though *Merychippus* still had three toes, the outer toes were reduced, barely touching the ground, and the leg had become, with its well-developed cannon bone, an efficient spring mechanism. This group, which marked the completion of the transition from browsing to grazing, was highly successful, numerous, and widespread. *Pliohippus,* the first one-toed horse, initially appeared in the Pliocene deposits. The two slender splint bones on each side of the cannon bone are the only vestiges of the other two toes. *Pliohippus* was succeeded in the Pleistocene by members of the genus *Equus* to which belong all the living Equidae—the horses, zebras, asses, and onagers.

In outline, the material just presented indicates the line of succession from the earliest known equids up to the present-day horses. The abundant fossils have made it possible to document the changes rather than having to attempt to fill gaps in the record by speculation or conjecture. The major changes from *Hyracotherium* to *Equus* were an increase in overall size, a reduction in the number of toes, a transition from browsing to grazing, and the associated increase in the height and complexity of the teeth.

To present this record without additional information, however, is to give a greatly oversimplified conception of how evolution actually took place in the horse. As presented, it appears to have been a linear process, perhaps with overtones of orthogenesis. Actually, this was far from the case. At each level from eohippus on, an adaptive radiation took place and numerous groups evolved, all of which except *Equus* are now extinct. *Miohippus,* for example, was ancestral not only to *Merychippus,* which completed the transition to grazing, but also to a line that culminated in the large three-toed browsing "forest" horses known as *Hypohippus,* and to at least three other distinct lineages. Similarly, *Merychippus,* successfully adapted to grazing, became the source of a number of three-toed grazing horses such as the highly successful genus *Hipparion,* as well as of the one-toed group *Pliohippus. Pliohippus* gave rise not only to *Equus* but also to the genus *Hippidion,* which reached South America in the early Pleistocene and there underwent adaptive radiation. Therefore, before reading any trends into the record, we must try to see whether they really exist. For example, horses in some cases did increase in size, but some lines remained essentially unchanged for long periods, and in others actual decreases in size occurred. The reduction in numbers of toes was by no means universal nor was it a gradual, inexorable process. The change from four front toes to three occurred in a relatively short period and was followed much later by the rapid transition from three toes to one. In each case it was an adaptive shift occurring in one among a number of existing groups. Finally, the change from low-crowned to high-crowned, more complex teeth was one adaptive shift in the evolution of the browsing horses that happened to be highly successful because it opened up a new ecological niche to exploitation. However, other types of trends can also be traced in the evolution of the teeth of browsing horses. Thus, this brief résumé indicates that both the rate and the direction of evolution may change and that the changes seem to be related to adaptation. Only so long as an evolutionary shift continues to bring improved adaptation will it continue. To this extent, evolutionary trends may be observed, but they are due to natural selection, not to orthogenesis impelled by some mysterious internal force. The most persistent trends would be expected in the improvement of those traits that confer adaptive advantage in any kind of environment.

Several obvious facts stand out from this brief review of the vertebrates' history. Not all of the major groups of vertebrates have been represented since the Ordovician; instead, new groups have appeared periodically. The more recent deposits contain vertebrates much more like living species than the most ancient fossils. Great numbers of species found as fossils have become extinct. Though gaps exist in the record, types intermediate between the major groups have been discovered. The most far-reaching and consistent explanation of the vast array of facts accumulated from the study of paleontology is the theory of evolution. The sequence of appearance in the rock strata depicts the phylogeny of the group (see Fig. 4-1). A major advance in the course of vertebrate evolution and hence of human evolution—for man fits into the overall scheme—was the acquisition of jaws and paired appendages by the Placodermi; another such advance occurred when the lobe-finned fishes gave rise to the four-footed amphibians, which breathed air with lungs derived from the air sacs or lungs of the fishes. Man and the dog and the horse show so many similarities—that complex of traits characteristic of placental mammals—because they had a common ancestry up until about 75 to 100 million years ago.

Although speculation as to what follows in vertebrate evolution is the next logical topic, we shall defer it until after our discussion of evolutionary mechanisms. Our purpose now is to present the evidence that evolution has occurred in the past, and of this evidence, fossils constitute the major portion.

SUMMARY ◄────────────────────────────────

The fossil remains of animals and plants are widely distributed over the earth. Absolute and relative dating methods show them to be of varying ages—some quite recent, others of great antiquity. These fossils constitute an actual record of the organisms that lived on the earth at different times in the past. An examination of this record shows that the kinds of living animals and plants changed gradually with time. Thus, species adjacent in time are more alike than species separated by vast time spans, and the more recent the fossils, the more they tend to resemble living species. The theory of evolution, of descent with modification, provides the most logical explanation for the fossil record. The living species of the past, forced to adapt to an ever-changing physical and biological environment, underwent gradual modifications through time. Many groups, unable to adapt, became extinct; others, more successful, survived and spread, only to be supplanted in turn by still better adapted types. These successful groups, however, did not arise *de novo,* but were descended from previously existing species of animals and plants.

SUGGESTED READING

Colbert, E. H., 1955. *Evolution of the vertebrates.* New York: Wiley.

Flint, R. F., 1957. *Glacial and Pleistocene geology.* New York: Wiley.

Moore, R. C., 1958. *Introduction to historical geology,* 2d ed. New York: McGraw-Hill.

Newell, N. D., 1959. "The nature of the fossil record," *Proc. Amer. Phil. Soc.,* 103:264-285.

Romer, A. S., 1945. *Vertebrate paleontology,* 2d ed. Chicago: University of Chicago Press.

———, 1958. *The vertebrate story.* Chicago: University of Chicago Press.

Simpson, G. G., 1950. *The meaning of evolution.* New Haven: Yale University Press. (New York: Mentor Books, 1951.)

———, 1951. *Horses.* New York: Oxford University Press.

———, 1953. *Life of the past.* New Haven: Yale University Press.

———, 1953. *The major features of evolution.* New York: Columbia University Press.

Stirton, R. A., 1959. *Time, life, and man. The fossil record.* New York: Wiley.

CHAPTER 5

The Origin of the Earth and of the Universe

Once it is known that the first fossils are several hundred million or a few billion years old, the next question inevitably concerns the origin of life and, beyond that, the origin of the earth and of the universe itself. Though cosmogony is currently making great strides, the answers to these questions are more speculative than those about the less remote events detailed in the fossil record. Nevertheless, a brief review of current thought on these questions is certainly worthwhile, as long as it is realized that this sort of information has a different basis and hence is less reliable than the reconstruction of past events based on actual fossil remains. The theories in these areas are much more likely to change as new information becomes available.

On the basis of narratives in the Old Testament, Archbishop Ussher in the seventeenth century calculated that the world was created in 4004 B.C. The delvers into such mysteries among the people of ancient India arrived at a date that would in 1962 make the world 1,972,949,063 years old. Modern estimates, which do not claim such precision, generally agree that the zero hour of the universe, as we know it, was a few billion years ago.

Age of the Universe

Science has used several approaches to estimate the age of the earth. One of these is a method that determines the age of the oceans. About 3 percent of sea water consists of dissolved salts.

These salts are constantly being leached from the rocks forming the earth's crust and are carried to the oceans by the rivers. The water evaporates from the surface of the oceans, falls on the land, and again flows to the sea in an ever-renewed cycle, but the salts remain in the sea, the salinity gradually increasing as time passes. Each year about 400 million tons of salt are added to the 40×10^{15} tons already present in the seas. Simple division indicates that the process has lasted for at least 100 million years. However, since the rate of erosion is now unusually high compared to other periods of geological time, because of the higher mountain ranges and man's activities, this estimate must be increased at least 20 to 30 times, which leads to an age of 2 or 3 billion years. The very fact that the oceans are not saturated with salt indicates their limited existence.

The age of the continents can be determined by estimating the age of the rocks composing them. The radioactive elements uranium and thorium are found in small quantities in many rocks, where both slowly decay into lead. Once the rock has solidified, the radiogenic lead cannot escape, but remains trapped in the rock with the original radioactive substances. The uranium/lead and thorium/lead ratios give a rather exact figure for the age of a given rock in much the same way an hour glass might if each grain as it fell were changed to lead. Different rocks give different ages, but the maximum estimate thus far is about 3 billion years. This value is fairly reliable, but must be regarded as the lower limit of the age of the earth, for the earth may well have been formed long before these rocks solidified into their present structure. Similar types of analyses have been run on meteorites in an effort to estimate the age of the solar system. The age of the meteorites was found to be on the order of 4.5 billion years; the earth, as a part of the solar system, must also be approximately of this age. Still another possible type of analysis is the determination of the age of the chemical elements themselves—that is, the matter that forms the solar system. These elements must have a finite age; otherwise, by now the radioactive elements would have disintegrated and disappeared. Estimates of their age range up to 6 billion years.

Astronomers have tackled the age of the universe in several ways. One method is to study stellar velocities within the Milky Way, the galaxy of which we are a part. When such a system has existed for a long time, the stellar velocities are expected to approach a limiting distribution with an equal partition of energy among all the stars. However, this distribution has not yet been realized, and the calculations indicate that the system has existed only a few billion years.

A second method is based on the rate at which a star burns up. Stars obtain their energy from the nuclear transformation of hydrogen into helium in their hot centers. Thus, the life span of a star is determined by its brightness or rate of burning and by its original hydrogen content. Larger stars burn out faster than the smaller ones such as the sun. The large stars that must have been formed several billion years ago are now in their death throes, pulsating and exploding, but the smaller sun has at least 5 billion years to go before reaching this stage.

A third method of estimating the age of the universe is based on what is called the "red shift." The Milky Way, containing billions of stars, is just one of about a billion such stellar systems or galaxies within the range of the 200-inch telescope at Mount Palomar, California. A peculiar feature about the distant galaxies is that the light from them, although similar to that from nearer ones, shows a peculiar shift of the spectral lines toward the red end of the spectrum. A simple physical explanation for this shift is that the galaxies are receding at high speeds, and hence the universe is expanding. The effect is similar to the apparent change in pitch of a train whistle as it approaches and then recedes from a crossing. Since this phenomenon, known as the Doppler effect, has also been reported in the rather new field of radio astronomy, both light and radio waves appear to be similarly affected.

This discovery led to still another method of estimating the age of the universe, on the assumption that the universe as we know it today arose as the result of the differentiation of some sort of rapidly expanding primordial matter. A date for the beginning of this expansion can be obtained by dividing the average distance between neighboring galaxies by the velocity of their recession. The original estimate by this method, 1.8 billion years, presented a puzzle because the geological estimates already were much greater than this. Recently, however, corrections in this method have led to estimates for the age of the universe as high as 7 to 10 billion years. Although some differences exist in the various estimates, they are not too important for our purposes. The age of the universe, as derived from several independent estimates, seems to be about 5 billion years or more.

Nature of the Universe

The findings of the astronomers have led modern cosmologists to two quite different conceptions of the nature of the universe. One is that of an evolving universe, the other a steady-state universe. Under the evolutionary theory the expansion indicated by the red shift is interpreted to mean that the universe started off with a "big bang." The matter within the universe was squeezed together so tightly and at such high temperature and density that it consisted only of protons, neutrons, and electrons, which did not form any larger elements. When, because of expansion, the temperature dropped, the neutrons started to decay to protons, and the neutrons and protons started to form aggregations of atomic nuclei. The rate of expansion determined the types of atoms formed. Physicists have calculated that the "cooking period" could not have lasted more than half an hour. If it had been less (a rapid expansion), the

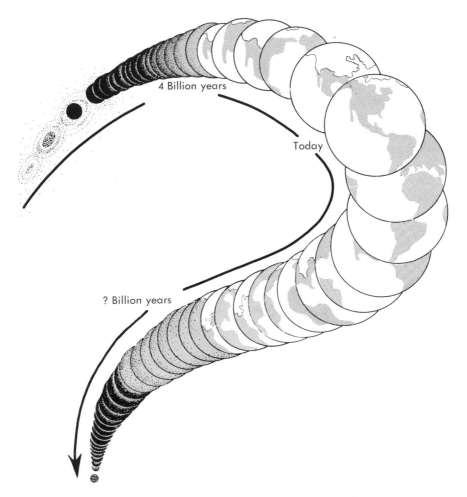

4 Billion years

Today

? Billion years

Fig. 5-1. The origin and evolution of the earth.

universe would contain mostly hydrogen; if longer, heavy elements would predominate.

For the next 250 million years, radiant energy was predominant over matter (the two being interconvertible with the now famous relationship $E = mc^2$ of Einstein). As expansion continued, the radiant energy was used to do the work of expansion, and matter became more prominent. At 250 million years the mass density of matter and radiation became equal. Prior to that time matter could be thought of as being "dissolved" in thermal radiation like salt in water.

At this time matter and gravitation became predominant, and the differentiation of the previously homogeneous system began. Gas balls were formed of the mass of a galaxy (about 40,000 light years radius and 200 million times the mass of the sun). These dark gas clouds next differentiated or condensed into stellar gas balls that contracted rapidly. The compression raised the temperature to 20,000,000 degrees, the threshold of nuclear reactions, and the stars began to shine. As most of the material fell toward the center of a star, the planets were formed from what was left behind. Colliding dust particles formed larger chunks of matter that swept through space, growing larger all the time. The process of star condensation and planet formation must have taken a few hundred million years. Since the moon is gradually moving further away from the earth, it appears that several billion years ago earth and moon formed a single mass, from which the moon has broken away. This conception of the universe extends the theory of evolution to the universe itself.

The steady-state theory, on the other hand, suggests that the universe is infinite in both space and time, that the density of its matter remains constant, and that new matter is constantly being created throughout space at a rate just compensating for the thinning of matter by expansion, with new galaxies constantly being formed.

The major difficulty with the theory of an initial 30-minute "cooking period" is that there are no stable atoms of mass 5 or mass 8, and therefore the build-up of the heavier elements by neutron capture could not get past helium 4. This shortcoming in the theory has led Gamow, one of its proponents, to agree recently that the bulk of the heavy elements may have been formed later in the hot core of stars.

Two recent tentative advances have lent still further support to the concept of an evolving universe. The steady-state hypothesis postulates that the density of matter in space remains contant. The density of radio stars, however, increases with distance. Since most radio stars are apparently due to collisions between galaxies, this latter finding indicates that galactic crack-ups were more common billions of years ago when these signals started on their way than they are today. Since the evolutionary theory postulates a denser universe then, with collisions between galaxies therefore more probable, this discovery, if confirmed, gives strong support to the theory.

In studying the red shift, distance is measured in light years rather than miles. The speed of light is 186,000 miles per second, yet some galaxies are millions of light years away. In viewing these far-distant galaxies, we are looking not only over great distances but also backward in time. A study of clusters of galaxies about a billion light years away has shown that a billion years ago the universe was expanding faster than it is today. If the rate of expansion is slowing down, then we must live in an evolving rather than a steady-state universe. Furthermore, the slowing down suggests that eventually expansion will stop and contraction will begin, ultimately reaching the superdense condition that existed some 5 or more billion years ago. The concept of a pulsating universe is thus further strengthened. As for the question of the structure of the universe prior to the colossal explosion that started it, it seems likely to remain inscrutable, for whatever previous structure existed was lost in the dense mass of energy, electrons, protons, and neutrons that gave rise to our present universe.

SUMMARY ◄

Our knowledge of the origin of the earth and of the universe is neither as specific nor as detailed as our knowledge of the evolution of plants and animals derived from the study of fossils. Nevertheless, progress in the fields of physics, chemistry, and astronomy has made it possible to attack this question on a rational, scientific basis. The results of these studies indicate that the earth was formed several billion years ago and that the age of the universe as we know it is approximately 5 to 10 billion years. Although the alternative hypothesis of a steady-state universe has been advanced, there is considerable evidence to indicate that the universe itself is an evolving system, changing through time.

SUGGESTED READING

Bondi, H., 1952. *Cosmology.* New York: Cambridge University Press.

Brown, H., 1957. "The age of the solar system," *Sci. Amer., 196*(4):80-95.

Gamow, G., 1951. "The origin and evolution of the universe," *Amer. Sci., 39:*393-406.

———, 1952. *The creation of the universe.* New York: Viking.

Hoyle, F., 1955. *Frontiers of astronomy.* New York: Harper. (New York: Mentor Books, 1957.)

Pfeiffer, J., 1956. *The changing universe.* New York: Random House.

Robertson, H. P. *et al.,* 1956. "The universe," *Sci. Amer., 195*(3):72-236.

Russell, B., 1958. *The ABC of relativity.* London: Allen and Unwin. (New York: Mentor Books, 1959.)

Schwarzschild, M., 1958. *Structure and evolution of the stars.* Princeton: Princeton University Press.

CHAPTER 6

The Origin of Life

Since man tends to seek final answers to all major questions, it is not surprising to find some sort of explanation for the origin of the world, of life, and of man in practically every human culture. These beliefs fall into the realm of myth or superstition in many cases or they may be a part of the religion of the society. So intriguing a question as the origin of life has a number of theories associated with it, most of which can be grouped into a few major categories. One category involves a belief in the creation of life by a supernatural creator, an explanation that is outside the realm of science and therefore not open to scientific study. Another category, however—that of spontaneous generation —does admit of such investigation.

Spontaneous Generation

For centuries, the problem of the origin of life did not loom large in men's minds, for it was common knowledge that life was arising *de novo* all around them all the time. As if by magic, worms appeared in their rain barrels, maggots in their meat, and mice in their rag bags; hence the spontaneous generation of worms, maggots, and mice, where none had previously existed, was a fact easily demonstrated from everyday experience. Among the Greeks, Thales, Anaximander, Xenophanes, and Aristotle all believed in some form of spontaneous generation. Even such scientists as Harvey, Newton, Descartes, and Paracelsus centuries later believed in it, and van Helmont, who did notable early work on plant nutrition, left a recipe for the spontaneous generation of mice—namely, a sweaty shirt plus some wheat germ.

Some of the fables are so fantastic that it is difficult to conceive how they originated. For example, according to the goose tree legend of the Middle Ages, geese were derived from barnacles, which in turn were formed in the fruits of trees. Since geese were thus obviously of vegetable origin, for centuries

Fig. 6-1. The goose tree legend.

they were an acceptable meat substitute during Lent. This belief was periodically reinforced by careful observations, often accompanied by imaginative drawings (see Fig. 6-1), and it persisted even to the beginning of the seventeenth century. One possible explanation for the origin of the legend is the coincidence of the time of attachment of the marine barnacles in the northern British Isles with the arrival of migrating young geese from the Arctic. These barnacles attach to a variety of things in the water, including fallen trees or branches, and this fact may have been the basis for the strange juxtaposition of beliefs.

Not until the seventeenth century were the first real doubts cast on the theory of spontaneous generation. The experiments of an Italian, Francisco Redi, showed that meat, covered with a cloth so that flies could not lay their eggs on it, never developed maggots. The idea nevertheless persisted, especially in relation to microorganisms. A century later, Spallanzani sealed some broth in a flask, boiled it, and showed that no microorganisms then developed and hence no spoiling occurred for an indefinite period. Needham, however, objected that the broth and particularly the air in the flask were changed by the boiling so that they would not support life. Breaking the seal on the flask, Spallanzani showed that the broth would still support life, but he failed to answer the criticism concerning the air. Hence, belief in spontaneous generation persisted not only among people generally but among biologists until less than 100 years ago. The experiments of Pasteur finally ended the argument, and the axiom became *Omne vivum ē vivo* for all beginning biology students. Pasteur's proof was a simple modification of Spallanzani's experiment. Rather than sealing the flask, he drew the neck out into a thin undulating tube, open to the air. After boiling, the broth remained sterile because dust and bacteria and mold spores were trapped in the neck of the flask even though the air molecules had free passage. After Pasteur had completed his painstaking series of experiments, no satisfactory explanation for the origin of life remained. Special creation was not a scientific explanation, and spontaneous generation had been shown not to occur. However, it might be noted at this point that negative proof can never be regarded as final.

An interesting twist in the theories was the concept that nonliving substances came from living things rather than vice versa, a form of vitalism based on the idea that life itself is eternal. Another more or less related theory involves cosmozoa, living particles dispersed throughout the cosmos that take up their abode and evolve whenever conditions become suitable. Various methods of their transmission through space have been suggested; Richter proposed floating particles, von Helmholtz that they arrived via meteorites, and Arrhenius that they were propelled by the pressure from light rays. There is, however, no evidence supporting the existence of cosmozoa; indeed, the known effects of temperature, ultraviolet rays, and radiation on living organisms make the theory very improbable. Even if it were correct, the question of the origin of life is not answered, but is simply removed to some more inaccessible part of the universe unless it is assumed, as has been done, that cosmozoa are eternal. The theory, in sum, is far from adequate.

In recent years, a new attack has been made on the problem, and the result has been, interestingly enough, a new version of spontaneous generation. The theory proposes that life originated on earth in the past when conditions were different from those of the present, and was preceded by a gradual chemical evolution that ultimately gave rise to self-duplicating molecules. Pasteur's experiments did not eliminate this possibility, for they demonstrated only that life did not originate spontaneously under his experimental conditions.

The Composition of Living Things

In order to discuss the conditions under which life might have originated in the past, we must have some idea of the nature of living things. They are composed of water, inorganic salts, and carbon compounds—organic substances known as carbohydrates, fats, proteins, and nucleic acids. The nucleic acids in combination with protein form the hereditary material; proteins form the structure of the organism; and the fats and the carbohydrates such as starch, glycogen, and the sugars are primarily a source of energy for cellular work. These compounds are highly organized into a smoothly functioning whole in the living organism. Thermodynamically, a living animal is a very improbable structure. The complex molecules are built up from relatively few elements, actually only 20 or so out of the 95 available on the earth. Carbohydrates and fats are formed from carbon (C), oxygen (O), and hydrogen (H) alone, and these three elements and the nitrogen (N) essential to protein formation form 99 percent of living protoplasm. Sulfur and phosphorus are two other important elements, found in proteins, for example. The inorganic salts are formed primarily from sodium, potassium, calcium, magnesium, and chlorine; traces of iron, copper, manganese, zinc, cobalt, nickel, iodine, vanadium, fluorine, boron, aluminum, and bromine have been found in various species of plants or animals.

The availability of the elements does not determine their utilization in living organisms, for some very common elements in the earth's crust are either absent or present in very low concentrations in organisms. Hence, some sort of selective process must be involved. The unique feature about hydrogen, oxygen, nitrogen, and carbon is that they are the smallest four atoms that can become stable by gaining 1, 2, 3, and 4 electrons respectively in their outer shell of electrons. They share electrons with other atoms to form chemical bonds that lead to molecule formation. Phosphorus and sulfur are in the same relative position in the periodic table as nitrogen and oxygen, but they are one group higher. The lightest elements (C, H, O, N) are the only ones that regularly share two or even three pairs of electrons with other atoms and hence permit the building up of chains of atoms. Silicon is chemically similar to carbon and much more available in the earth's crust, but, lacking this electron-sharing ability, is seldom found in living organisms. The trace elements such as the iron in hemoglobin or the magnesium in chlorophyll are complex formers, holding together big molecules.

Water, which is a major component of organisms, is a unique substance. It is the best solvent known, and has a long liquid range—that is, a high boiling point and a low freezing point. It promotes the ionization of salts through its high dielectric constant, and it expands from 4° C down to 0° C, its freezing point.

Formation of Organic Compounds

Our previous discussion of the formation of the present universe indicated that the elements were not likely to be bound together in large molecules; in other words, organic compounds such as carbohydrates, fats, and proteins were not present on the earth during its formative period. Life could not have originated on the earth until the earth had assumed more or less its present form; thus, before we can talk of the origin of life, we must discover what conditions prevailed on the earth several billion years ago and what means were available to cause the synthesis of the more complex compounds from the very simple ones that existed then. Unfortunately, these questions are not easy to answer. For example, it is not certainly known whether the earth's atmosphere then contained free oxygen; prevailing opinion is that no free oxygen was present and that the atmosphere was reducing in character. However, several mechanisms have now been demonstrated experimentally by which more or less complex organic molecules can be obtained from simple carbon compounds such as formic acid or methane and nitrogenous substances such as ammonia or nitric acid or nitrates. Shown below are some of the structural formulas of compounds mentioned in the text.

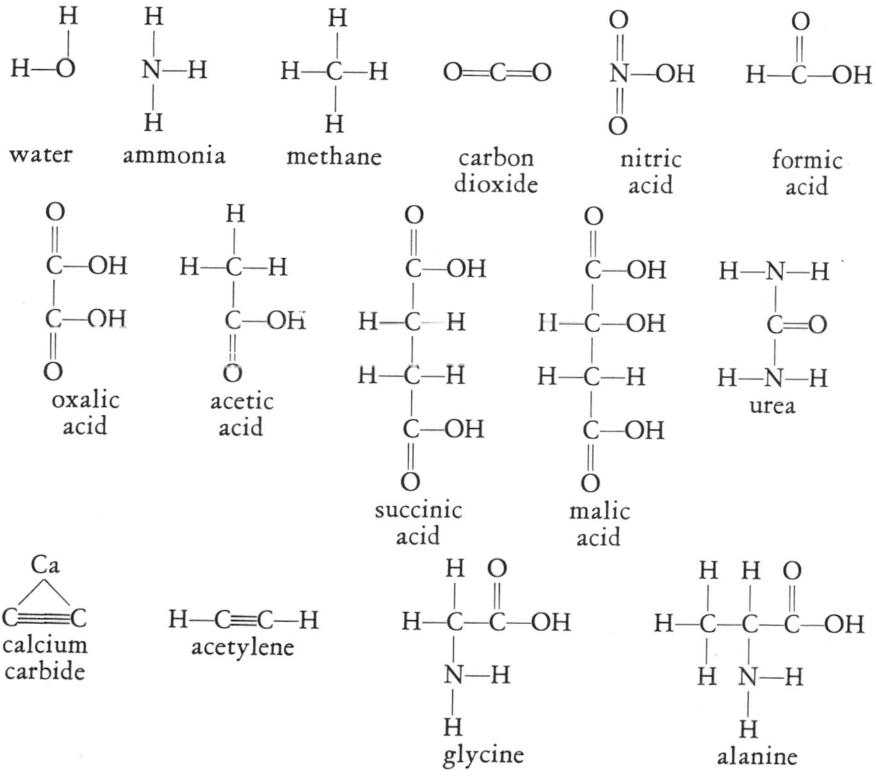

water   ammonia   methane   carbon dioxide   nitric acid   formic acid

oxalic acid   acetic acid   succinic acid   malic acid   urea

calcium carbide   acetylene   glycine   alanine

At present, living things directly or indirectly get their free energy from sunlight by means of the photosynthetic process in green plants. Before the evolution of photosynthesis, other energy sources had to be used because simple molecules such as CH_4, H_2O, NH_3 and so on do not absorb light in the visible spectrum. Only after the appearance of compounds like the porphyrins (for example, chlorophyll) or other pigments did absorption in the visible spectrum become possible. The energy sources that could have made significant contributions to the early synthesis of organic compounds appear to have been primarily ultraviolet light and electric discharges such as lightning. The possible contributions of energy from cosmic rays, radioactivity, or volcanoes seem to have been very slight. Although thermal synthesis of organic compounds has been suggested, its significance has been questioned. The surface of the primitive earth is thought to have been cool, as the result of its formation from the condensation of a cold cloud of cosmic dust, and therefore unfavorable to this type of synthesis.

A number of experiments to demonstrate possible methods for the synthesis of organic compounds prior to the existence of living organisms have been performed. One type of experiment involved the illumination of aqueous solutions of these simple compounds with ultraviolet light; the result was formation of amino acids and heterocyclic or ring compounds. In another experiment, water vapor, ammonia, methane, and hydrogen, substances all thought to have been present in the primitive reduced atmosphere, were passed over an electric spark to simulate the effects of electric discharges in the upper atmosphere. The amino acids, glycine and alanine, plus several others were recovered after a week. Still another method was suggested by the Russian biochemist, Oparin, who initiated the recent discussions on chemical evolution with his book *The Origin of Life* published in 1936. He suggested that the earth, cooling from a hot miasma, had its carbon primarily in the form of metallic carbides, which, on coming in contact with water, formed the hydrocarbon, acetylene. The acetylene then could polymerize under the influence of catalysts to form the longer carbon chain molecules. Furthermore, the thermal production and conversion of amino acids from malic acid and urea has also been demonstrated. Finally, a fifth method to be tested experimentally was the effect of very high energy radiation such as that from cosmic rays or from radioactive minerals. In this manner solutions of carbon dioxide and water have been irradiated to form formic acid; the formic acid has then produced the 2-carbon compounds, oxalic acid and acetic acid, and even the 4-carbon compound, succinic acid, but all in very low concentrations. Just which conditions prevailed and which mechanisms were important billions of years ago cannot yet be stated with certainty. The important point is that several mechanisms have been demonstrated by which organic compounds, those with carbon-carbon or carbon-hydrogen bonds, can be formed without the mediation of living organisms.

Granted, then, that organic compounds could have been formed; the next logical question concerns their stability. Today, organic substances are rapidly destroyed, primarily by decay or oxidation. Decay is due to the activities of living microorganisms, but since no life existed at the time we are discussing, the organic compounds were not then subject to this kind of decomposition. Furthermore, since it is generally thought that free oxygen was virtually absent from the earth's early atmosphere, organic matter was not subject to oxidation either, and hence could accumulate on the earth's surface. A further point of interest is the belief that carbon dioxide, like oxygen, was essentially absent from the early atmosphere though now both are common in the air. The conclusion to be drawn is that both oxygen and carbon dioxide are present in the atmosphere because of the activities of living organisms; oxygen because of its release during photosynthesis by plants, carbon dioxide due to the respiration or metabolic activity of almost all living things.

Although the early organic compounds were not subject to decay or oxidation, they were not entirely stable. Just as "spontaneous" formation of organic matter was undoubtedly possible, so was "spontaneous" decomposition, since chemical reactions are reversible, and some sort of equilibrium between synthesis and decomposition is achieved. Furthermore, because of the energy relations between the various compounds, the equilibrium point is usually far on the side of decomposition. Thus, although amino acids have a certain probability of uniting to form polypeptides or even proteins, the probability that a protein or polypeptide will break up into its constituent amino acids is far greater.

At this point in our chronology we have a more or less random assortment of simple, relatively stable organic molecules, such as amino acids, in the form of a dilute aqueous solution—a rather thin broth—still a far cry from even the simplest of living organisms. Present-day organisms can only maintain themselves and grow by a constant expenditure of energy drawn from their environments. A living organism is, in a sense, a chemical machine, which, because of its organization and metabolic activity, is able to take up materials and energy from the environment and incorporate them in order to survive, grow, and reproduce itself. The next question is the crux of the problem of the origin of life: How, from the dilute broth of organic compounds, did higher types of organization arise, persist, and ultimately lead to self duplicating entities? Unfortunately, our knowledge here is only a beginning toward complete understanding. However, various suggestions have been made as to ways in which large molecules, once formed, are kept from breaking up. If the molecules are removed from solution by precipitation, they no longer are so apt to disintegrate. Similarly, by becoming attached to other molecules, they are "trapped" in their more complex form. In this fashion, molecular aggregates of considerable complexity could have been built up in a stepwise fashion. Furthermore, the orderly propensities of matter—their tendency toward forming crystals, for example—could also have played a role in bringing structure to the random assortment of substances. This order is inherent in the molecules. Muscle or cartilage fibers, after being dissolved, will return, on precipitation, to their original molecular patterns. Proteins are composed of long chains of amino acids connected by peptide linkages (that is, a bond formed between the carboxyl group (—COOH) of one amino acid and the amino group (—NH$_2$) of the next with the elimination of H$_2$O). Since these bonds are broken or hydrolyzed in water, it has also been proposed that the long polypeptide chains were first formed by polymerization in, for example, a dried-up pool in the absence of water rather than in the primordial "soup."

Perhaps the most characteristic trait of living things is their ability to reproduce their own kind. It is at this point that we must begin to think in terms of chemical evolution governed by a selective process akin to natural selection. Some chemical compounds are catalysts for their own formation; in a more or less random group of molecules or aggregates, an autocatalytic compound will have a selective advantage over the others, for it will tend to transform the others into itself or, in the competition for substrate, it will win out as each new unit in turn catalyzes the formation of others like itself. Furthermore, the more efficient autocatalysts will win out in competition with the less efficient types so that in time very efficient self-duplicating systems will arise. If these molecular aggregates become unstable when they exceed a certain size, they will break up, and the cycle of self-duplication will then start anew.

Sources of Energy and Food

Finally, we should consider the ways in which living organisms get the energy they need to continue to exist. This energy must be externally derived by the organism. Not only must the energy be obtained, but it must be available in such a form that the organism can make use of it. Today living things obtain their energy by means of coupled reactions in which one reaction gives off energy to another that absorbs it. Probably the most important of such coupled reactions in present organisms is oxidative phosphorylation, by means of which the energy from burning (or oxidizing) sugar is made available to do cellular work rather than being lost as heat. Instead of being released in one large burst, the oxidation is stepwise, and at each step a little parcel of energy is tied up as chemical energy in a molecule known as adenosine triphosphate (ATP). The formation of a single peptide linkage in a protein requires a small amount of free energy, energy that can be obtained through a coupled reaction with an ATP molecule. The energy exchanges involving ATP are useful not only in protein synthesis but also in muscle contraction and in a variety of other ways in the cell. The unique feature of the ATP molecule is that two of its three phosphate groups are linked together by what are known as "energy-rich" or "high-energy" phosphate bonds. The significant property of these phosphate groups is that in transfer to another compound they carry with them a certain amount of free energy, and in this way supply the energy needed to do cellular work at the time, in the place, and in the amounts needed. The efficient energy-coupling systems involving ATP and catalyzed by enzymes undoubtedly are the product of the evolutionary process and are probably derived from simpler, less efficient systems in the past.

In addition to energy, the living organism if it is to live, grow, and reproduce requires food. The source of food for primitive organisms, formed under the conditions described previously, must have been the other organic molecules in the aqueous broth. Since oxygen was absent, the only process available was fermentation, by which energy is obtained from the breakage and rearrangement of organic compounds in the absence of oxygen. A typical fermentation is that of sugar by yeast to yield alcohol, carbon dioxide, and energy.

$$C_6H_{12}O_6 \rightarrow 2CO_2 + 2C_2H_5OH + \text{energy}$$

glucose　　　　carbon　　　ethyl
　　　　　　　dioxide　　　alcohol

The CO_2 and alcohol are waste products in the cell and must be eliminated. Fermentation is a destructive process, however, and the exhaustion of the available organic compounds would have led to a cessation of life.

The next step must have been the evolutionary invention of photosynthesis, made possible by the quantities of CO_2 released by fermentation. Thus it became possible for living organisms to synthesize their own organic molecules, using the energy from the sun. The equation

$$6CO_2 + 6H_2O \xrightarrow[\text{light}]{\text{sun-}} C_6H_{12}O_6 + 6O_2$$

carbon　　　water　　　　glucose　　oxygen
dioxide

shows the synthesis of sugar; nitrogen was available from inorganic nitrates or ammonia, and therefore all of the necessary organic compounds could be synthesized. Living things now were no longer dependent on the accumulated organic matter from the nonliving era, but could synthesize needed materials by photosynthesis and obtain necessary energy by fermentation.

The oxygen production by photosynthesis provided a much more efficient source of energy, however. The waste products of fermentation—alcohol, lactic acid, formic acid, etc.—are poisonous, and the energy yield is low. The process of respiration, or the combination with oxygen, is much more efficient, for the energy produced is about 35 times as great for the same amount of sugar consumed. All possible energy is extracted; thus a maximum amount of energy is obtained from a minimum amount of material. Furthermore, the waste products, carbon dioxide and water, are harmless and easily disposed of. The equation for respiration is

$$C_6H_{12}O_6 + 6O_2 \rightarrow 6CO_2 + 6H_2O + \text{energy}$$

glucose　　oxygen　　　carbon　　water
　　　　　　　　　　　dioxide

The processes of photosynthesis and respiration have made life, as we know it today, possible. In tending to pride ourselves on our progress and on our control over the environment, we sometimes overlook man's complete dependence on energy from the sun for his very existence. Since fermenting organisms have never evolved to a very high degree of organization and complexity, it seems reasonable to suppose that only with the origin of respiration did the evolution of more complex organisms, including man, become possible.

Therefore, the current hypotheses of the origin of life envision initially the random formation of more or less complex organic compounds from the simpler molecules present in what was probably a reducing atmosphere. Autocatalytic molecules, having a selective advantage over the other types, tended to increase in frequency. At what point one should stop speaking of molecules and start referring to living organisms is rather difficult to say. However, since a self-duplicating system capable of mutation is frequently regarded as the fundamental criterion for life, by this standard we are already discussing living systems. The original organisms were heterotrophic, obtaining their essential constituents from the environment rather than synthesizing them from carbon dioxide and water. Evolution of additional enzyme systems as a result of the selective process then led to autotrophic organisms capable of carrying out increasingly complex and efficient syntheses from very simple precursor substances. The exact steps by which cellular life as we know it today arose through the process of chemical evolution cannot be stated with certainty. Nevertheless, some of the basic questions involve the origin of protein synthesis, of deoxyribonucleic acid as the genetic material, of high-energy organic phosphates such as ATP, of catalytic compounds or enzymes, particularly the porphyrins, and the origin of cell structure. Although answers to these questions are at present rather speculative, active research in this field is in progress, and at a recent symposium on evolution, a panel of experts was unanimous in agreeing that the synthesis of life was both conceivable and possible in the not too distant future.

Hence, the origin of life cannot be regarded as a mysterious, unique process but, rather, one that was practically inevitable and, moreover, will occur whenever and wherever similar conditions exist. Since billions of planets like the earth are scattered throughout the universe, it is conceivable that life exists in many more places than the earth. The astronomer Harlow Shapley has estimated very conservatively that there are approximately 100,000,000 planets in the universe capable of supporting life similar to that on the earth. None of the details of this account can be taken too seriously or as finally established, and to some people it may seem no more than a modern fable of the origin of life, comparable to those of the ancients and with a similar purpose. Nevertheless, there is sufficient evidence to consider it a reasonable hypothesis worthy of further study.

▶ *SUMMARY*

Again, as with the origin of the universe, recent scientific advances have made it possible to attempt to answer the question of the origin of life on a rational basis and even to tackle it experimentally. Present theories recognize that life arose when the physical conditions on the earth were quite different from those at present. A long period of chemical evolution is thought to have preceded the origin of the first self-duplicating particles that could be called living. The earliest forms of life are thought to have been saprophytic, deriving energy from the fermentation of organic compounds in the environment. Only later did living cells evolve the ability to synthesize complex molecules from simple precursors, a trend that culminated in the evolutionary invention of photosynthesis. Respiration, a far more efficient process of energy extraction than fermentation, only became possible after the oxygen in the atmosphere increased as a result of photosynthesis.

SUGGESTED READING

Blum, H. F., 1955. *Time's arrow and evolution,* 2d ed. Princeton: Princeton University Press.

Calvin, M., 1956. "Chemical evolution and the origin of life," *Amer. Sci.,* 44:248-263.

———, 1959. "Evolution of enzymes and the photosynthetic apparatus," *Science,* 130:1170-1174.

———, 1959. "Round trip from space," *Evolution, 13:*362-377.

Fox, S. W., 1956. "Evolution of protein molecules and thermal synthesis of biochemical substances," *Amer. Sci.,* 44:347-359.

Gaffron, H., 1960. "The origin of life," *Evolution after Darwin,* Vol. I, *The Evolution of life.* S. Tax, ed. Chicago: University of Chicago Press.

Miller, S. L., 1953. "A production of amino acids under possible primitive earth conditions," *Science, 117:*528-529.

———, and H. C. Urey, 1959. "Organic compound synthesis on the primitive earth," *Science, 130:*245-251.

Oparin, A. I., 1957. *The origin of life on the earth,* 3d ed. New York: Academic Press.

———, et al., eds., 1959. *The origin of life on the earth.* Pergamon Press. Reports of the Moscow Symposium on the origin of life. August 1957.

Pringle, J. W. S., 1953. "The origin of life," *Symposium Soc. Exp. Biol.,* 7 (Evolution):1-21. New York: Academic Press.

Wald, G., 1954. "The origin of life," *Sci. Amer., 191*(2):44-53.

CHAPTER 7

Geographical Distribution

The physical evidence for evolution consists of living organisms and the remains of organisms that have lived in the past. Although the fossil record presents concrete evidence that species differing from all living species lived long ago, it is often sketchy or incomplete on critical points. If the record were complete, we would have before us the complete phylogeny of all living things and there would be no need to seek further information by more indirect methods. However, because of the paucity of the fossil record, it has been necessary to turn to living organisms to plot more fully the course of past evolution. The study of the present geographical distribution of animals and plants has lent considerable support to the theory of evolution.

In our discussion of adaptation we noted that organisms are adapted to their environments. It is now necessary to analyze this situation still further. Within a given geographical area, the environment is not uniform; in other words, a great variety of different types of habitat exist. In the state of Minnesota, for example, three major types of terrestrial habitat can be recognized: the deciduous forest in the southeast, the coniferous forest to the north, and the prairie in the west and southwest. If the variety of fresh-water habitats to be found in the thousands of lakes, and in the streams, swamps, bogs, and rivers is included, the range of possible habitats becomes even wider. Yet each species has its own ecological niche, its own unique requirements of the environment; where these are not met, that species is not to be found. To use a painfully obvious example, the fish in Minnesota are confined to the water. Much more subtle differences than that between fresh water and dry land may determine whether a species will be found in a particular spot; thus, within a given area such as Minnesota, the ecological conditions may vary widely, and the species present will vary also in accordance with the changes in ecological factors. Though no physical barrier exists, the animals and plants to be found in the deciduous forest areas of southeastern Minnesota are distinctly different from the animals and plants to be found in the coniferous forests to the north, and surprisingly few species are common to both areas.

But, and this is a very important "but," there is another aspect to distribution, which can be most readily outlined by quoting from Darwin.

Neither the similarity nor the dissimilarity of the inhabitants of various regions can be wholly accounted for by climatal and other physical conditions . . . . There is hardly a climate or condition in the Old World which cannot be paralleled in the New—at least as closely as the same species generally require . . . . Notwithstanding this general parallelism in the conditions of the Old and New Worlds, how widely different are their living productions.

For example, the climates of parts of Australia, South Africa, and western South America are very much the same, but the fauna and flora in each region are strikingly different. In South America, on the other hand, the species south of 35° latitude and those north of 25° latitude are clearly quite similar, although they live under markedly different climatic conditions.

Biogeographical Realms

Because species living in the same region tend to resemble each other despite considerable differences in climate and habitat, it has been possible to delimit biogeographical realms, within which the existing groups of animals and plants show many similarities. These realms, shown in Fig. 7-1, are the

1. Nearctic—North America down into the Mexican plateau in central Mexico.
2. Palearctic—Asia north of the Himalayas, Europe, and Africa north of the Sahara Desert. Since the species of the Nearctic and Palearctic regions are much alike in many respects, these two regions are sometimes grouped together as the Holarctic.
3. Neotropical—Central and South America.
4. Ethiopian—Africa south of the Sahara.
5. Oriental—Asia south of the Himalayas.
6. Australian.

Though the absence of a species because of an unsuitable environment is easy to appreciate, its absence when the environment is favorable poses other questions. There is little doubt that many species can survive and even thrive in regions other than the one in which they normally occur. The rapid increase and spread across the United States of the English sparrow and the starling introduced from Europe within the past century is a case in point. Further examples are the depredations of the Japanese beetle and the gypsy moth, two other species recently introduced into the United States. Many of our common roadside weeds and flowers also had their origin in Europe, but were brought here with seeds or escaped from gardens. The phenomenal increase in the number of rabbits in Australia, where they have become a serious pest in the absence of the predators found in their usual range, is striking evidence that ecological factors alone do not determine the distribution and numbers of animals.

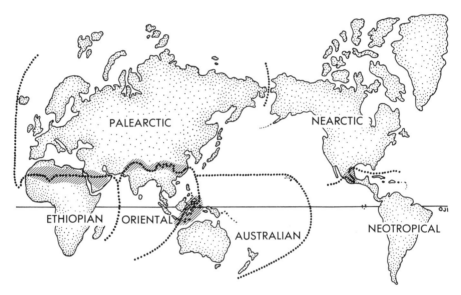

Fig. 7-1. The biogeographical realms.

Table 7-1 shows the distribution of some significant groups of mammals; a few comments may help emphasize some of its important aspects. The similarities between the Nearctic and Palearctic are quite obvious. The single metatherian or marsupial in the Nearctic is the opossum, and the edentate is the armadillo, both of which appear to have spread north from South America. The few primates of the Palearctic are found on the fringes of the Ethiopian and Oriental realms. Although no members of the camel group now exist in the Nearctic, large numbers of fossils indicate their presence in the past. Not only the same major groups but closely similar species within these groups are to be found in the Nearctic and Palearctic.

The Neotropical realm is a curious mixture of "modern" and "primitive" mammals. The edentates are also characteristic and quite numerous.

The Ethiopian or African region has the richest mammalian fauna but lacks completely the monotremes and marsupials. The hoofed mammals or ungulates are a large and important group with many representatives of both the *Perissodactyla* (odd-toed) and *Artiodactyla* (even-toed) orders. There are many rodents, carnivores, insectivores, and primates.

In the Oriental region, similarities to both the Ethiopian and Palearctic realms can be seen. For example, elephants, rhinoceroses, and antelope are common to the Ethiopian and Oriental; deer (*Cervidae*), and sheep and goats to the Palearctic and Oriental (and Nearctic).

TABLE 7-1
Distribution of Certain Mammalian Groups

Group	Biogeographical Realm					
	Neotropical	Nearctic	Palearctic	Ethiopian	Oriental	Australian
Monotremes	—	—	—	—	—	2
Marsupials	+	1	—	—	2	+
Edentates	+	1	—	—	—	—
Bats	+	+	+	+	+	+
Ungulates (Artiodactyls & Perissodactyls)	few	+	+	+	+	—
Rodents	⊕	+	+	+	+	⊕
Carnivores	+	+	+	+	+	—
Primates [a]	+	—	few	+	+	—
Insectivores	few	+	+	+	+	—
Lagomorphs	+	+	+	+	+	(introduced)
Tapirs	+	—	—	—	+	—
Camels	+	—	+	—	—	—

+ -representatives of group are present.
— -representatives of group are absent.
1, 2 -only 1 or 2 species of group are present.
⊕ -group is well represented but species differ markedly from those in other parts of the world.
[a] -exclusive of man.

In Australia, very few groups are represented; the marsupials predominate, and only the rodents and bats are well represented among the Eutheria. The only living egg-laying mammals or monotremes are found there.

From this brief sketch of mammalian distribution, it is clear that the different regions of the world have their own distinctive faunas, though adjacent regions tend to show more similarities than more remote areas. It should also be noted that the *Chiroptera,* the bats, are the only order rather uniformly distributed throughout the world. The widely distributed rodents have endemic groups (that is, peculiar to a particular locality), especially in Australia and the Neotropical region. Similar findings have emerged from the study of other animal and plant groups. The above facts suggest that in addition to the ecological factors that set limits on distribution, the other major limiting factor on distribution is what we may term the historical. A species or group will only be present in a given region if, at some time in the past, it was able to reach that region. For most species, oceans or deserts or mountain ranges have been barriers to the further expansion of their ranges. The bats, however, with their great mobility, have spread easily throughout the world, even to the most remote oceanic islands. This explanation raises almost as many problems as it solves, for the implication is that each species has had a single center of origin. The questions that arise in connection with any species are, then, where was its center of origin and when did it originate.

Present distribution is intelligible only on the assumptions that each species has originated only once, that species have had their origins in practically all habitable parts of the earth, and that they have originated throughout the geological history of the earth. Each species tends to expand like a gas from its center of origin, the pressure being due to its high reproductive capacity; migration will then fill all available areas until further expansion is blocked by physical barriers or by unfavorable environmental conditions. New species can evolve only after a population of an existing species has become to some degree physically isolated from the parental species. Hence related species or groups will tend to be found in adjacent areas. We will now consider some specific examples of geographical distribution and see how they are explained in terms of the theory of evolution plus a knowledge of the geological history of the earth.

Primitive and Modern Mammals in the Neotropical

The mixture of "primitive" and "modern" mammals in the Neotropical region has already been mentioned. The "primitive" group includes anteaters, sloths, armadillos, many marsupials, primitive primates (platyrrhine monkeys and marmosets), and a unique group of rodents. All of these are peculiar to South America. The "modern" group is very similar to the fauna of North America though for the most part the species are different. Included are deer, various cats, wolves, otters, many rodents, guanacos, and llamas.

With the assumption of evolution, the explanation is relatively simple. Marine fossils similar to those of the Miocene elsewhere are found on land in Panama; thus Panama, the link between North and South America, must have been submerged during the mid-Tertiary. The "primitive" group of mammals reached South America in the late Cretaceous and Paleocene from North America and then evolved in isolation during the period of submergence. Re-emergence of the land gave rise first to island chains and then Panama rose again above the surface of the sea during the Pleistocene. The "modern" mammals invaded South America via this new land bridge. Many of the "primitive" forms in South America could not compete with the more efficient new immigrants and became extinct. Their history is known from the extensive fossil record. Only a few species of the South American fauna were adaptable enough to spread their ranges into North America, among them the armadillo, the opossum, and the porcupine.

Nearctic and Palearctic

The similarities in the biota of North America and Eurasia have already been mentioned as warranting the inclusion of both areas in one biogeographical realm, the Holarctic. Though these two land masses are now isolated, the evidence is clear that in the late Tertiary, a land bridge in the Bering Sea region was repeatedly formed and broken. The fossil record indicates that the camels originated in North America and flourished here, evolving into a variety of species, some of which migrated to South America or to Asia. At present the group is entirely extinct in North America, but the curiously disjunct distribution of the group is intelligible when the fossil record and geological events are known. However, migration more frequently was from Asia to North America; the bison, mammoths, bears, cats, and deer, for example, originated in the Eurasian land mass and spread to North America. It should be realized that during this period climatic conditions underwent changes as well. Early in the Cenozoic, North America was relatively flat, and the Bering land bridge formed a broad connection between the two continents. Fossils deposited at that time indicate that the climate was much milder than at present, for the fossil record shows that alligators, sassafras trees, and magnolias were more or less continuously distributed from southeastern United States to eastern China, from the banks of the Yangtse to the banks of the Suwanee. In the late Cenozoic, the Rockies rose, western North America became colder and drier, and these species were eliminated from much of their former range. Next came the glaciers, which wiped out practically everything in their paths. In North America their extreme southern limits were, roughly, the Ohio River and the Missouri River (see Fig. 7-2). During this invasion by the ice, southeastern United States and eastern China were only slightly affected, and in these two areas the alligators, the sassafras, and the magnolias survived. In the million years since these populations became isolated from each other they have evolved to the extent that they are now recognized as distinct species of the same genus; there are other species (for example, skunk cabbage) that are apparently the same in both areas.

Relict Alpine Populations

In the Northern Hemisphere it is often observed that species at the higher altitudes in mountainous areas are similar to those at lower altitudes farther north rather than to the species living at the foot of the mountains. For

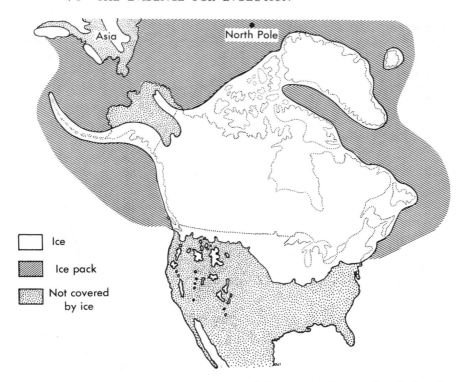

Fig. 7-2. The approximate extent of the glaciers in North America during the Pleistocene.

example, some of the species in the Great Smoky Mountains of Tennessee are only found again hundreds of miles to the north in Canada, and some plants on Mt. Washington in the White Mountains of New Hampshire are isolated populations of species found in Labrador. It seems probable that species adapted to arctic or subarctic conditions retreated to the south as the glaciers advanced, and were forced into more southern areas of North America. As the glaciers retreated, the species migrated north and also up the mountainsides, continuing to survive in areas to which they were adapted. In this way relict populations were left behind on the mountains.

Primitive Southern Fauna

Not only South America but the other southern land masses, Africa and Australia, have "primitive" fauna, each, however, quite unique. Australia's mammals are primarily marsupials, and among the insects are found primitive bees, termites, and butterflies. In Africa, "primitive" primates such as the lemurs, and other species such as the aardwolf and the chevrotain still exist. Each of the three areas has a genus of the lungfish. This concentration of primitive species in the Southern Hemisphere has led some investigators to believe that these land masses were at one time united but later split apart and gradually drifted northward to their present positions. This interesting theory of "Continental Drift" postulates that at one time there were two major land masses— Gondwana, centering on the South Pole, and Laurasia in the vicinity of the equator. These masses drifted gradually northward, Laurasia splitting into North America and Eurasia, and Gondwana splitting up to form Africa, South America, Antarctica, and the Arabian and Indian peninsulas. The drifting was very slow and not completed until the Tertiary. Although the fossils of tropical species in Alaska and the lungfish genera and other similarities between Australia, Africa, and South America could be explained on this basis, the geological evidence for the split is not impressive and the theory poses about as many biogeographical problems as it solves.

Some form of Matthew's theory of climate and evolution seems a more reasonable explanation for the geographical distribution of living and fossil species. Matthew suggested that the continents and ocean basins have occupied relatively permanent positions at least since the Mesozoic, but that the climate of the earth has fluctuated between warm, moist periods and cold, dry periods. During the warm phases, the seas have covered the continental lowlands, and tropical and subtropical species have expanded their ranges far to the north. During the cold phases, the continents were elevated, glaciers expanded southward, and only the tropics remained mild. The land masses were primarily north of the equator, and the southern continents remained more or less isolated and warm even during the cold periods. In the glacial periods, species had to adapt to the changing conditions, or migrate, or perish. Major new evolutionary types seem to have appeared on the major land masses, the southern continents serving as refuges. This theory explains geographical distribution, then, by means of climatic changes and known land bridges, with no major shifts in the position of the continents or the oceans. The most probable explanation of the fossil record appears to be that the earliest mammals—monotremes and marsupials—originated in Eurasia or North America and were able to migrate into all the major land areas. When the placental mammals arose, also in the Northern Hemisphere, they replaced the marsupials in the Holarctic; the former connection to Australia was completely broken, however, and Africa and South America were partially isolated by barriers of desert or water, and the more "primitive" forms there were at least partly protected from competition with the more "modern" and efficient mammals that continued to evolve to the north.

Continental and Oceanic Islands

Two distinct types of islands, continental and oceanic, can be identified. The continental islands are generally separated from a continent by a shallow sea. The rock formations on both the land mass and the island are similar, with the islands basically formed from stratified rock. The continental islands are separated from the mainland if the sea level rises or the land sinks. Typical of the continental type are the British Isles, Borneo, Sumatra, and Java. Oceanic islands are usually volcanic in origin, hence formed of igneous rock, and are separated from the major land masses by deep water. The Hawaiian Islands and the Galápagos Islands are examples of oceanic islands. Not only do continental and oceanic islands differ in their mode of origin, but they have quite different types of fauna.

Each of the oceanic islands or island groups has its own distinctive fauna, different from the faunas in all other parts of the world. Compared with the continents, the oceanic islands have depauperate faunas. There are seldom any mammals except bats, though rodents, possibly introduced by man, are sometimes present. The only fresh-water fishes are those capable of adapting to life in salt water. Such small animals as snails, lizards, insects, and land birds are found. The fauna of continental islands is clearly derived from the nearby continent; though the species may sometimes be different, the similarities are quite striking. There is a distinct relationship between distance and the similarity of the species on island and mainland. The British Isles have essentially the same species as the European mainland; Ireland, however, lacks some elements found on the continent. Though St. Patrick has long received credit for the absence of snakes there, their inability to cross an ocean barrier in postglacial times is a more reasonable, though less romantic, explanation. Where the distance is greater or the connection to the continent less recent, as in Sumatra, Java, or Borneo, different species have had a chance to evolve, but they are similar to the mainland species that originally populated the island and from which they are descended. On Sumatra, for example, a small edition—a different species—of the rhinoceros found on the mainland has evolved. For some reason, island species are frequently smaller than their close relatives on the mainland, but the adaptive significance of this tendency requires further study.

After a volcanic eruption the oceanic islands must have formed a barren mass of rock in the vast distances of the sea. The explosion of Krakatoa in 1883 has provided an actual example of such an event for study. Once formed, the island will become inhabited only by those species capable in one way or another of traversing the formidable barrier of ocean and sheer distance that confronts the terrestrial species. Chance thus plays a large role in determining which species happen to bridge the gap. Some groups, however, are much more capable of wide dispersal than others; for example, the probability is great that such groups as birds and bats will be present, but it is practically zero for elephants. Among the birds, chance again may play a major role in determining which species reach the island. The Hawaiian honey creepers and Darwin's finches on the Galápagos Islands are instances of arrays of species that have evolved on the islands from original immigrant groups, perhaps even a single flock wandering or blown far from its usual haunts.

Thus, the present distribution of species is most intelligible if interpreted in terms of the ecological conditions, the historical factors that have limited their expansion, and the theory of evolution. Within this framework, the peculiarities of island distribution, alpine distribution, regional similarities, and the many other facets of biogeographical distribution can be fitted. No other system has a logical, rational explanation for so many of the facts.

 **▶ SUMMARY**

Plants and animals are not uniformly distributed over all parts of the world. The spread of many species is quite obviously limited by the prevailing ecological conditions. Nevertheless, the suitability or unsuitability of the environment is not alone a sufficient explanation for the distribution of the flora and fauna, for introductions have shown that many species can thrive far beyond the limits of their natural range. On the other hand, within a given land mass, even though a variety of habitats exists, the species tend to evidence many similarities despite their adaptation to different conditions. These facts are most easily explained by the theory of evolution. Within a given region the variously adapted groups have evolved from a common ancestral stock; hence their underlying resemblances that made possible the identification of biogeographical realms. The changing, evolving species in one area can only spread into other parts of the world if there are no barriers to their expansion. Thus, distribution has an historical as well as an ecological basis. The details of continental, alpine, and island distributions of living species have become increasingly well understood as knowledge of paleontology and past geological and climatic changes has increased. Nevertheless, the theory of evolution is essential to a complete understanding of present-day distribution, for the species have obviously been dynamic and changing rather than static entities.

SUGGESTED READING

Cain, A. S., 1944. *Foundations of plant geography.* New York: Harper.
Darlington, P. J., 1957. *Zoogeography.* New York: Wiley.
Darwin, C., 1839. *The voyage of the Beagle.* New York: Bantam Books (1958).
Du Toit, A. L., 1937. *Our wandering continents.* Edinburgh: Oliver and Boyd.
Lack, D., 1947. *Darwin's finches.* New York: Cambridge University Press.
Matthew, W. D., 1939. Climate and evolution, 2d ed. New York: New York Academy of Science.

Simpson, G. G., 1950. "History of the fauna of Latin America," *Amer. Sci.*, 38:361-389.
———, 1953. *Evolution and geography.* Eugene: Oregon State System of Higher Education.
Wallace, A. R., 1876. *The geographical distribution of animals,* 2 vols. London: Macmillan.
———, 1911. *Island life,* 3d ed. London: Macmillan.
Wegener, A., 1924. *The origin of the continents and oceans,* 3d ed. (J. G. A. Skerl, tr.) New York: Dutton.

CHAPTER 8

Systematics

Taxonomy is one of the oldest biological disciplines, but today it is increasingly being pushed into the background by the rapid developments in such fields as physiology, ecology, embryology, and genetics. Yet taxonomy remains as the foundation stone for all biological research simply because the starting point in any biological experiment is an organism, and in order to conduct and describe an experiment properly, you must know and know with certainty what organism you are using. Otherwise, it may be impossible for you or anyone else to confirm or to duplicate your results. This fact has all too often been slighted or overlooked, particularly by experimental biologists, who may speak of using "liver" or "frog muscle" as if all livers and all frog muscles were alike. In at least one instance, a series of experiments was abandoned after it was found to be impossible to identify the organisms being used.

Classification

All of us are taxonomists to some extent, in that we learn to identify the animals and plants that we encounter frequently. Taxonomy, or systematics as it is often called, grew out of the study of local faunas and floras. As information accumulated, the taxonomic problems quickly became more complex than those encountered in a local, essentially nondimensional system. It is virtually a biological axiom that no two organisms are identical. Yet it is also true that some organisms are much more alike than others. The taxonomist's problem, essentially, is to seize upon the significant similarities and thus try to bring some sort of order out of this chaos of variation. Many different systems are possible. Plants, for example, may be grouped by the color of their flowers as is often done in popular flower guides, or by their habitats, or by their size, and so on. The method used, which is not quite so simple, is known as the "natural system of classification" and stems from Aristotle. It is based on the degree of similarity in morphological characters, for it has been found that many individuals are very much alike and can be grouped together as a species. All house cats, for example, belong to the species *Felis catus*. Certain species, in turn, are quite similar and hence are grouped together in a higher category, the genus. The house cat, *Felis catus,* the mountain lion, *Felis concolor,* and the lynx, *Felis lynx,* all belong to the genus *Felis*. Certain genera are much more alike than other genera and thus can be combined into a family; the genus *Panthera,* which in- cludes the "big cats" such as lions, tigers, and leopards, together with the genus *Felis* belongs to the family Felidae. The family Canidae (dogs, foxes, and wolves), the Ursidae (bears), the Mustelidae (weasels, skunks, mink, etc.), the Felidae, and several other families are grouped together in a higher group, the order Carnivora, or the flesh eaters. The orders can be arranged in still higher categories, the classes and phyla, thus forming a complete hierarchy. Each family, for example, can be characterized by a constellation of traits that sets it apart from all other families and that describes not only each genus within the family, but each species, and even each individual. Hence, to assign a species to a par- ticular higher group characterizes it at once with respect to a certain combination of traits, and the problems of dealing with over a million different species are thereby greatly simplified. Even though this hierarchical pattern of variation was recognized and used for centuries, it remained a puzzle as to why organisms fell into this particular pattern rather than some other geometrical configuration.

Variation

At this point it is well to consider the nature of variation within groups of related individuals. First of all, it must be reemphasized that there is not a continuum in the pattern of variation. There are, for example, no individuals who are intermediate in their traits between a house cat and a dog. Even in cases where the resemblance is much closer than that between a dog and a cat, inter- mediates do not exist. The thrushes of the genus *Hylocichla* are very difficult to identify in the field, but even though five different kinds—the veery, and the wood, hermit, olive-backed, and gray-cheeked thrushes—are found in the same region, intermediate types will not be found. Without now attempting a species definition, we say that there are five species, each composed of similar but not identical individuals. As in this case, species are for the most part quite distinct from each other.

Considerable variation may exist within a species, for within a given population two or more different expressions of a trait may appear, a type of variability called *polymorphism*. The most familiar example undoubtedly is a human population with its variety of sizes, shapes, eye and hair colors, and so on and on, but populations of other species show similar variability. Whether it be screech owls, deer mice, fruit flies, or turtles, variations may range from very minor differences to such a striking specimen as an albino snapping turtle. These differences between individuals may be either genetic or nongenetic in origin. Some differences are simply seasonal or age differences. The spring and fall plumage of many migratory birds and the differences between a caterpillar and a butterfly or a tadpole and a frog represent merely different stages in the life of the same individual; in some species like the aphids, seasonal generations exist. The impact of the environment can also cause wide variations. The form of corals in the surf is quite different from that found in quiet lagoons, and dandelions growing in an alpine habitat differ in form from those in the valleys below. The hereditary variations include the differences between the sexes, which may be as striking as the presence and absence of wings in some insects or antlers in deer, as well as the great array of hereditary variations of greater or lesser degree to be found in all sexually reproducing populations.

Though local populations are polymorphic, other patterns of variation emerge when wider areas are examined. A *cline* is said to exist when a trait or a group of characters is observed to change more or less continually and gradually as one moves from one part of the species' range to another. The song sparrow, *Melospiza melodia*, is widely distributed and common in North America but is by no means uniform throughout its range. In the prairies and in the arid regions of the Southwest the birds are paler in color; in the more humid regions to the east and up the Pacific coast the birds are duskier in color, the transition being more or less gradual even though at least 20 subspecies have been named. Where the species is broken up into more clearly defined geographical races or subspecies, it is said to be *polytypic* (see Fig. 8-1). For example, in the Philippines a small kingfisher inhabits a number of the islands, but each island's population is isolated from and easily distinguished from that of the other islands. Man, too, is polytypic as well as polymorphic, for the human species is readily subdivided into three major geographic races, the Negroid, Mongolian, and Caucasian.

The Binomial System

Modern taxonomy stems from the 1758 edition of *Systema Naturae*, a volume by Linnaeus, a Swedish botanist. The binomial system of nomenclature that he introduced was simple yet precise—two characteristics needed for a workable system. For example, a small fish can easily be singled out if it is known that it is pale brown "with a dark bar behind the opercles and

Fig. 8-1. The bobwhite quail, a polytypic species. Each of the five males, shown in dorsal and ventral views, is representative of a different population in the United States or Mexico. All five, so distinctive in appearance, are considered to be members of the same species, *Colinus virginianus.*

across the dorsal and anal fins, which are bright orange in spring males. The lips are thick and fleshy. The intestine is very peculiar, it is wrapped many times around the swim bladder. The scales are 7, 49-55, 8. The dorsal fin has 8 rays, the anal fin 7. The teeth are 4-4. This species reaches a length of 8 inches." (Eddy and Surber) Though it is accurate, no one in his right mind would try to use this description in everyday conversation. And yet the common name, stoneroller, is no more satisfactory, for what is one man's stoneroller may be called stonelugger by another, or doughbelly, or even rotgut minnow. The more picturesque common names suffer from their lack of precision, but the binomial, *Campostoma anomalum,* is both precise and brief, and has been assigned to the "minnows" of the family Cyprinidae fitting the above description.

At one time the scientific name was assigned to a single specimen, the type specimen, and all individuals collected subsequently were referred to it in order to determine whether they belonged to the same or a different species. One of the major advances in modern systematics is that the type concept has been almost entirely abandoned. The fallacy of the type concept can be easily made clear. Suppose, for example, you were told to go out and collect the type specimen for the species *Homo sapiens.* Would it be male, or female? If you could settle this question to your own satisfaction, how would you then decide which member of your sex to bring in? The basic facts of biological variation have made it abundantly clear that the type specimen is not typical of anything. The important point to determine is the range of variation in the species. For this purpose adequate sampling methods must be used so that statistical analyses can be applied. Hence, taxonomic studies are becoming studies of populations rather than of individuals. The type specimen has become the individual to which the species name is attached; in case what was originally thought to be one species later turns out to be two, the original name will be reserved for individuals similar to the type and a new name assigned to the other group.

As mentioned earlier, the natural system of classification, stemming from Aristotle and formalized by Linneaus, with its hierarchy of taxonomic groups of different levels of morphological similarity was always something of a biological puzzle because it worked so well even though there was no obvious reason why this particular geometrical configuration should exist rather than some other. The publication of *The Origin of Species* in 1859 offered a simple solution to the puzzle—that is, the theory of evolution. When different species are similar, the similarities are due to descent from a common ancestry. The closer the similarities, the more recent the divergence and the closer the genetic relationship between the species. After Darwin, the natural system, based on morphological similarities, became a phylogenetic system based on degree of relationship. It might be expected that changing the criterion for classification would drastically change the classification system itself, but no major changes were necessary. Perhaps the main inference to be drawn is that the system of classification is not arbitrary but natural, reflecting the objective state of species in nature. And systematics has become more than classification; it has become the study of evolution.

Some Taxonomic Problems

Although the binomial system generally works beautifully, anomalous situations occasionally arise that are very difficult to resolve satisfactorily. For example, the purple grackle breeds in a belt between the Appalachians and the Atlantic from just north of New Jersey to Florida and southern Louisiana, and the bronzed grackle breeds in New England and in the St. Lawrence and Mississippi Valleys. Yet where the ranges of the purple and bronzed grackles meet, all along the Appalachians, they interbreed, and intermediate types of individuals are found. At present, the two groups are considered separate species, *Quiscalus quiscula,* the purple grackle, and *Quiscalus versicolor,* the bronzed grackle. Where such extensive interbreeding occurs over such a large area, it would seem just as reasonable to consider them as two subspecies of the same species, which replace each other geographically.

A somewhat different situation exists in the leopard frog, *Rana pipiens,* the most widely distributed frog in North America, ranging from Mexico far into Canada. In this case it has been shown that when frogs collected in Florida or Texas are crossed with those from Wisconsin or Vermont, the hybrids are deformed and unviable. In other words, members of what is generally regarded as a single species are not even capable of interbreeding.

One further instance may be cited. Butterflies of the genus *Junonia* are distributed from Florida along the Gulf Coast, into Mexico and Central America, across northern South America, and up through the West Indies (see Fig. 8-2). The populations gradually change in their characteristics as one proceeds around the ring, but adjacent populations are similar and are capable of interbreeding. This ring of races, or *Rassenkreis* as it is often called, is closed in Cuba, for there butterflies resembling those in Florida coexist without interbreeding with butterflies like those to the south in the West Indies. In Cuba, then, these two populations behave like two distinct and well-defined species, yet there is no single place around the ring where it is possible to say that here one species stops and the other begins.

For the taxonomist who is trying to work out a satisfactory scheme of classification, situations such as the three cited pose very real and very tricky problems—and there are many others even more complex. For the student of evolution, however, these taxonomic difficulties furnish still another argument in favor of evolution. If evolution is a gradual process that has been in progress through time, then indications that species are now undergoing change should be expected among living species. The existence of these puzzling taxonomic

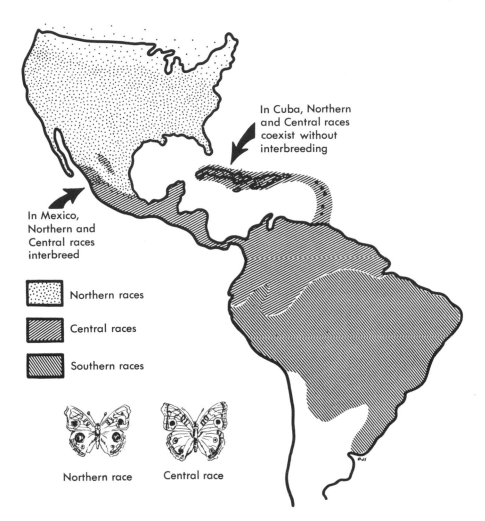

In Cuba, Northern
and Central races
coexist without
interbreeding

In Mexico,
Northern and
Central races
interbreed

Northern races

Central races

Southern races

Northern race   Central race

Fig. 8-2. The distribution of geographic races of the butterfly *Junonia lavinia
(Precis lavinia)* commonly known as the Buckeye. (Based on Forbes.)

problems is evidence that species are not static, inflexible units, but rather are
capable of change. The very hierarchy of genera, families, orders, and so forth is
in itself evidence for the correctness of the theory of evolution, for that is the
pattern that evolution should cause to develop.

SUMMARY ◄

At first acquaintance, the living world may seem a chaos of variation. It is, however, possible to bring order from this chaos, to arrange living things in a reasonable, workable system of classification. The "natural system of classification" that has developed, culminating in the Linnaean binomial system, is based on the degree of similarity in morphological traits. When arranged under this scheme, living things fall into a hierarchy with the similarities becoming more specific at each level from phylum to genus. The theory of evolution furnished a cogent explanation for this pattern of variation. The similarities so readily observed are the result of descent from a common ancestry and are a reflection of the actual genetic relationship between the species. The taxonomically difficult groups merely confirm the theory of evolution, for the difficulties largely arise in groups that are in the process of diverging to become distinct species—clear evidence of the operation of evolution.

SUGGESTED READING

Eddy, S., and T. Surber, 1947. *Northern fishes.* Minneapolis: University of Minnesota Press.

Huxley, J., ed., 1940. *The new systematics.* New York: Oxford University Press.

Mayr, E., 1942. *Systematics and the origin of species.* New York: Columbia University Press.

———, E. G. Linsley, and R. L. Usinger, 1953. *Methods and principles of systematic zoology.* New York: McGraw-Hill.

CHAPTER 9

Comparative Embryology

Each individual starts his independent existence as a single cell, the fertilized egg or zygote. The hereditary material contained by each zygote is the surviving product of millions of years of evolution. Each zygote develops in an environment of some sort. The characteristics of the adult organism are determined by the interaction between the developing embryo and its environment. Abnormalities either in the transmitted germ plasm or in the environment may cause abnormal development in the individual. The zygote itself is a spherical object bearing little or no resemblance to the adult form, which is only reached by gradual stages. The sequence of stages from the single cell to the adult and beyond—that is, the individual's developmental history from fertilization to old age—is known as the *ontogeny* of the individual. The various adult forms of an evolving species may also be considered as a series of stages in the history of the species, a series which is called its *phylogeny*. With two such series available, it was almost inevitable that someone would compare them. Haeckel, who made such a comparison, propounded the biogenetic "law" or the Theory of Recapitulation, which states, "Ontogeny recapitulates phylogeny." In other words, the embryo in its development retraces its evolutionary path, or climbs its family tree from the one-celled ancestor up to the present. The adult stages of ancestral forms are repeated, but they are now to be found in the earlier stages of ontogeny. For example, the stage early in development, in which gill slits are visible in birds and mammals, was considered by Haeckel to be equivalent to the adult fish ancestors in the phylogeny of these groups. Thus, evolution was thought to be occurring in the adult, with new adult forms being tacked on to the old at the end of the developmental period. This concept has had considerable appeal, especially to zoology professors, for the zygote could be compared to the single-celled protozoan ancestor, the blastula to a colonial flagellate such as *Volvox,* the gastrula stage to a two-layered coelenterate like *Hydra,* and so on. Phylogeny then became not only the explanation but the cause of ontogeny, a conclusion that actually hampered research into the causative mechanisms in development.

von Baer's Dicta

Haeckel's generalization was too sweeping. The earlier statements of von Baer, though less striking, were more accurate. He had observed that in development the general traits appear before the more specialized, that the embryos of different species are more alike than the adults and depart progressively from each other during ontogeny, and that the young stages of a species are not like the adults of species lower in the phylogenetic series but rather like their embryonic stages. There is a germ of truth in the biogenetic law even though it is demonstrably false if taken too literally; hence it would be more proper to say, though von Baer did not, that "Ontogeny recapitulates ontogeny." Vertebrate embryos do show many similarities, for which the most reasonable explanation is their common ancestry.

In the development of the mammalian heart, for example, the number of chambers is initially two, then three, and finally in the adult, four. The mammalian phylogeny includes first the fishes with a two-chambered heart, then the amphibians with three, and the reptiles with four. The basic number of aortic arches in vertebrates is six, the living fishes having arches 3 through 6 complete and traces of the first two. These arches break up into capillary beds in the gills and then regroup to form the dorsal aorta. The lower amphibians have arches 3 through 6, but the lower part of the 6th aortic arch has now become the pulmonary artery to the lungs. In the higher amphibians and reptiles the 5th arch is also missing in the adult, the 3rd becomes the carotid arteries to the head, the 4th, the systemic arteries to the rest of the body, and the 6th remains pulmonary in function. In the adult mammals only the 3rd, the left half of the 4th arch (in birds, the right half), and the lower part of the 6th are all that remain functional of the six arches that make their transient appearance during development. (See Fig. 9-1).

Man's evolutionary past sometimes manifests itself in strange ways. From time to time we read of so-called "blue babies," who are suffering from insufficient oxygenation of their blood. There are two major causes for this condition: either the opening between the right and left auricles of the heart does

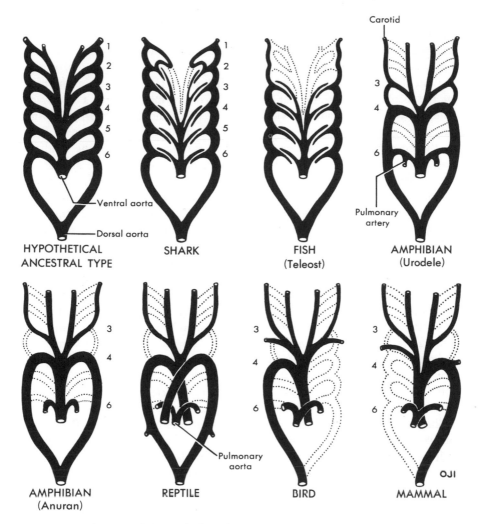

Fig. 9-1. Diagram of the evolution of the aortic arches in the vertebrates (ventral views).

not close, or the duct of Botallus, a vessel connecting the pulmonary artery directly to the dorsal aorta, fails to close. Both opening and duct are devices by which the blood of the fetus is shunted past the nonfunctional lungs prior to birth. Since the opening between the auricles represents a persistence of the ancestral two-chambered fish heart and the duct of Botallus is actually the upper half of the 6th aortic arch, these blue babies are living evidence of man's evolutionary past.

The gill arches and the gill slits in the mammalian embryos do not represent the adult ancestral fish, but are similar to those of a fish embryo at a comparable stage of development. They then differentiate into structures quite different from those in the fish. All of the gill slits close and disappear except the one that forms the Eustachian tube, which connects the pharynx at the back of the mouth to the middle ear. The gill arches themselves have a variety of fates. In the most primitive jawless fishes, of which the lamprey is a surviving relict, the gill arches number seven. The first arch became the basis for the jaws in the fishes, but the bones forming the jaw articulation in fishes, the quadrate and the articular, by an unusual turn of events have moved into the middle ear of the mammals during the course of evolution. There, as the incus (or anvil, formerly the quadrate) and the malleus (or hammer, formerly the articular), they form two thirds of the chain of small bones that conduct sound across the middle ear to the inner ear. The third bone in this chain, the stapes or stirrup, is derived from the second gill arch, which as the hyomandibular in fish more or less anchors the jaws to the brain case. The rest of the 2nd gill arch forms the body and the anterior horn of the hyoid apparatus, the posterior horn coming from the 3rd gill arch. The hyoid apparatus and other cartilaginous structures in the throat region such as the thyroid, arytenoid, and cricoid cartilages, derived from the 4th and 5th arches, are relatively insignificant compared to their size and functional importance in fish. (See Fig. 9-2.) All of the above statements are well grounded on embryological and anatomical evidence. The obvious question is why there should be a stage in the mammalian embryo where gills and gill arches, which never function as such, are nevertheless present, even though they differentiate into quite different adult structures. The most obvious answer is that the mammals are descended from fishlike ancestors and that in the course of evolution modifications in development have occurred; the similarities which still persist in the ontogeny of fish and mammals are indicative of a fundamental similarity in their genotypes due to their common ancestry.

Modifications of Development

The notochord, characteristic of the Phylum Chordata, to which the vertebrates belong, is crowded out by the vertebrae almost as soon as it is formed in the vertebrate embryo. Why, then, is the notochord retained? It might seem to be a clear-cut case of recapitulation, but this can hardly be so. The cells that form the notochord are intimately bound up with the organizing and inducing of the essential axial structures of the embryo—the spinal cord and brain, the heart, kidneys, muscle, and so on; thus if this function is to be retained, the cells themselves must be retained. Because natural selection acts on living organisms at all stages of their existence, not just upon the adults, embryonic as well as adult stages and structures may be changed, added, or eliminated. Since selection must act within the limits imposed by the modifications possible in already existing stages, the retention of stages similar to those of ancestral forms is to be

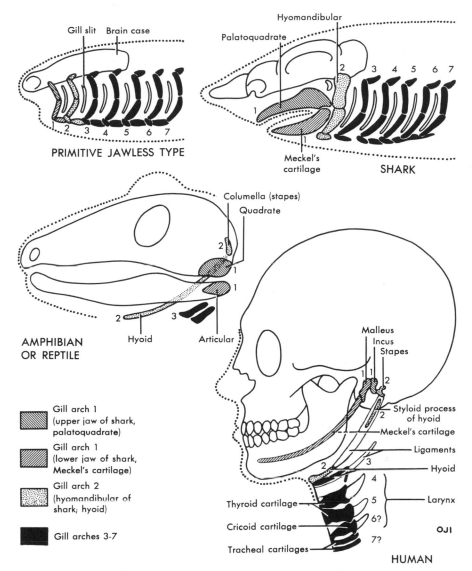

Fig. 9-2. Evolution of the gill arches in vertebrates.

expected even though their subsequent developmental fates may differ. Many kinds of modifications of developmental patterns may be observed.

In the typical frog, for example, the small eggs laid in water hatch after a few days into free-living, gill-breathing tadpoles that metamorphose after several weeks or months—or even years, in the bullfrog—into the adult frog. In the *Hylodes* of the West Indies, however, the large eggs laid on leaves hatch in two or three weeks directly into frogs, although a brief tadpole stage exists prior to the hatching of the frogs from the eggs. The elimination of the functional tadpole stage has taken place, but the tadpole nevertheless continues to appear; thus, although a secondary modification of the basic plan of frog development has occurred, the change has not been sufficiently drastic to eliminate the stage completely. Such information is evidence not only for evolution, but for its gradual nature.

The fossil evidence and other evidence make it abundantly clear that the Amphibia are ancestral to the reptiles, birds, and mammals. The three latter groups are known as the amniotes, for their embryos develop within the watery cradle made possible by embryonic membranes known as the amnion and chorion. Yet since the amphibians lack these membranes, they must be new structures evolved during the evolution from amphibians to reptiles. In the mammals, a modification in function led to the utilization of the chorion as a part of the placenta. Thus new structures or modification of existing structures for new functions can evolve in the embryo as well as in the adult.

In some instances precocious sexual maturity has led to the elimination of the adult stage, a phenomenon known as paedogenesis. In the axolotls, salamanders of the genus *Ambystoma* having a gill-breathing, water-dwelling larval stage, the larvae may mature sexually and reproduce without undergoing metamorphosis. That this is an example of paedogenesis is proved by the fact that the axolotl, under certain environmental conditions, metamorphoses into the adult lung-breathing, land-dwelling form. Compared to the other primates, man has an extended developmental period; in fact, human adults show more resemblance to immature anthropoids than to the adult great apes. The lack of hair and of well-developed brow ridges, the relatively flat face, and the slow closure of the skull sutures have all been singled out as indicative of a tendency toward paedogenesis in man.

New and different stages in the life cycle have also evolved. Among the primitive insects, the immature forms are rather similar in appearance and function to the adults or imagoes. In the more recent groups of insects, the egg hatches into a larva quite different in form, function, and, usually, habitat from the adult into which it later metamorphoses. The caterpillars that become butterflies and the squirming maggots that, after a quiescent pupal stage, emerge as flies, are familiar examples of insect metamorphosis. An example can even be cited much like Haeckel's concept of evolution: in the development of the crab, the megalopa stage resembles a lobster or crayfish, near relatives of the crabs, and the adult crab, with abdomen folded under, is a stage that appears to be tacked on to the ancestral form.

Thus, it is clear that many changes in ontogeny have occurred: new embryonic stages not affecting the adults, for example, parasitic larvae of free-living adults; wide divergence of adults with similar embryos, for example, fish and mammalian embryos; adult forms that may resemble larval stages of ancestors, that is, paedogenesis; or appearance of a new adult stage apparently added to the previous adult stage. These changes must be due to the action of natural selection, producing changes in relative rates of development of various structures as well as modifications in the function and structure of existing stages and structures. Where repetition of ancestral stages occurs, it is not simply a case of Haeckelian recapitulation, but rather an indication that similar groups of genes are operative and that the embryonic structures they control are still essential to normal ontogeny, and hence have not been eliminated by natural selection. Therefore, the study of embryology is helpful in determining relationships, and the rejection of Haeckel's dictum does not imply a rejection of all embryological evidence relating to evolution, for similarities in ontogeny are often indicative of phylogenetic relationship. In fact, they may often be the best evidence available. In the free-living shrimp (*Penaeus*), the sessile barnacle (*Lepas*), and *Sacculina,* a parasitic sac in the crab, the Nauplius larval form of all three is the best evidence that these three diverse adult types are members of the Crustacea. Here and in many other instances, similarity in ontogeny is an indication of genetic affinity but is not necessarily evidence as to the adult form of the ancestors.

 ▶ *SUMMARY*

Despite the diversity of form among such groups as fish, amphibians, reptiles, birds, and mammals, the embryos of all of these vertebrates look very similar and have many features such as gill slits, aortic arches, neural tube, and notochord in common. Thus, the adult diversity results from the modification during development of the same basic embryonic plan. The assumption that these groups are all descended with modification from a common fish ancestry renders this situation intelligible. Other theories are quite inadequate to account, for example, for the presence of gill slits in birds and mammals, which never at any stage in their life cycle require functional gills. The recapitulation theory of Haeckel, as originally stated, represents an oversimplification of the facts, for the developing embryo does not recapitulate the adult stages of its ancestors. Rather, the embryo will in most instances show more resemblance to the embryos of ancestral or related groups than it will to their adult forms. For this reason comparative embryology can be a fruitful source of phylogenetic information. The evidence indicates that evolution must operate within the framework and limitations imposed by existing patterns of development. Although the end products in some cases have been as diverse as a fish darting through the water and a bird soaring in the sky, their embryos still carry the clues to their common ancestry.

SUGGESTED READING

DeBeer, G. R., 1958. *Embryos and ancestors,* 3d ed. New York: Oxford University Press.

Nelsen, O. E., 1953. *Comparative embryology of the vertebrates.* New York: Blakiston.

Willier, B. H., P. A. Weiss, and V. Hamburger, eds., 1955. *Analysis of development.* Philadelphia: Saunders.

CHAPTER 10

Comparative Anatomy

The similarity between different species was one of the fundamental reasons for the development of the theory of evolution, and comparative anatomy has been one of the cornerstones of evidence for the theory ever since Darwin's time. In a sense, comparative embryology and comparative anatomy are one and the same study, differing only with respect to the stage of development of the organism, but historically and traditionally two disciplines have existed rather than one. Unfortunately, not all similarities between members of different species are due to a common ancestry, and the concept has sometimes been considerably overworked. Lamarck and especially St. Hilaire argued that all animal species conformed to a common archetype, a clearly erroneous idea that was strongly and effectively attacked by Cuvier. The fallacy of the archetype concept can be seen through a comparison of such "higher" animals as a mammal, an insect, and a mollusk like the snail; neither in general nor in particulars can they be truly said to conform to a common pattern at any stage. Lamarck's adherence to this concept undoubtedly weakened his arguments for evolution and may well be responsible for the fact that we now associate the theory of evolution with Darwin rather than Lamarck.

Homology and Analogy

There are apparently two major reasons for similarities between species—heritage and habitus. Heritage refers to a common ancestry, with similar genetic systems responsible for the resemblances. However, species with similar modes of life are often very much alike even though not closely related. The mechanism responsible for this type of similarity is natural selection, similar selection pressures bringing about similar adaptations to similar environments. The problem, of course, is to be sure that relationships attributed to heritage are not actually due to habitus, a distinction not always easily made. Two concepts have arisen in connection with these

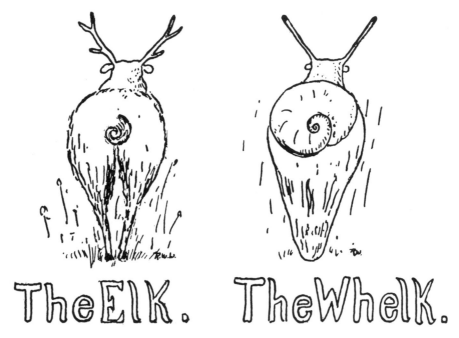

Fig. 10-1. Analogy. (From *Animal Analogues* by R. W. Wood.)

differences that aid in clarifying the ideas involved; structures that are similar because of similar function or habitus are said to be *analogous,* whereas structures that are similar because of common ancestry and a similar genetic basis are said to be *homologous.*

The wings of a swallow and a dragonfly, though used by both in flight, are analogous since their origin and structure are clearly different. The fins of a trout and a dytiscid water beetle are also analogous. In both of these examples the structural differences between the vertebrate and the insect are fairly obvious, but this is not always the case. The camera-type eye with a focusing lens and a sensitive pigment layer has appeared in two groups of animals, the vertebrates and the cephalopod mollusks such as the squid and the octopus. The physical requirements for this type of eye are such that they must be quite similar structurally if the eye is to function at all. Both have a lens, a sensitive pigment layer, and a layer of nerves, all housed in a spherical chamber, and superficially are much alike. However, the embryology of the eye in the two groups is quite different. Most striking, perhaps, is the fact that the vertebrate eye is, in a sense, arranged backward; that is, the layer of nerves carrying the impulses to the brain lies in front of the pigment layer rather than behind it, the latter being a more sensible arrangement and the one that is found in the cephalopod eye. It is clear from these examples that a similar problem, whether it be flying, swimming, or seeing, is apt to have similar solutions in different groups. Even though, at the outset, the heredity may be very different, the end products of the operation of natural selection are much alike. The evolution of widely divergent groups toward greater similarity due to common functions or adaptations is known as *convergent* evolution. The resemblances, however, are always superficial.

Homologous structures, on the other hand, may or may not function alike; homology rests not on function but on a similar developmental origin and hereditary basis. A human hand, a bat's wing, and a cat's forepaw, for example, are homologous, for all are five-toed (pentadactyl) structures, functionally quite different, but of similar location and embryology in three different mammals.

The distinction between homology and analogy may seem relatively clear-cut, but cases do arise where the decision will depend on point of view rather than any fixed criterion. The wing of a bird, the wing of a bat (a mammal), and the wing of a pterosaur (a flying reptile) are all derived from the vertebrate tetrapod forelimb and are thus homologous, in one sense. However, flight originated independently in these three groups, and the three types of wings are quite different in the details of their structure. In the bat wing all five digits of the pentadactyl forelimb are present. The wing of a bird utilizes only digits 1, 2, and 3, and in quite a different manner, with the fourth and fifth digits completely lost. The pterodactyl had four digits, with only the fourth elongated to support the wing and the fifth missing (see Fig. 10-2). With respect to their adaptations for flight, then, these wings should more properly be regarded as analogous rather than homologous.

Homologies in Vertebrates

Obviously, it is not possible to explore in detail the great wealth of material on comparative anatomy that has been amassed for many different groups. Volumes have been written even for a single group such as the vertebrates (see references at end of chapter). Careful study of these texts and first-hand experience with the organisms themselves give an extremely convincing demonstration of the reality of evolution. However, some selected examples will serve to illustrate the nature of this type of evidence.

Characteristically there are seven cervical vertebrae in the mammalian neck; a mouse, an elephant, and even a giraffe have the same number of cervical vertebrae. These mammals have a defined neck region and are capable of turning their heads, whereas the porpoise, a mammal with the torpedolike shape characteristic of the fishes, lacks a distinguishable neck region and cannot turn its head. Nevertheless, the seven cervical vertebrae are present in the porpoise although they are much shorter than in mammals of comparable size and are fused to-

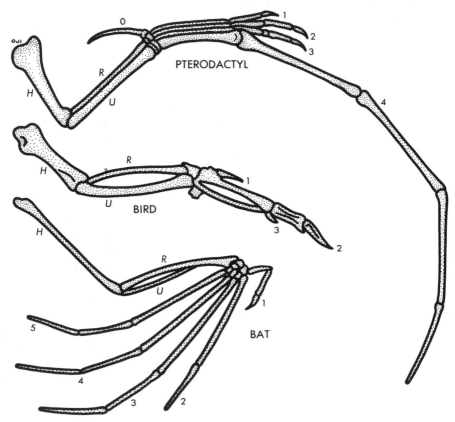

Fig. 10-2. Homology in vertebrate wings.

gether so that flexibility has been lost. To the obvious question as to why animals differing so greatly in size, in structure, and in mode of life should have the same number of vertebrae in their necks, the theory of evolution presents a simple, plausible answer. All these varied forms, and the many other mammals, are descended, with modifications, from an ancestral mammalian stock that was characterized by seven cervical vertebrae.

The evolution of the vertebrate skull, in which homologies have been traced from the fish up through the amphibians and the reptiles to the present-day mammals, illustrates the amount of change that has taken place in the many millions of years of vertebrate history. The mammalian skull, an apparently unitary structure, has been shown to have been formed from three quite distinct components found in the fish skeleton: the endoskeletal brain case, the dermal bony armor in the head region, and the visceral skeleton supporting the gill arches (see Fig. 10-3). The original braincase housed the major sense organs—

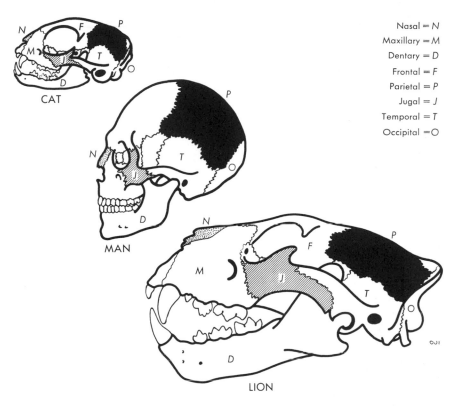

Nasal = N
Maxillary = M
Dentary = D
Frontal = F
Parietal = P
Jugal = J
Temporal = T
Occipital = O

Fig. 10-3. Homology in the bones of the skull.

of sight, hearing, and olfaction—and was shielded by a complete roof of dermal bones imbedded in the skin. The jaws were originally derived from the gill arches. By a series of extensive changes involving modification, fusion, or loss of the bones in the fish skull, the mammalian skull such as that of the cat has arisen. Although the homologies between the fish and cat skull are by no means obvious without adequate study of the many forms representative of the numerous intermediate stages, and many people find it difficult in any event to accept that modern man's gum-chewing jaws are derived from structures that originally supported the gills of fish, the homologies between the cat (*Felis catus*) and the lion (*Panthera leo*) skulls are quite clear. The homologies are not so obvious between these skulls and that of man, in a different mammalian order, but study of the diagrams will show the many similarities between them.

The pentadactyl appendage has already been mentioned as the characteristic condition in tetrapods, but not all tetrapods have five toes on each appendage, and it may be questioned whether some of them ever did have five toes. In addition to the embryological evidence and the vestiges of digits that indicate the previous presence of additional digits, another type of evidence, from guinea pigs, is now available. The guinea pig has four toes on each forefoot, but only three on each hind foot; a hereditary variant, called pollex, has been discovered that produces the five-toed condition on all four feet. Though it could be argued that such a mutation has no evolutionary significance, it seems more reasonable to suppose that it has restored the ancestral condition, and in any case it certainly establishes that guinea pigs *can* have five toes.

Genetic Homology

Morphological homologies are actually based on homologies in the hereditary materials or genotypes of different species, of which they are the most obvious manifestations. It is therefore significant that when it has been possible to study genetic homologies more directly, homologous genes have been demonstrated in closely related species. In different species of flies of the genus *Drosophila,* similar mutations affecting eye color, body color, the bristles, and other traits have been shown to exist. The homologies have been based not only on the similarities in phenotype, but on the location of these genes in homologous regions of the chromosomes and in some cases by crosses as well.

Serial homology is a somewhat different concept from the one we have been considering, but it, too, has evolutionary significance. The segmented animals such as the vertebrates and the arthropods are composed of a series of segments, each of which is basically similar to the others, and the structures in one segment can be compared and homologized to those in other segments. Serial homologies are clear-cut in an animal like the earthworm, an annelid, where most of the segments are replicas of each other. Even in arthropods such as the lobster and crayfish in which considerable differentiation of the segments has occurred, the homologies between various appendages such as the mandibles, the legs, the claws, and the antennae are easy to visualize. The segmentation of many insect larvae shows relatively little differentiation, and the homologies are therefore easily established; but in adult insects, the great degree of differentiation serves to mask not only the homologies but even the segmentation itself to some extent. Nevertheless, in the insects the mouth parts, the antennae, and the legs have been considered to be serially homologous despite their dissimilarity in appearance and function. The discovery of the so-called homeotic mutants in *Drosophila* has tended to reinforce these conclusions. The aristapedia mutant causes the development of a leglike structure in place of the antenna, and proboscipedia causes a similar change in the proboscis. Thus, the homeotic mutants cause one of a series of parts to assume the character of another member of the series, and by demonstrating the common potentialities of these varied appendages have tended to confirm the conclusions previously drawn.

In most orders of insects there are two pairs of wings located on the second and third thoracic segments. In the two-winged flies of the order Diptera, the second segment bears the single pair of wings and the third bears the halteres, a pair of gyroscopic devices. The inference that the halteres are homologous (and serially homologous) to wings has been strengthened by the discovery of the homeotic mutants tetraptera, which produces a four-winged dipteran, and tetraltera, which causes flies with four halteres to develop. The discovery of mutants that change the ordinal characters of individuals carrying them has led some students, notably Goldschmidt, to believe that the higher taxonomic groups have originated in this fashion, an interesting speculation that does not appear, however, to be borne out by the facts.

Vestigial Organs

Another type of evidence for evolution is derived from the so-called vestigial structures. Not only do they suggest relationships, but they also raise questions about the mechanism of evolution; many vestigial organs have lost their adaptive function, and it may well be asked why they should continue to persist. Man himself is virtually a walking museum from his head to his feet. Many people, for example, have small nodes on their ears, known as Darwin's points, which are thought to be vestiges of the somewhat larger and more pointed ears of our ancestors. And even though we can no longer rotate our ears to test the sounds carried by each vagrant breeze as do the deer, nevertheless vestiges of these muscles remain that permit small boys and gentlemen at parties to show off by wiggling their ears. Human facial contortions are controlled by the remnants of the muscles with which our remote fish ancestors aerated their gills. When cold, our mammalian relatives fluff out their fur to increase the insulation of their bodies; we get goose pimples or duck bumps under the same conditions, but the attempt is abortive, for even though the muscles for fluffing the hair are present, the hair itself has virtually no insulating capacity. When angry or excited or frightened, your dog may raise the hackles along his neck, something we also try to do when we get the "chills" in a horror movie. The appendix and the coccyx are classical examples of human vestigial organs. The coccyx is all that remains of our tail, and the appendix seems to be of more trouble than value as an adjunct to the human intestine. Even the human footprint, showing the arch and the big first toe, is a vestige of our simian ancestry and our former habitat in the trees.

The theory of evolution gives a simple explanation for the presence of vestigial structures. The presence of a pelvic girdle in the python and the whale, a reptile and a mammal respectively, neither of which has hind limbs, is clear evidence that they are descended from tetrapod ancestors. Any other explanation is extremely difficult to apply or to accept.

SUMMARY ◄

Comparative anatomy rests on the distinction between homology and analogy. Homologous structures have a similar developmental origin and hereditary basis, but may or may not have a similar function. Analogous structures, though functionally similar, are otherwise different. The existence of many organs diverse in function yet clearly similar in structure—for example, the human hand, a seal's flipper, and a bat's wing—constitutes a conundrum best explained by evolution. The list of morphological homologies can be almost endlessly extended, but the interpretation remains the same—namely, descent with modification. The persistence of nonfunctional vestigial organs of all kinds is still another biological phenomenon best accounted for by the theory of evolution. The serial homologies demonstrated in segmented animals are indicative of the evolution of segmental diversification from more uniformly segmented ancestral stocks. The assumption that anatomical homology and genetic relationship go hand in hand has been strongly reinforced by the discovery of homologies at the level of the chromosomes and the genes.

SUGGESTED READING

Davis, D. D., 1949. "Comparative anatomy and the evolution of the vertebrates," *Genetics, paleontology and evolution.* G. L. Jepsen, E. Mayr, and G. G. Simpson, eds. Princeton: Princeton University Press.

Gregory, W. K., 1951. *Evolution emerging,* 2 vols. New York: Macmillan.

Romer, A. S., 1955. *The vertebrate body,* 2d ed. Philadelphia: Saunders.

———, 1959. *The vertebrate story,* 4th ed. Chicago: University of Chicago Press.

Spencer, W. P., 1949. "Gene homologies and the mutants of *Drosophila hydei,*" *Genetics, paleontology and evolution.* G. L. Jepsen, E. Mayr, and G. G. Simpson, eds. Princeton: Princeton University Press.

Young, J. Z., 1950. *The life of vertebrates.* Oxford: Clarendon Press.

CHAPTER 11

Comparative Biochemistry

Some biochemical traits are so fundamental that they are universally present in living things; others are widespread, characterizing large groups of animals or plants; still other biochemical properties are species specific or may even be unique to a given individual. Within this array of similarities and differences is to be found considerable evidence for evolution and for the solution of specific phylogenetic problems. The term "homology" is customarily associated with morphological characteristics, but biochemical as well as structural homologies can be recognized. Common ancestry may be indicated just as clearly by homologous biochemical compounds as by homologous morphological structures. This type of evidence, which gives essentially an independent check on the conclusions drawn from comparative studies in embryology and anatomy, was unavailable to Darwin. Since biochemical traits generally seem to change more gradually than morphological traits, the conclusions drawn from biochemical evidence are apt to be more soundly based. In some cases, biochemical evidence has made it possible to trace relationships where previously no reliable conclusions could be drawn from morphology. As might be expected, analogous biochemical compounds also exist; for example, both hemoglobin and hemocyanin function as oxygen-carrying respiratory pigments, but they are analagous rather than homologous, for hemoglobin is an iron-porphyrin protein whereas hemocyanin is a copper protein.

Although different species may differ radically in their gross morphology, nearly all of them are formed from similar compounds, which are used metabolically in similar ways. An elm tree and an elephant, a bacterium and a Bantu may at first glance appear to have little in common, but at the biochemical level they are much alike. The hereditary materials in both plants and animals, for example, are nucleic acids, while the stucture of the organism is erected primarily with protein molecules. The carbohydrates and fats, on the other hand, serve as the major sources of energy for carrying on metabolic work. The photosynthetic process makes possible the nutritional independence of the green plants, which are able to synthesize organic compounds (carbohydrates, fats, proteins, nucleic acids, etc.) from simple substances such as carbon dioxide, water, and inorganic salts. Other organisms, with few exceptions, are either directly or indirectly dependent on green plants for their energy. Even for a top carnivore (which does not serve as prey to another carnivore) such as a polar bear, this relationship can be traced back through the food chain to its origin in the chlorophyll of green plants. Despite the diversity of form and function found among the different species of plants and animals, certain chemical compounds play similar key roles in their metabolism. In the digestion of carbohydrates in animals, the complex polysaccharides are hydrolyzed and broken down into their constituent simple sugars or monosaccharides, of which the most important is glucose. The glucose molecules, after absorption from the intestine, become the building blocks for the formation of the animal's carbohydrates such as glycogen or, by stepwise oxidation, they become the major source of energy for the variety of processes going on within the cells. Similarly, proteins are broken down to amino acids, and fats to fatty acids and glycerol, which then, after absorption, enter into the metabolism of the animal. Furthermore, these substances are to a large extent interconvertible. The amino acids, for example, may undergo deamination or loss of the amino group, which then contributes to urea formation. The deaminized portion may be oxidized, ultimately to carbon dioxide and water, or it may be synthesized into glucose or a fatty acid or even into another amino acid. Thus, although the types of carbohydrates, fats, and proteins in different species are distinctive, many of the amino acids, fatty acids, and simple sugars of which they are composed are identical in both plants and animals. The metabolic pathways they follow are also similar. For example, the ornithine cycle, the Krebs tricarboxylic acid cycle, the cytochrome system, the metabolism of aromatic amino acids, glycolysis, the roles of actomyosin and adenosine triphosphate (ATP), and many other metabolic sequences have been identified in a wide variety of species. For this reason, it is possible to study cellular or general physiology, a field that concentrates on the phenomena common to the cells of many different species. The conclusion seems inescapable that the existence of these fundamental similarities must be regarded as evidence for an underlying kinship among all living things. It seems advisable, therefore, to examine in further detail the biochemical evidence relating to evolution.

Plant Pigments

Some rather interesting information about evolution can be derived from a consideration of various plant pigments. Chlorophyll is present in all photosynthetic organisms, and this biochemical common denominator seems indicative of an affinity among these species. Several types of chlorophyll have been identified, but all have the same basic porphyrin or tetrapyrrole structure with magnesium attached to the ends of the pyrroles:

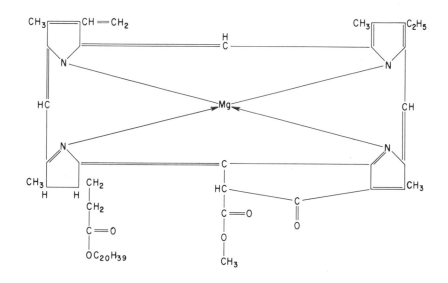

Chlorophyll *a* occurs in almost all types of photosynthetic organisms, but the other kinds of chlorophyll have a more limited distribution (see the listing below). Even the sulfur bacteria contain chlorophyll-like compounds.

group of plants	chlorophylls
green plants	*a* and *b*
brown algae	*a* and *c*
diatoms	*a* and *c*
red algae	*a* and *d*
yellow-green algae	*a* and *e*
blue-green algae	*a*

The chlorophylls are bound to proteins in the chloroplasts and differ from each other only in the side chains attached to the outer ends of the tetrapyrrole nucleus. Descent with modification from a common ancestry seems clearly indicated for these photosynthetic species.

The anthocyanins and anthoxanthins are water-soluble pigments found in the cell sap of plants, and are responsible for most of the flower and fruit colors in higher plants and for much of the color in autumn foliage. The anthocyanins vary in color from red to purple to blue; the anthoxanthins, though chemically quite similar to the anthocyanins, appear yellow or white. The anthocyanins are always combined with sugars to form glycosides, and the anthoxanthins are usually found as glycosides also. The color, particularly of the anthocyanins, changes with the acidity of the cell sap, becoming bluer as the acidity decreases.

pelargonidin
(anthocyanin; pink)

apigenin
(anthoxanthin; ivory)

(aglycone
residues)

The anthocyanins and anthoxanthins of many hundreds of species of flowering plants have been studied both genetically and biochemically in one of the pioneer studies of biochemical genetics. The results have shown that these pigments are apparently derived from a common precursor and that the differences among them are due to simple gene substitutions, which determine the state of oxidation and methoxylation of the side phenyl ring, the pH of the cell sap of the petals, and the position, number, and nature of the attached sugars. Such similarities, extending through many families of plants, certainly seem a strong argument for a common origin.

Photoreceptors

Even more remarkable, perhaps, are the biochemical homologies involved in photoreceptor systems, both animal and plant. Phototropism, phototaxis, and vision are apparently all dependent on the yellow to red fat-soluble carotenoid pigments. The carotenes and the related xanthophylls are found in the chloroplasts, where their color is usually masked by the chlorophyll. Although relatively few studies have been made in plants or among the lower invertebrates, the available evidence implicates the carotenoids or their derivatives in the light reactions of these groups. Shown below is β-carotene, the most familiar of the carotenoid pigments.

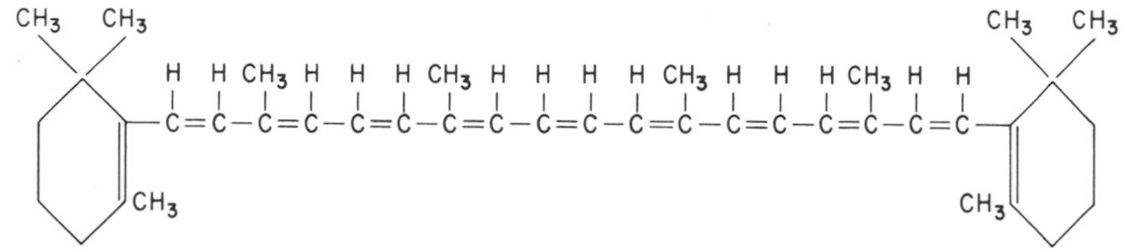

β-carotene

The taxonomically intermediate position of the green flagellates such as *Euglena,* which have been claimed as algae by the botanists because they possess chloroplasts and as Protozoa by zoologists because of their other traits, is confirmed by the presence of the carotenoid, astaxanthin, in the eyespot. Since this group contains both chlorophyll, a plant pigment, and astaxanthin, which is an exclusively animal carotenoid, it cannot properly be assigned to either the plant or the animal kingdom.

The vertebrates and the higher invertebrates such as arthropods and mollusks cannot synthesize their carotenoids and must obtain them in their nutrition as the A vitamins, ultimately derived from plants. That the A vitamins are similar to the carotenes may be seen from the structure of vitamin A_1.

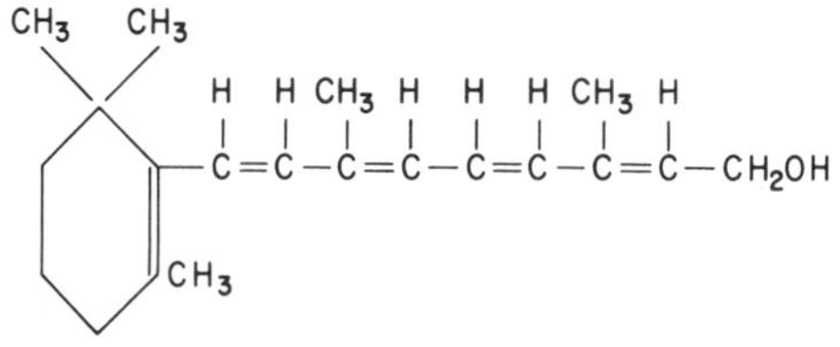

vitamin A_1

The carotenoid pigments play a fundamental role in photoreception in the arthropods, mollusks, and chordates. These phyla independently have developed image-forming eyes, each of a distinct type, and yet each utilizes the A vitamins in the photoreception process. The details have been most carefully studied in the vertebrate eye. Photoreception takes place in the retina, where two types of photoreceptors are found: the rods, specialized for vision in dim light, and the cones, specialized for vision in bright light and for color vision. The action of light on the photosensitive carotenoid-protein pigments in these cells causes the carotenoid to split off from the protein, giving rise to nervous excitation, which is transmitted as a nervous impulse from the retina through the optic nerve to the brain where it gives rise to visual sensations. The chemistry has been most carefully worked out in the rods. Here the photosensitive pigment is rhodopsin, a rose-colored compound that is broken down by light through a series of steps to the protein, opsin, and to vitamin A_1 or its derivative, retinene$_1$. The bleached products can regenerate rhodopsin spontaneously in the dark. Under continuous light the whole system goes into a steady state with the continuous restitution of rhodopsin permitting vision to persist indefinitely. The phenomenon of dark adaptation, during which the ability to see in a dimly lit room markedly increases, can readily be explained as due to the resynthesis of rhodopsin, which was previously somewhat depleted in the light. The details of the changes in the rods are outlined in the diagram. (It may be noted that the rhodopsin is formed only from the so-called *cis* optical configuration of retinene$_1$ but that it breaks down to the *trans* form.)

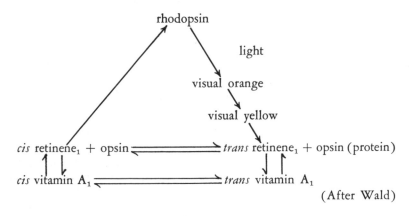

(After Wald)

The rhodopsin system utilizing vitamin A_1 is widely distributed, being found in the retinas of marine and terrestrial vertebrates. The crustaceans and the squid, a cephalopod mollusk, also use A_1 or retinene$_1$ in their visual pigments. However, the retina of fresh-water fishes contains a different light-sensitive pigment, a purple substance known as porphyropsin. The opsins are essentially the same as in rhodopsin, but the carotenoids are vitamin A_2 and retinene$_2$, which differ from A_1 and retinene$_1$ in having just one extra double bond in the ring. This finding poses some very intriguing questions, for there are no fundamental phylogenetic distinctions between marine and fresh-water fishes; closely related species may be found in either environment.

The available evidence indicates that the ancestral vertebrates lived in fresh water and had porphyropsin as their visual pigment. The evolution of the vertebrates gave rise to species that invaded the oceans or the land, and in both cases the invasion of the new habitat was accompanied by a shift from porphyropsin to rhodopsin. Study of the types intermediate in their habitats such as amphibians or fishes migrating between the sea and fresh water has shown that they also are intermediate in their visual pigments. These findings are summarized below.

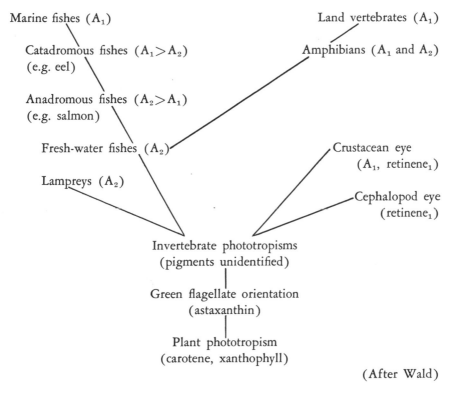

Marine fishes (A_1)

Catadromous fishes ($A_1 > A_2$)
(e.g. eel)

Anadromous fishes ($A_2 > A_1$)
(e.g. salmon)

Fresh-water fishes (A_2)

Lampreys (A_2)

Land vertebrates (A_1)

Amphibians (A_1 and A_2)

Crustacean eye
(A_1, retinene$_1$)

Cephalopod eye
(retinene$_1$)

Invertebrate phototropisms
(pigments unidentified)

Green flagellate orientation
(astaxanthin)

Plant phototropism
(carotene, xanthophyll)

(After Wald)

The type of pigment is not simply an adaptation directly determined by the environment, for one exceptional group of fish, the wrasse fishes (Labridae), is exclusively marine yet all have porphyropsin. Furthermore, the sea lamprey, which migrates from the ocean to fresh water to spawn, already has vitamin A_2 and porphyropsin as it starts its migration from the sea. Thus, genetic control of the type of visual pigment is clearly indicated.

The lampreys are the most primitive living vertebrates and only distantly related to the fresh-water bony fishes or teleosts. Hence, the presence of porphyropsin in this group places this type of pigment close to the origin of the vertebrate visual system. The lungfish, which have evolved along a separate line of descent from the modern fresh-water teleosts, also have vitamin A_2 in their retinas.

Among the teleosts the salmon and the eels also migrate between the sea and fresh water. Migratory fish may be divided into two groups: anadromous, which migrate from the sea to fresh water to spawn, and catadromous, which migrate from fresh water to spawn in the sea. The retinas of anadromous salmon contain both rhodopsin and porphyropsin, vitamins A_1 and A_2, but the porphyropsin predominates. The catadromous eels that return to the sea to spawn also have both pigments, with the rhodopsin predominant. Among all of the fish in these groups thus far studied, it has been found that their visual pigments are predominantly or exclusively the kind ordinarily associated with their spawning environment.

The amphibians, which, as their name suggests, live on land or in the water or a little bit of both, are intermediate between a fresh-water and a terrestrial existence. Their visual systems parallel their habitat, for those living in fresh water, such as tadpoles or the mud-puppy Necturus, a permanently larval aquatic form, contain vitamin A_2, whereas terrestrial forms such as adult frogs have rhodopsin and vitamin A_1. Even within a given species the type of visual pigment changes when metamorphosis makes possible a change in habitat.

The vitamin A_1-retinene$_1$-rhodopsin system appears to have originated somewhere in the evolutionary history of the invertebrates, and the vitamin A_2-retinene$_2$-porphyropsin system appears to be closely associated with the origin of the vertebrates. A major unanswered question is why a change from porphyropsin to rhodopsin should have taken place when fresh-water vertebrates evolved into marine or terrestrial species. The conclusion that porphyropsin confers an adaptive advantage in the fresh-water environment and rhodopsin is better suited to either an oceanic or terrestrial existence seems inescapable. The change from one system to another within the life cycle of a single individual seems the best indication that adaptation is involved. It must be remembered, however, that these changes are under genetic control and hence must have been brought about by natural selection and not by the direct influence of the environment.

Immunology

Some unusual and valuable information about evolution has been derived from still another type of biochemical study—namely, immunology. The immunity of an organism is based upon what is called the antigen-antibody reaction. An antigen is a foreign substance of biological origin that is usually a protein although some polysaccharides are also antigenic. In response to the entrance of an antigen into the body, an antibody, which is a protein capable of combining specifically with that antigen, is formed. If the antigen subsequently enters the body again, the antibodies already present will combine with it, and the individual becomes immune to its harmful effects. Antibodies can be developed not only against bacteria and viruses but against a variety of other substances as well, and this fact has been utilized to study the relationships of organisms.

If the blood serum or body fluid of an animal is injected into a rabbit, the rabbit forms antibodies in its blood against the foreign serum proteins. By withdrawing the rabbit's blood and removing the cells from the serum it is possible to carry out the antigen-antibody reaction (foreign serum-rabbit antiserum) in a test tube, where a precipitate is formed. This so-called precipitin test or various refinements of it have been used in a number of phylogenetic studies, a few of which will be mentioned here.

Some of the earliest studies were conducted by Nuttall. Perhaps the most exciting at the time was the discovery that rabbit serum containing anti-human antibodies reacted almost as strongly with chimpanzee serum as it did with human serum; somewhat less strongly with sera from the other apes; still less with monkey sera; only slightly with carnivore and ungulate sera; and essentially not at all with insectivore, rodent, and marsupial sera. Because of the specificity of the antigen-antibody reaction these cross reactions are a measure of the degree of similarity of the serum proteins in the different species. They tend to confirm, therefore, the relationships of man to the Primates and particularly to the anthropoid apes.

In another experiment Nuttall's group showed that the horseshoe crab, Limulus, once classified with the other crabs among the Crustacea, belonged instead much nearer the Arachnida, for an anti-Limulus serum reacted strongly with spider sera, but scarcely at all with crustacean sera. A more recent study by Wilhelm has shown a close serological relationship between echinoderms and hemichordates, which confirms the morphological evidence. Boyden has demonstrated that whales, which because of their adaptations to marine life were difficult to place taxonomically among the mammals, are most closely related to the cloven-hoofed Artiodactyls. Another study by Moody indicated that rabbits and hares, long classed with the rodents, properly belong in the separate order Lagomorpha with closer affinities, actually, to the Artiodactyls than to the rodents. Thus, the serological approach has been very fruitful, particularly in instances in which the standard morphological methods were not too reliable.

▶ SUMMARY

The field of biochemistry has developed since Darwin's time to the point where it now can make notable contributions to our knowledge of evolution. Biochemical as well as structural homologies can be recognized, and they furnish reliable evidence of relationship independent of the conclusions based on comparative morphology. The chemical composition of living organisms, based on nucleic acids, proteins, carbohydrates, and fats, is itself evidence for the underlying kinship of all forms of life. Detailed studies of plant pigments, photoreceptor systems, immunology, and many metabolic systems have led to a variety of detailed biochemical evidence on relationships within and between groups. This evidence, unavailable to Darwin, has confirmed and extended our knowledge of evolution, for no other theory is adequate to interpret these data or so fruitful in suggesting further research in the field.

SUGGESTED READING

Boyden, A. A., 1942. "Systematic serology: a critical appreciation," *Physiol. Zool.,* 15:109-145.

———, 1953. "Fifty years of systematic serology," *Systematic Serol., 2:*19.

Florkin, M., 1949. *Biochemical evolution* (S. Morgulis, tr.). New York: Academic Press.

Nuttall, G. H. F., 1904. *Blood immunity and blood relationship.* New York: Cambridge University Press.

Prosser, C. L., 1960. "Comparative physiology in relation to evolutionary theory," *Evolution after Darwin,* Vol. I, *The evolution of life.* S. Tax, ed. Chicago: University of Chicago Press.

———, ed., 1958. *Physiological adaptation.* Washington, D. C.: American Physiological Society.

Wald, G., 1952. *Biochemical evolution. Modern trends in physiology and biochemistry.* New York: Academic Press.

———, 1958. "The significance of vertebrate metamorphosis," *Science, 128:*1481-1490.

CHAPTER 12

Biochemical Adaptation

Biochemical as well as morphological adaptations can be discerned. The morphology of the animal in a sense simply reflects its functioning; it is the net result of all of the genetic and environmental influences acting upon the developing organism. Regulation of the composition of the body fluids in different kinds of environments has led to a variety of biochemical adaptations. One of the fundamental similarities among living species of animals is in the relative ionic composition of the body fluids. Although they may differ in their absolute composition, nevertheless on a relative basis the plasma of such diverse species as the jellyfish, lobster, frog, and man is quite similar, and furthermore is much like sea water (see Table 12-1). These similarities suggested to Macallum that the body fluids of animals were originally derived from sea water. Since it is widely believed that life originated in the sea, the suggestion seemed quite reasonable. He even accounted for the discrepancies between the concentrations of potassium and magnesium in human plasma and sea water by the fact that the ocean millions of years ago contained less magnesium and more potassium than at present. The major difficulty with this theory is that it assumes that the body fluids, since being closed off from the sea, presumably at different times for different species, have somehow remained of the same composition despite the vicissitudes of existence and evolution in the history of each species. Since the evidence is clear that the ionic composition of the body fluids is actively maintained by living cells, the theory is obviously far too simple. An alternative explanation may be that life can exist only within rather narrow limits and arose at a time when the ionic composition of the ancient seas was similar to that of the plasma of present-day animals. These ionic limitations have remained essentially unchanged; consequently, all subsequent evolution, no matter what direction it took, of necessity was accompanied by the development of mechanisms for maintaining the ionic composition of the body fluids within the limits that would support life. It is known that one of the requirements for life is enough water containing the proper concentrations of the right kinds of salts.

TABLE 12-1

Relative Ionic Compositions of the Bloods and Tissue Fluids of Some Different Animals (After Macallum from Baldwin)

	Na	K	Ca	Mg	Cl	SO$_3$
Sea water	100	3.61	3.91	12.1	181	20.9
King crab						
Limulus	100	5.62	4.06	11.2	187	13.4
Jellyfish						
Aurelia	100	5.18	4.13	11.4	186	13.2
Lobster						
Homarus	100	3.73	4.85	1.72	171	6.7
Dogfish						
Acanthias	100	4.61	2.71	2.46	166	—
Sand shark						
Carcharias	100	5.75	2.98	2.76	169	—
Cod						
Gadus	100	9.50	3.93	1.41	150	—
Pollack						
Pollachius	100	4.33	3.10	1.46	138	—
Frog						
Rana	100	—	3.17	0.79	136	—
Dog						
Canis	100	6.62	2.8	0.76	139	—
Man						
Homo	100	6.75	3.10	0.70	129	—

Aquatic Life

The maintenance of the proper concentration of salts is apparently a relatively simple matter for most marine animals. A word about osmosis is appropriate at this point. When two different solutions are separated by a semipermeable membrane, which permits passage of the solvent but not of the dissolved substances, the solvent will flow toward the solution of higher concentration, thus tending to equalize the concentrations. This movement is known as osmosis or the osmotic flow, and the pressure resulting from this flow is osmotic pressure. Another way to think of osmotic pressure is as that amount of pressure necessary to prevent any fluid from flowing. A comparison of the freezing point of an aqueous solution with that of pure water serves as a simple yet precise indirect measure of the osmotic strength of that solution. In the coelenterates, echinoderms, and mollusks the freezing point depression of the body fluids does not differ essentially from that of the medium in which they live, and therefore their osmotic problems are not considered serious. However, the concentration of salts in fresh water is very low, and fresh-water animals have mechanisms for regulating their osmotic concentrations so that they are osmotically independent of their environments. Various methods have evolved in fresh-water species for osmotic regulation. Their problem, in essence, is to get rid of excess water. Semipermeable boundary membranes permit the retention of salts, but water is constantly seeping into the cells by osmosis, and must be eliminated in some way if the cells are not to swell up and burst due to the osmotic pressure. In the fresh-water protozoans contractile vacuoles constantly pump water out of the cell. Some protozoans can eliminate in this fashion a volume of water equal to their own volume in as little as two minutes. Species in other groups may have most of the body surface impermeable to both salts and water. The chitinous exoskeleton of crustaceans such as the crayfish, the keratin in the integument of various vertebrates, and the slimy surface of many fresh-water species all serve, to various degrees, to render the body surface impermeable. Excess water is still absorbed, but is eliminated by the excretion of a copious dilute urine through the kidneys of species such as the fresh-water bony fish and frogs. A frog, for example, excretes on the average one-third of its body weight in water each day. Man, with quite different osmotic problems, excretes only one-fiftieth of his weight per day. If the salt concentration is to be kept higher than that of the environment, osmotic work must be done in order to absorb salts against the concentration gradient. Fresh-water fish have special cells in the gills that carry out this function; mosquito larvae absorb chloride ions through their anal papillae.

The marine teleosts or bony fishes, in contrast to the marine invertebrates, have an osmotic concentration only about one-half as great as that of sea water. Dessication is therefore a constant threat, for they tend to lose water to their environment. With the Ancient Mariner, they can croak, "Water, water, everywhere, nor any drop to drink." Although they swallow large quantities of sea water, nevertheless their blood remains more dilute in salts than the sea water (see Table 12-2). The sea water is absorbed, salts and all, from the intestine, but the excess salt is excreted by the so-called "chloride secretory cells" in the gills. Thus in both fresh-water and marine bony fish, osmotic regulation is achieved only by the expenditure of energy to do osmotic work in specially adapted cells in the gills. The salts move in opposite directions, of course, through the cells of these two groups. Whereas fresh-water teleosts excrete a copious dilute or hypotonic urine, marine teleosts waste a minimum of water, a valuable material to them, in the formation of urine, and their urine is nearly isotonic with the blood. The numerous glomeruli in the kidneys of fresh-water fishes appear to be adaptations for filtering off large amounts of water. Marine fishes, with the problem of conserving water, have few glomeruli and this region

TABLE 12-2
Freezing Point Depression of Body Fluids in Animals (°C)
(After Heilbrunn)

Marine animals	Body fluid	Outer medium
Coelenterata		
Alcyonium palmatum	2.195	2.2
Echinodermata		
Asterias glacialis	2.295	2.195–2.36
Annelida		
Sipunculus nudus	2.27–2.31	2.29
Mollusca		
Ostrea edulis	2.23	2.11–2.14
Octopus vulgaris	2.16	2.11–2.14
Arthropoda		
Limulus polyphemus	1.90	1.82
Homarus americanus	1.82	1.80
Maja verrucosa	2.13	2.17
Tunicata		
Ascidia mentula	2.08	1.98
Chondrichthyes		
Mustellus vulgaris	2.36	2.29
Raja undulata	1.89	1.84
Teleostei		
Conger vulgaris	0.77	2.14
Charax puntacco	1.04	2.29
Fresh-water animals		
Mollusca		
Limnaea stagnalis	0.22–0.23	0.02–0.03
Annelida		
Hirudo officinalis	0.43	
Crustacea		
Daphnia magna	0.20–0.67	
Telphus fluviatile	1.17	
Osteichthyes		
Cyprinus carpio	0.50	
Salmo fario	0.57	
Terrestrial animals		
Annelida		
Lumbricus terrestris	0.45–0.51	
Mollusca		
Helix aspera	0.37	
Insecta		
Decticus albifrons	0.50	
Lymantria dispar	0.48	
Bombyx mori	0.73–0.79	
Amphibia		
Rana esculenta	0.40	
Reptilia		
Emys europea	0.47	
Aves		
Chicken?	0.615	
Mammalia		
Pig	0.615	
Horse	0.564	
Cat	0.638	

of the kidney has the appearance of having degenerated. This difference in the kidneys of marine and fresh-water species is also considered to be evidence for the fresh-water origin of the fishes.

The marine elasmobranchs (sharks, skates, and rays) have about the same amount of salts in their blood as the marine teleosts, but they have in addition about 2 percent urea (ordinarily a nitrogenous waste product), which brings the total osmotic pressure to slightly higher than that of sea water. The solution of the osmotic problems posed by life in the sea is quite different, therefore, in teleosts and elasmobranchs. The urea is retained because the gills are relatively impermeable to urea in low concentrations, and the renal tubule contains a special segment that reabsorbs urea from the glomerular filtrate. The shark and its relatives resemble the fresh-water teleosts in certain respects, for its kidney is glomerular, the osmotic gradient tends to drive water into the fish, and the urea-absorbing segment corresponds to the salt-absorbing segment of the renal tubule in fresh-water bony fish. Certain elasmobranchs live in fresh waters, and it is believed that they are descended from forms that at one time lived in the sea and later invaded the rivers. The salt content in the plasma of marine and fresh-water elasmobranchs is almost the same, but the fresh-water species have only about 0.6 percent urea rather than 2 percent. Since a more copious dilute urine must be produced than even that of the fresh-water teleosts, it would appear advantageous if the urea content were further reduced or even eliminated entirely, but this is apparently impossible. During the long period of marine life, the physiology of the elasmobranchs became so completely adapted to the presence of a high concentration of urea that the heart of fresh-water elasmobranchs will not beat in its absence.

The presence of the glomerulus, a device for excreting water, is evidence to indicate that all of the fishes originated in fresh water. Invasion of the sea led to degeneration of glomeruli in the teleosts; in the elasmobranchs, the retention of urea furnished a different means of minimizing water loss. See Fig. 12 1.

Terrestrial Life

Life on land poses still other biochemical problems, for the environment consists of air, with an abundance of oxygen but a scarcity of water. Furthermore, the excretion of nitrogenous waste products is more difficult in an environment where water is at a premium. The problems involved in biochemical adaptation to terrestrial life suggest that the first land vertebrates, the early amphibians, arose from among the fresh-water fishes rather than among the marine species living in the littoral zone. Two of the major adaptive changes required were the ability to obtain oxygen from the air rather than from water and the ability to withstand dessication. In warm, shallow, stagnant, fresh-water pools, the oxygen supply may be virtually depleted, and survival in this habitat may depend on the ability of the species to obtain the necessary oxygen from air rather than water. The air sac in fish is used as a lung by many species, particularly those dwelling in stagnant waters or in areas with seasonal droughts. The Dipnoi or lungfishes are perhaps the most familiar group of this kind, but the more primitive ray-finned fishes (Actinopterygii) such as the spoon-billed cat (*Polyodon*-Chondrostei) and the gar pike and bowfin (*Lepisosteus* and *Amia-*

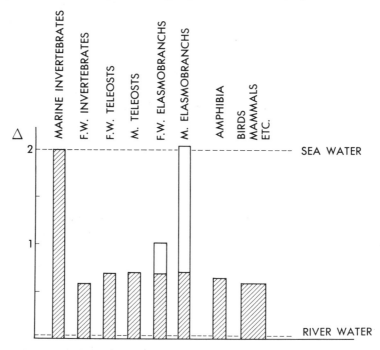

Fig. 12-1. Osmotic pressures of bloods of various animals compared with those of fresh and sea waters. Δ = freezing point depression. (After Baldwin.)

Holostei) also use the air sac as a lung for getting oxygen from the air. The use of the air sac as a swim bladder or hydrostatic organ in the teleosts appears to have been a subsequent development in marine fishes. The modern lungfish *Protopterus,* during the seasonal drought in its habitat in Africa, estivates in a slimy cocoon, breathing by means of its lungs so that it is able to withstand dessication and obtain oxygen from air, the two requirements mentioned above. Furthermore, the fresh-water fish typically have an integument of low surface permeability to water, although water enters quite freely through the gill and oral membranes. Thus, in making the transition from fresh water to land, the problem is to control water loss at these points rather than over the entire body surface.

It is doubtful that marine fishes were the first vertebrates to invade the land, since the littoral zone is a rather stable environment with an abundant oxygen supply and is therefore unlikely to require the major adaptive shifts that accompanied the origin of terrestrial vertebrates. Some of the most slowly evolving groups, such as the oysters (Mollusca) and the horseshoe crab (Arthropoda), inhabit the littoral zone, and their slow rate of evolution can probably be attributed to the stability of their environment and hence to the absence of major shifts in the pressures of natural selection that would be expected to produce rapid evolutionary change.

Among terrestrial vertebrates water conservation is a major problem. In most of the amphibians, evaporation from the body surface occurs at a fairly rapid rate even though the skin is not completely permeable to the outward flow of water. No amphibian is altogether independent of a moist environment, for even the desert toads tend to burrow and seek out damp and humid places. The integuments of the reptiles, birds, and mammals are far more effective protection against surface evaporation, for their permeability to water is extremely low. The arthropods, the other major group of animals to have achieved virtually complete independence from a moist environment, are protected against surface evaporation by the chitinous exoskeleton. Both chitin and the cuticular wax contribute to the impermeability of the cuticle.

Water loss during excretion is minimized in terrestrial forms in various ways. The ancestral vertebrates were fresh-water fishes whose kidneys primarily functioned, by means of large glomeruli, to rid the body of excess water. The frog kidney still functions in this fashion. In living reptiles, water loss has been reduced through a decrease in the size of the renal corpuscles, and consequently a smaller volume of filtrate is produced. In the snakes and lizards, the urine may even be solid or semisolid. The birds and mammals have renal corpuscles of normal size and therefore produce a large volume of filtrate, but the kidney tubule is modified by the presence of the long, thin loop of Henle in which it is thought most of the water resorption occurs. Some water is reabsorbed in any type of kidney tubule, but in man, for instance, with a long kidney tubule including the loop of Henle, scarcely 1 percent of the filtrate from the glomeruli ever reaches the bladder. The urine therefore is hypertonic to the blood in the birds and mammals. In birds, further water absorption occurs in the cloaca, and thus the urine becomes a semisolid mass. Insects, too, conserve water by reabsorption from the excretory wastes, which are discharged from the Malpighian tubules into the hind gut where resorption occurs.

Terrestrial animals obtain water by drinking, or with their food, or as a product of metabolism. Absorption of water occurs in the small and large intestine, and so the feces are usually semisolid or solid. The oxidation of organic compounds is a major source of water for some species, particularly desert species or such insects as clothes moths. The figures below indicate the efficiency of formation of metabolic water:

Oxidation of 100 g of	G of water
protein	41.3
carbohydrate	55.5
fat	107.1

Thus the fats, which are frequently stored by desert mammals, produce almost twice as much metabolic water per gram oxidized as the other compounds.

Development of amniote embryos on land is possible despite the fact that they are essentially aquatic. A watery environment is provided for reptilian and avian embryos by the shelled egg and for mammalian embryos by the uterus of the mother. Among the amphibians the majority of species lay their eggs in the water, and an aquatic larva, the tadpole, lives there for a considerable period. However, a variety of adaptations exist in various species of Amphibia for getting the eggs out of the water and minimizing the larval period. The reptilian egg may be regarded as the most successful of these adaptations. Viviparity is a further modification of reptilian development that has appeared not only in the mammals but also independently in certain reptilian groups as well.

Nitrogen Excretion

Nitrogenous wastes from protein metabolism are excreted in a variety of forms, with the type of waste product clearly related to the availability of water in the environment of the organism. Species with an abundant water supply excrete nitrogen primarily in the form of ammonia, a soluble but highly toxic compound. Although no group excretes just one nitrogenous waste product, the aquatic invertebrates and the fresh-water teleosts primarily eliminate ammonia, much of it through the gills in these teleosts rather than the kidneys. Marine teleosts, with quite a different osmotic problem as described earlier, excrete considerable ammonia, but they also excrete some urea and up to a third of their nitrogen as trimethylamine oxide, the latter two substances being soluble and relatively nontoxic. The elasmobranch fishes, which retain up to 2.5 percent urea in the blood, also excrete it from the gills. Terrestrial animals primarily excrete urea or else uric acid, which has a low toxicity and is relatively quite insoluble, hence can either be stored or eliminated as crystals.

In frogs, the tadpoles eliminate 40 percent or more of their nitrogen as ammonia, but adult frogs, with a greater need for conservation of water, excrete less ammonia and about 80 percent urea. Salts and some water are reabsorbed in

NH₃
ammonia

CH₃
|
CH₃—N—CH₃
‖
O
trimethylamine
oxide

NH₂—C—NH₂
‖
O
urea

H—N—C=O
| |
O=C C—NH
| ‖   >C=O
H—N—C—NH
uric acid

the kidney tubules, and the evidence indicates that urea is actively secreted into the tubules. Mammals also excrete urea, during both embryonic and adult stages, and the urea may be concentrated up to 100 times its level in the blood by the reabsorption of water in the kidney tubules.

Insects, birds, snakes, and lizards eliminate a semisolid urine containing uric acid crystals, thus minimizing water loss more than any other group. It should be noted that in these species with eggs protected against water loss (cleidoic eggs) the insoluble, nontoxic uric acid crystals can be stored in the allantois during the development of the embryo.

Metamorphosis from a tadpole to a frog involves a number of dramatic morphological changes taking place in a relatively short time. As a result the organism changes from an aquatic gill-breathing herbivore to a terrestrial lung-breathing carnivorous tetrapod. Just as striking as the changes in structure are the biochemical changes that accompany metamorphosis. At that time nitrogen excretion shifts over primarily to urea from amomnia, the visual pigment changes from porphyropsin to rhodopsin, and the hemoglobin changes to a type with a decreased affinity for oxygen. It also has a declining affinity for oxygen as the acidity increases, the so-called Bohr effect. Tadpole hemoglobin exhibits no Bohr effect and has a relatively high affinity for oxygen. These three changes can be regarded as adaptive for terrestrial life although the evidence that this is so for rhodopsin is not yet available. They may also be considered as instances of biochemical recapitulation. The ancestors of the amphibians were fresh-water fishes, which excreted primarily ammonia, had porphyropsin in their retinas, and possessed hemoglobin of high oxygen affinity and a small Bohr effect. It is difficult to avoid the conclusion that the developing frog manifests not only morphological but biochemical recapitulation of a phylogenetic sequence.

From this brief review, it seems clear that the biochemical approach to evolutionary problems and, conversely, the evolutionary approach to biochemical problems, are promising fields for further work, for this is an area of research where the surface has only been scratched.

SUMMARY ◄──────────────────────────────────

The adaptations of living organisms to their environments are biochemical in addition to being morphological and behavioral. Despite the varied osmotic problems posed by the sea, fresh water, and the land, living things must maintain the ionic composition of their body fluids within rather narrow limits. Water intake, water conservation, and the excretion of metabolic waste products are interrelated problems, the solutions of which vary greatly depending upon the environment. The invasion of fresh-water and terrestrial habitats became possible only when species had evolved methods of osmotic regulation in these new habitats. Evolutionary theories, therefore, must account for the origin of biochemical adaptation as well as the somewhat more obvious morphological adaptations.

SUGGESTED READING

Baldwin, E., 1949. *Comparative biochemistry,* 3d ed. New York: Cambridge University Press.

Prosser, C. L., and F. A. Brown, Jr., 1961. *Comparative animal physiology,* 2d ed. Philadelphia: Saunders.

Smith, H. W., 1953. *From fish to philosopher.* Boston: Little, Brown.

CHAPTER 13

Evolution in Animals

Approximately a million species of animals have been described; in some groups such as birds and mammals virtually all species are known, but in others many more species undoubtedly remain to be discovered. The great number of living species probably represents less than 1 percent of all of the species that have ever existed. These species have been arranged into a relatively small number of phyla, although there is no universal agreement among zoologists as to just how many phyla there are. The common practice of arranging the different groups into a phylogenetic sequence is frequently a useful teaching device. The record is spotty, however, and its better known parts consist largely of modern species out at the tips of the evolutionary branches. Since the phylogenetically significant portions of the record may be obscured far in the distant past, too great stress on the phylogenetic arrangement of known groups may confuse the student rather than convince him of the validity of the postulated relationships.

One of the problems in the discussion of evolution in the animal kingdom is the lack of familiarity of many people with the major groups of animals. This need not be an insurmountable obstacle. Most Americans can recognize at sight not only the make but the model and year of any car they spot on the highway. The number of phyla of animals is roughly comparable to the number of makes of American automobiles, and it should be no more difficult to learn to distinguish the phyla than it is to identify cars. Furthermore, to remain unfamiliar with at least the major animal groups is to be painfully ignorant of the world in which we live. Therefore, with no further apologies, we shall consider the major groups of animals and the ways in which they are thought to be related to one another. Obviously, many details must be omitted in our discussion, and if further information about any of the groups is desired, the references at the end of this chapter should be consulted.

A word or two may be in order about the nature of an animal. Anyone can tell the difference between a tree, which we call a plant, and a cow, which is an animal. The tree stands still and ignores you; the cow moves about, appears to see you, and may even, if so inclined, kick or toss or bite you. The tree makes its own food by photosynthesis from simple inorganic substances, but the cow cannot. However, not all animals can move, and not all plants are sessile, and distinctions based on behavior and nutrition soon begin to weaken. They break down completely in the flagellates or Mastigophora, which have traits regarded as characteristic of both animals and plants. The free-living flagellate, *Euglena,* is in many respects like an animal yet it contains chlorophyll and can therefore synthesize its own food. On the other hand, it can also absorb nutrients from its environment. It is not surprising that both botanists and zoologists have laid claim to such species, the botanists classifying them among the algae, the zoologists among the Protozoa. The truth of the matter is that there is no sharp line of demarcation by which animals may be separated from plants. The living world is not divided into two camps, one plant, the other animal; rather, it forms a continuum. It is generally thought that the other Protozoa and the higher multicellular animals or Metazoa as well as the higher plants have arisen from ancestral primitive flagellates.

Protozoa

The Protozoa are fundamentally single-celled animals. Although some form colonies, nevertheless each cell is typically morphologically and physiologically independent. (The Protozoa have also been called acellular animals because the high degree of complexity in some Protozoa outstrips anything to be seen in any individual metazoan cell. However, since the Metazoa seem to have been derived from the Protozoa, metazoan cells may perhaps best be thought of as having lost some of the versatility of the ancestral protozoan cell in their evolution to their present well-differentiated and specialized functions. The Protozoa do have a nucleus, cytoplasm, a plasma membrane, and the other structures usually associated with cells; hence by the usual criteria it is difficult to avoid the conclusion that they are cells, highly versatile cells, but cells nevertheless.) The classification of the Protozoa into five classes based primarily on their mode of locomotion is as follows:

1. Flagellata (Mastigophora)—propelled by one or several flagella. (A flagellum is a long whiplike cell process, often regarded as a very long mobile cilium.)

2. Sarcodina (Rhizopoda)—amoeboid movement by means of pseudopodia (temporary protrusions of the protoplasm).
3. Sporozoa—all are internal parasites without locomotor organelles, usually producing spores.
4. Ciliata—move by means of numerous cilia (short hairlike cell processes capable of vibratory movement).
5. Suctoria—ciliated only in the young stages; as adults, have one or more suctorial tentacles.

The relationships among the Protozoa are by no means clear, and their classification is to some extent quite arbitrary. Some of the green flagellates can hardly be separated from the green algae, and other flagellates, known as the chrysomonads, are continuous with the filamentous brown algae (Chrysophyceae). The chrysomonads show affinities in several directions; they may lose their flagella and resemble algae, or lose their chromoplasts and resemble animallike protomonads, or by the loss of both flagella and chromoplasts come to resemble typical amoebae or rhizopods. Loss of the chloroplasts in the different orders of flagellates has apparently given rise to the colorless animal forms. Furthermore, some parasitic flagellates with sporulation as a means of reproduction suggest the affinities of this group with the Sporozoa. The relationship between the flagellates and the Sarcodina is also suggested by the Rhizomastigina, which typically have both flagella and pseudopodia, as well as by the sporadic occurrence of amoeboid forms among various groups of flagellates. That the Sarcodina are derived from the flagellates rather than vice versa is suggested by the fact that they very often have flagellate immature stages, while the flagellates do not have amoeboid young stages.

The flagellates may very well be a polyphyletic group—that is, derived from a number of different sources, in this instance, spirochaetes and bacteria, which in many cases also have flagella. The rhizopods, like the flagellates, also appear to have a polyphyletic origin from several different groups of flagellates. The origins of the Sporozoa are again somewhat of an enigma; possibly they are polyphyletic also. The ciliates and the suctorians are probably related, but their relations to the other protozoa are unclear although it has been suggested that the cilia are derived from flagella.

Porifera

The enormous diversity of form and function among the Protozoa, from the simplest amoeba to the most complex ciliate, is so great that the Protozoa are sometimes regarded as a subkingdom, separate from all of the multicellular animals or Metazoa. Among the multicellular animals the sponges or Porifera (pore bearers) are regarded as an evolutionary dead end from which no other groups have evolved. Therefore, they have been placed in a separate

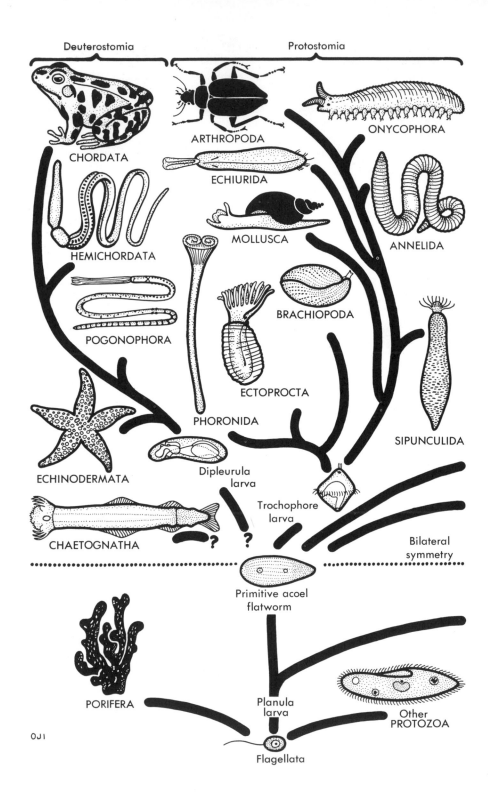

Deuterostomia   Protostomia

CHORDATA   ARTHROPODA   ONYCOPHORA

ECHIURIDA

HEMICHORDATA   MOLLUSCA   ANNELIDA

POGONOPHORA   BRACHIOPODA

ECTOPROCTA   SIPUNCULIDA

PHORONIDA

ECHINODERMATA   Dipleurula
larva

Trochophore
larva

CHAETOGNATHA   ?   ?   Bilateral
symmetry

Primitive acoel
flatworm

PORIFERA   Planula
larva   Other
PROTOZOA

OJI

Flagellata

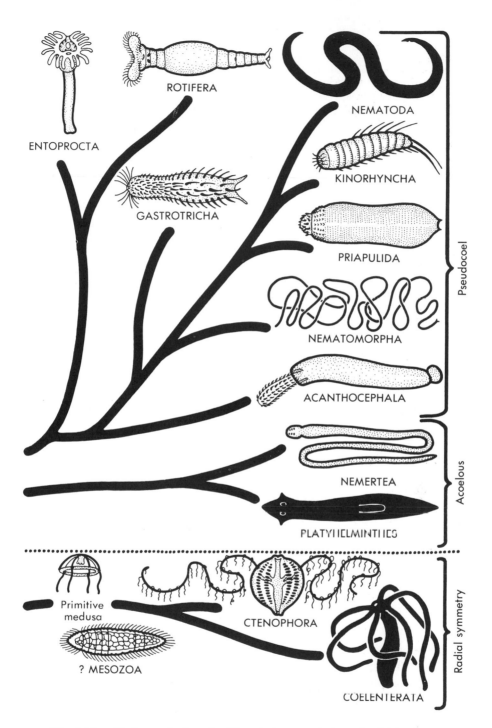

ENTOPROCTA

ROTIFERA

NEMATODA

GASTROTRICHA

KINORHYNCHA

PRIAPULIDA

NEMATOMORPHA

ACANTHOCEPHALA

NEMERTEA

PLATYHELMINTHES

Primitive
medusa

CTENOPHORA

? MESOZOA

COELENTERATA

Pseudocoel

Acoelous

Radial symmetry

Fig. 13-1. (facing and above). The phylogeny of the animal kingdom.

branch of the Metazoa called the Parazoa. The sponges are rather simple sessile organisms, either asymmetrical or with radial symmetry. They have a cellular grade of construction with special cells for special functions. There are no organs, no mouth, and no nervous tissue. The body is permeated with pores and canals through which water currents flow. The currents are generated by the flagella of the collar cells or choanocytes that line the canals or chambers. Food particles are trapped by the collar cells and are digested intracellularly. There is an internal skeleton of spicules or of spongin fibers, which the Greeks used to line their helmets and which we use today to wash windows or automobiles. Because of their characteristic choanocytes the sponges have been considered descended from the group of flagellates known as the choanoflagellates. However, it is also true that sponge larvae have typical flagellate cells rather than choanocytes and hence the Porifera could have originated from some more generalized flagellate stock. The sponges have not evolved too far beyond the stage reached by colonial flagellates; although the cells are somewhat differentiated and specialized for particular functions, coordinated activity has not been possible because of the absence of any sort of a nervous system. Evolution in the sponges has led to increased complexity in the skeleton and in the system of water canals but not to any higher or more complex organisms.

Mesozoa

The phylogenetic position of the Mesozoa is not at all clear. One reason for this difficulty is that all of the species in the group are invertebrate parasites, and it cannot be said with certainty whether their simple structure is truly primitive or the result of the degenerative changes so frequent in parasites. The Mesozoa are small wormlike animals of extremely simple two-layered solid construction. Whereas the inner layer of the Metazoa is digestive in function, in the Mesozoa it consists of only one or a few reproductive cells. The outer layer of ciliated cells carries on intracellular digestion. This type of structure shows some resemblance to the ciliated planula larva of the coelenterates, and the Mesozoa have sometimes been treated with this group. In other cases they have been considered as degenerate flatworms. In view of the doubts about their origin and affinities it seems best to put them in a separate branch of the Metazoa. Until more evidence is available, however, it seems unwise to place too great emphasis on their phylogenetic importance as possibly the most primitive group of Metazoa.

Coelenterata

The Coelenterata (coel-enteron = hollow gut), which include such forms as corals, jellyfish, and sea anemones, have a gastrovascular or digestive cavity with a mouth but no anus, whence their name. They are tentacle-bearing, radially symmetrical Metazoa with a tissue level of construction. Their cells, unlike the Porifera, are organized into an outer protective epithelium or ectoderm and an inner digestive layer or endoderm. Though commonly called diploblastic (having two tissue layers), the coelenterates also have, to varying degrees, indications in the mesogloea of a third intermediate mesodermal layer. Their activities are coordinated by a nerve net so that food can be seized by the tentacles and brought to the mouth. Whether in the form of a sessile cylindrical polyp or a free-floating bell-shaped medusa or jellyfish, the tentacles typically bear stinging cells or nematocysts.

Ctenophora

The Ctenophora, the comb jellies or sea walnuts, are a small group of about 80 marine species; although frequently included in the Coelenterata, they are sufficiently distinct to warrant being placed in a separate phylum. They take their name, comb-bearing, from eight rows of ciliary combs used for locomotion. Tentacles are present in most species, but nematocysts, so typical of coelenterates, are completely absent. Symmetry is biradial, a combination of radial and bilateral traits. They resemble the coelenterates in having a gastrovascular cavity and in having essentially a tissue level of construction, but the presence of mesenchymal muscle fibers in the abundant mesogloea and of an aboral sensory region suggests a higher level of organization than that of the coelenterates.

Platyhelminthes

In the flatworms or Platyhelminthes, still greater complexity of organization can be observed. The flatworms are bilaterally symmetrical; that is, they have anterior and posterior ends, dorsal and ventral surfaces, and right and left sides, one the mirror image of the other. Here there are clearly three germ layers with the mesoderm between the ectoderm and endoderm giving rise to muscles and other structures permitting greater complexity and efficiency. The flatworms have an organ level of construction, for their tissues are associated to form various organs. The excretory system is of the protonephridial type, consisting of terminal flame bulbs leading into excretory ducts. The flame bulbs lie in the body fluid and wastes diffuse across them into the ducts where a ciliary tuft (the "flame") presumably sets up a current in the duct. The nervous system has a pair of enlarged anterior ganglia and one to three pairs of longitudinal nerve cords. Hence, it is a central nervous system rather than a nerve net. Like the coelenterates, most of the flatworms have a gastrovascular cavity with a single opening that serves both as a mouth and anus. They completely lack any sort of body cavity comparable to the coelom of higher forms. Included in the Platyhelminthes are three quite distinct classes, the free-living flatworms such as

Planaria of the class Turbellaria, the parasitic flukes or Trematoda, and the intestinal parasites of vertebrates, the tapeworms or Cestoda. Associated with the parasitic habit, the parasitic flukes and tapeworms show varying degrees of change from the free-living turbellarians.

Origin of the Metazoa

While there is fairly wide agreement that the Porifera are derived from the choanoflagellates, the origin of the other Metazoa has been a moot question. A variety of possibilities has been raised, but no one theory can be said to have a preponderance of evidence in its favor. However, in a negative sense it is possible by a brief review of these theories to see which phyla are not likely to have been involved, and thus narrow the field considerably. The Metazoa simplest in structure are the Porifera, Mesozoa, Coelenterata, Ctenophora, and the Platyhelminthes. We have already considered and more or less discarded the Porifera and Mesozoa, which leaves the other three phyla. Of these, the coelenterates and the flatworms are the two groups most commonly considered as lying closest to the original Metazoa. It should be realized that the fossil record has been of no help in settling the question of the origin of the Metazoa, for the presence of most of the major phyla among the fossils of the early Paleozoic, when the record first becomes fairly good, indicates that the Metazoa must have arisen well back in the Pre-Cambrian. Therefore, the various theories are primarily speculative and all could very well be wrong. The following theories are among the more prominent concepts thus far advanced.

1. The gastraea theory of Haeckel may be regarded as the classical theory of metazoan origin, certainly it is the most widely quoted. In its current form, colonial flagellates similar to *Volvox,* which forms a hollow, spherical colony, are equated with the hollow spherical blastula stage in the embryology of the Metazoa. This hypothetical organism, termed the blastaea, was supposed to have a single layer of flagellated cells and to swim about with one end always forward so that an antero-posterior axis was established. The first differentiation was assumed to be into somatic or body cells and reproductive cells, a phenomenon also observed in *Volvox.* Next the posterior cells of the blastaea were thought to become adapted or specialized for digestive functions, the assumption being that separation of the digestive and locomotor functions would have an adaptive advantage. If one side of the sphere is pushed inward or invaginated—as can be done with a deflated basketball, for example—so that it comes in contact with the other side, a pouchlike, two-layered, radially symmetrical structure is formed that approaches the basic structure of the coelenterates. It also has the form of the two-layered or diploblastic gastrula stage of the metazoan embryo —whence the name, gastraea, of this hypothetical organism.

The two-layered coelenterate ancestors were then supposed to have given rise to the flatworms by becoming bilaterally symmetrical and developing a third germ layer, the mesoderm, between the outer ectoderm and the endoderm. The small ciliated planula larva of the coelenterates has been compared with the ancestral type that gave rise to the bilaterally symmetrical flatworms presumably like the very simple ciliated free-living flatworms of the order Acoela of the class Turbellaria. The appeal of the theory lies in its synthesis of a great deal of information drawn from the embryology and morphology of existing forms. In fact, it might be said that it is almost too good to be true. For example, the origin of the internal digestive layer, or endoderm, in lower forms, is generally not by invagination but rather through the inward migration of many cells from the ectoderm, and the planula larva and acoeloid flatworms have an internal solid mass of cells rather than being hollow. Other criticisms have also been directed at the theory as outlined above, but it seems likely that it will remain a strong contender for some time to come.

2. Another suggestion is that the coelenterates, like the sponges, are off the main path of metazoan evolution and arose independently of the rest of the Metazoa. The flatworms then would become ancestral to the higher Metazoa. However, the presence of a gastrovascular cavity in both coelenterates and flatworms and of a mesogloea between the ectoderm and the endoderm of the coelenterates comparable to the mesoderm of the flatworms suggests a relationship between them. Furthermore, the Ctenophora, while not necessarily in a direct line of relationship between the two groups, appear to show some similarities to both.

3. Still another hypothesis is that the coelenterates have evolved from the flatworms rather than vice versa as in the gastraea theory. In this case multinuclear ciliates were postulated to give rise to the Turbellaria Acoela by the formation of cells around the nuclei. From the Acoela were descended the higher Turbellaria from which the higher invertebrates arose and from which the coelenterates and the ctenophores were separately and independently evolved. On this view bilateral symmetry was the primitive condition, and the radial symmetry of the coelenterates was a secondary development associated with their sessile mode of life.

4. Quite a different concept is that the Metazoa, except for their mode of nutrition, are more like multicellular plants than like Protozoa and that the earliest organisms were multinuclear and photosynthetic plants, which were ancestral to the Metazoa and, independently, to the flagellates and the other Protozoa.

Although other theories or other versions of the above theories have been advanced, these give some idea of the diversity of opinion on the subject. The concept followed in the phylogenetic chart in Fig. 13-1 is that of the planula-acoela line of descent, not only because it is currently perhaps the most highly regarded of the various possibilities but also because it is less of a strain on the imagination. One reason is that the transition from radial to bilateral symmetry can be more readily visualized. This change was a major one, leading to the evolution of the higher phyla, all of which are bilateral. As noted above, however, since it cannot even be stated with assurance that the change was in this direction, further emphasis on the origin of bilaterality seems unwarranted. However the stage of the primitive acoeloid flatworms may have been reached, a stage similar to this seems very likely to have been ancestral to the higher bilateral groups. Although again all of the relationships among the various phyla cannot be discerned, two major lines of descent can be recognized: one, the Protostomia, leading to the Arthopoda and Mollusca; the other, the Deuterostomia, leading to the Chordata. The distinction between the Protostomia and the Deuterostomia is based on their mode of development. In the Protostomia, the mouth forms from (or in the region of) the blastopore whereas in the Deuterostomia the anus forms from (or in the region of) the blastopore, and the mouth is formed *de novo*. In the Protostomia, furthermore, embryonic development typically proceeds by spiral cleavage and is determinate; that is, specific cells of the early embryo are fated to give rise to specific parts of the larva and their extirpation results in a deficient larva. The trochophore larva characteristic of this group, more or less spherical in shape, has an apical tuft of cilia, a ciliated band (the prototroch) at the equator, and a complete L-shaped digestive tract.

Nemertea

The flatworms were mentioned earlier as lacking a coelom or body cavity, and one other phylum, the Nemertea (also known as Nemertinea and Rhynchocoela) or ribbon worms, is also acoelomate. They resemble the flatworms in several respects, having, for example, a ciliated ectoderm and flame bulbs for excretion. They differ, however, in having a complete digestive tract with mouth and anus, an eversible proboscis not connected with the alimentary canal, and a simple blood vascular system, differences so fundamental that assignment to a separate phylum seems necessary.

Acanthocephala

A fairly large number of groups have a body cavity known as a pseudocoel, since it lacks the mesodermal lining characteristic of the coelom. The spiny-headed worms or Acanthocephala are parasitic as larvae in various arthropods and as adults in the intestine of vertebrates. Though having a pseudocoel and circular as well as longitudinal muscles, they entirely lack a digestive tract, the retractable proboscis serving as an organ of attachment and the food being directly absorbed from the host's intestine. The excretory organs appear to be nephridia with modified flame bulbs, and in some, a type of superficial segmentation appears. Although these traits in general resemble those of the other pseudocoelomates such as the nematodes, the embryology tends to resemble that of the flatworms. Therefore, the Acanthocephala, even though a small group, have generally been accorded the status of a separate phylum.

The next six groups of pseudocoelomate animals to be considered show many similarities and therefore have sometimes been placed in one phylum, the Aschelminthes. These groups, which here are treated as separate phyla, are the Nematomorpha (Gordiacea) or horsehair worms, the Priapulida, the Kinorhyncha (Echinodera), the Nematoda (Nemathelminthes) or roundworms, the Gastrotricha, and the Rotifera. These more or less wormlike animals all have a complete digestive tract with a posterior anus.

Nematoda

Of these six groups, the nematodes include by far the largest number of species, for there are literally thousands of free-living and parasitic forms, some of an extremely unusual nature; one species, for example, has been found only in the poison gland of the rattlesnake. A roundworm is a rather simply constructed animal. In addition to the traits noted above, the body is covered by a tough cuticle, and the body wall has only a single layer of longitudinal muscle cells. There are no respiratory or circulatory organs, and the excretory system, when present, is a simple canal system unlike that of any other phylum. The nervous system consists of a circumenteric ring around the pharynx and a simple system of associated ganglia and nerves.

Nematomorpha, Kinorhyncha, and Priapulida

The Nematomorpha are much like the nematodes except that no excretory system is present, the alimentary canal is always more or less degenerate, and there is just a single ventral nerve cord. The long, thin adults, thought to resemble "horsehair," are free-living, but the larvae are insect parasites. Another small group, the Kinorhyncha (Echinodera), are superficially segmented into 13 or 14 rings and have a retractable spiny anterior end. There are two excretory tubes or protonephridia each with a single flame bulb. The Priapulida, with only three known species, are also superficially segmented, but have circular as well as longitudinal muscles. The spiny retractile anterior end calls to mind the kinorhynchs, as does the type of nervous system. The soft posterior processes with gill-like outgrowths seem to be unique. The excretory system consists of protonephridia and solenocytes (similar to flame bulbs except that they have a single flagellum rather than a tuft of cilia). Although the priapulids have been grouped with the sipunculid and the echiurid worms either in a separate phylum Gephyrea or else as a class of annelids, this seems clearly in error, for their greatest affinities are with the kinorhynchs and nematodes, and they also show certain traits similar to those of the rotifers and gastrotrichs.

Gastrotricha and Rotifera

Typical gastrotrichs are minute spiny animals that glide about by means of ventral cilia. Each lobe of the forked posterior end has an adhesive gland for temporary attachment. The excretory system consists of paired protonephridia each with a single flame bulb. The rotifers have a similar excretory system, an anterior retractile ciliated disc or corona, and a posterior forked "foot" with adhesive glands. The internal jaws in the pharynx are unique and quite distinctive. The rotifers are generally the smallest of all of the Metazoa.

The gastrotrichs are probably closest phylogenetically to the nematodes, but they also have several features in common with the rotifers, such as external cilia, the forked foot, and the excretory system. The rotifers, because of their resemblance to the trochophore larva characteristic of the annelid-mollusk line of descent, are thought to be in some way related to the common ancestor of these phyla. However, the rotifers also resemble the free-living flatworms, perhaps more than they do any other group, as well as showing affinities with the gastrotrichs and nematodes. Hence they should probably be regarded as a group relating the turbellarian flatworms to the aschelminths.

Entoprocta and Ectoprocta

The final pseudocoelomate phylum, the Entoprocta, was formerly placed with the Ectoprocta as a class in the phylum Bryozoa (or Polyzoa), but the resemblance is superficial. The entoprocts have a pseudocoelom, a U-shaped digestive tract with both mouth and anus opening within the circle of tentacles, and they have protonephridia with flame bulbs for excretion. The ectoprocts, a much larger group, have a true coelom lined with mesoderm, an anus that opens outside the lophophore bearing ciliated tentacles, and no excretory organs. The similarities lie primarily in the crown of tentacles and the sessile mode of life, which is usually in colonies. However, since the tentacular crown of the entoprocts is not comparable or homologous to the lophophore of the ectoprocts, it is clear that the two groups should be separated. The group nearest the entoprocts would seem to be the rotifers. Despite the many well-defined differences between adult entoprocts and ectoprocts, both types develop from a type of larva known as the trochophore, although the entoproct larva departs in some respects from the typical trochophore larva.

Among the animals with a pseudocoel, then, are six groups quite clearly similar and two phyla, the Acanthocephala and the Entoprocta, rather different from the others. Here, too, although fundamental morphological similarities exist that clearly seem to indicate relationship, the exact phylogenetic sequence is obscured in the mists of the past and may never be known with certainty.

Brachiopoda and Phoronida

In addition to the Ectoprocta, two other coelomate phyla, the Brachiopoda and the Phoronida, also have a lophophore, and these three phyla, though quite different in some respects, nevertheless appear to be related. They are similar also in having a trochophore-like larva but differ in that both phoronids and brachiopods have a simple circulatory system and an excretory system with nephridia, both of which are lacking in the ectoprocts. The nephridial system of coelomate invertebrates is typically of the metanephridial type, in which the nephridial tubules begin as coelomic openings, draining wastes from the body cavity.

Very few species of phoronids are known. Sedentary, wormlike animals, they are all marine, living in a self-secreted tube from which the lophophore is extended to feed. The brachiopods or lamp-shells have a superficial resemblance to the bivalve mollusks such as the oyster, but the two halves of the shell are dorsal and ventral rather than right and left halves as in the bivalves. An unusual feature of brachiopod development is the formation of the mesoderm by enterocoely (out-pocketing from the gut), a mode of mesoderm formation more characteristic of the Deuterostomia and therefore suggesting affinities with the echinoderms and chordates. The brachiopods have a long, extensive fossil record, and the living species represent only a small remnant of the species and genera of the past. One living genus, *Lingula,* has persisted virtually unchanged from the Ordovician period of the Paleozoic, some 400,000,000 years ago, and is therefore probably the oldest living genus.

Mollusca

The Mollusca are the second largest group of invertebrates, having five classes, quite diverse in appearance but with an underlying fundamental similarity. The body consists of a head (absent in bivalves and tooth shells), a ventral muscular foot, and a dorsal visceral mass covered by a mantle, which usually secretes a calcareous shell on its upper surface. The five classes are as follows:

1. Amphineura—chitons
2. Gastropoda—snails, slugs, limpets, whelks, abalone, periwinkle, conches, etc.
3. Scaphopoda—tooth shells
4. Pelecypoda—bivalves such as clams, oysters, scallops, and mussels
5. Cephalopoda—nautili, squids, and octopi

The radula, a rasping organ in the mouth of most mollusks, is unique to the group, and here, for the first time, we encounter respiratory organs either in the form of gills (ctenidia) or lungs. Though mollusks are coelomate, the coelom is reduced to the cavities of the gonads, the pericardium, and the nephridia. Both circulatory and excretory systems are well developed. The nervous system varies widely from the simple system of ganglia in bivalves like the clam to the complex centralized system with a "brain" and camera-type eyes of cephalopods such as the squid.

The mollusks were a large, well-defined group with all of the living classes already represented at the beginning of the Paleozoic. The trochophore larva typical of many mollusks clearly indicates their relationship to the line of descent that also led to the annelids and arthropods, although the separation must have occurred long ago. Most of the Mollusca show little or no evidence of segmentation, and the group is usually referred to as unsegmented. However, the recent discovery of a living mollusk, *Neopilina galatheae,* in the depths off the west coast of Mexico has raised serious questions as to whether the ancestral mollusks were segmented (see Fig. 13-2). *Neopilina* belongs to the Amphineura, generally presumed to be closest to the ancestral mollusks because of their relatively simple bilateral structure as compared with the other classes of mollusks. *Neopilina* has five pairs of small gills, and each gill is associated with a nephridium; there are, furthermore, five pairs of dorso-ventral muscles associated with the foot. Clearly, this arrangement represents well-defined segmentation, and the possibility must now be admitted that ancestral mollusks were segmented, the modern forms representing a secondary loss of the segmented condition. If such is the case, then the mollusks may be closer to the annelids than had been previously suspected.

Annelida

The members of the phylum Annelida, to which belong the earthworms, polychaete marine worms, and leeches, are usually conspicuously segmented both externally and internally, with the body composed of many essentially similar segments or somites. This segmentation can be observed not only in the appendages and muscles, but in the serial repetition of the parts of the nervous, excretory, circulatory, and reproductive systems. Each somite also typically bears small rodlike appendages or setae. The circulatory system consists of a closed system of vessels with a circulating fluid containing a respiratory pigment. The larva, when present, is a trochophore, and the early development of annelids and mollusks is quite similar.

Since segmentation is present in the two dominant phyla of animals of the present time, the Arthropoda and the Chordata, it must represent a major evolutionary advance. However, although various theories of the origin of seg-

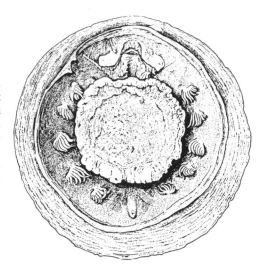

Fig. 13-2. Neopilina galatheae, a recently discovered living mollusk of the class Amphineura, with definite signs of segmentation, suggesting a closer relationship between the mollusks and the segmented annelids than had previously been suspected. (With permission of Lemche.)

mentation have been advanced, there is little evidence to favor any one theory over the rest. Furthermore, segmentation in the annelid-arthropod line appears to have arisen independently of segmentation in the chordates.

Sipunculida and Echiurida

The sipunculid and echiurid marine worms are undoubtedly related to the annelids and, perhaps because they are rather small groups, have sometimes been classified as annelids. Since they are quite different from the earthworm and other annelids, however, more recently they have been placed in separate phyla. Both Sipunculida and Echiurida have trochophore larvae, large coeloms, and somewhat similar circulatory and nephridial systems. The sipunculid or "peanut" worms are gourd-shaped with a narrow retractile anterior end crowned with a circle of ciliated tentacles. The anus is anterior and dorsal. The echiurids have a troughlike proboscis, which cannot be withdrawn into the anterior end of the body like that of the sipunculids, and the anus is posterior. Bristlelike setae are present, and the larvae show definite signs of segmentation. Thus the echiurids quite definitely belong close to the annelids.

Onycophora, a Living Link

Whereas the evidence for the relationships among the various groups presented thus far has been rather tenuous in most cases, the evidence for the relationship between annelids and arthropods is much more clearcut. These phyla show many similarities both in mode of development (although a trochophore larva is absent in arthropods) and in adult structure. The arthropods differ from annelids in having a thick chitinous exoskeleton, jointed appendages, and muscles in functional groups rather than simple continuous sheets. The coelom of the arthropods is much reduced and is more or less replaced by the haemocoele of the circulatory system, and the excretory and reproductive systems are concentrated rather than segmental.

Fig. 13-3. Peripatus (*Macroperipatus geayi*) of the phylum Onycophora, a connecting link between the annelids and the arthropods. (Photo by Ralph Buchsbaum.)

These two phyla are the only major invertebrate groups with conspicuous true segmentation. One other small phylum, the Onycophora, is also segmented, and has a unique mixture of annelid and arthropod traits. They are like annelids in having segmental nephridia, simple eyes but no well-defined head, a soft cuticle, short unjointed appendages, and muscles in continuous sheets. Arthropod traits include the reduced coelom with the haemocoele as the adult body cavity, the tracheal respiratory system, and the circulatory system with a dorsal "heart." The Onycophora, represented by *Peripatus* (Fig. 13-3), have been classed with the arthropods and also as annelids, but it seems best to place them for the present in a separate phylum, for their features, although re-

sembling those in both groups, are different enough to suggest that the Onycophora are a very old group. Rather than being a missing link between Annelida
and Arthropoda, they perhaps represent a third independent line of descent from
the ancestral stock that gave rise to modern annelids and arthropods. In any
event their very existence tends to reinforce the postulated relationship between
those two phyla.

Arthropoda

The Arthropoda have by far the greatest number of species of any
phylum. The following classes have been recognized, most of them including
very familiar forms.

1. Trilobita—extinct aquatic forms
2. Crustacea—shrimps, copepods, crabs, lobsters, etc.
3. Arachnida—spiders, ticks, mites, scorpions, horseshoe crabs, eurypterids (ex-
      tinct), etc.
4. Myriapoda—centipedes, millipedes
5. Insecta—butterflies, beetles, bees, dragonflies, etc.

The Arthropoda may be described as segmented animals with jointed appendages, a haemocoele, and a thick chitinous exoskeleton. This body plan has been
enormously successful in all sorts of habitats. Different species have adapted to
life in the depths of the sea, on land, and in the air. The exoskeleton undoubtedly made possible the invasion of the land by protecting the animals against
dessication, and, by providing rigid points of attachment for the muscles, it also
is related to their speed of movement. Furthermore, the great morphological
specialization and diversification of the exoskeleton into various types of legs,
wings, and mouth parts has made possible adaptation to a great variety of ecological niches.

Chaetognatha and Pogonophora

The phyla remaining to be considered, Chaetognatha, Echinodermata,
Pogonophora, Hemichordata, and Chordata, all belong to the Deuterostomia.
The arrow worms or Chaetognatha resemble in the simplicity of their structure
(no excretory, respiratory or circulatory systems) some of the pseudocoelomate
groups. However, they have a large true coelom and their early embryology resembles that of the echinoderms and chordates. A post-anal tail is found only in
this group and among the chordates. The bristles about the mouth, from which
the phylum gets its name, aid in the capture of food. Although the arrow worms
appear to belong among the Deuterostomia, they show no obvious relation to
any other members of this group. The Pogonophora, sedentary worms living in

long tubes in the depths of the Pacific, were originally thought to be polychaete annelids, but more recently they have been placed in a separate phylum with their closest affinities to the Hemichordata. Because of the complex tentacles at the anterior end, somewhat like the lophophore of the phoronids, ectoprocts, and brachiopods, they have been placed between the hemichordates and the lophophorates. However, the exact status of this group will not be well established until it has been more extensively studied.

Echinodermata

The Echinodermata, which include such species as starfish, crinoids, brittle stars, sea urchins, and sea cucumbers, have ciliated, free-swimming, bilaterally symmetrical larvae and radially symmetrical adults, presumably a secondary development related to the adults' sessile mode of life. Although a starfish is a far cry from a vertebrate, nevertheless the echinoderms, hemichordates, and chordates clearly form a related group. The relationship is based primarily on the similarities in their embryological development. In the Deuterostomia not only is the mouth newly formed, the blastopore becoming the anus, but cleavage is indeterminate, and the mesoderm and the coelom originate from pouches formed from the wall of the primitive gut (enterocoely). Furthermore, the echinoderm skeleton is derived from the mesoderm as it is in the chordates, unlike its mode of origin in any other invertebrate group. The different groups of echinoderms have several distinctive types of larvae, but in the early stages of development all echinoderm larvae pass through a dipleurula stage during which they show several traits in common. The dipleurula larvae are bilaterally symmetrical, swim by means of longitudinal looped ciliated bands, and have an anterior coelom that opens to the dorsal surface through a pore. There is an anterior tuft of sensory cilia, a ventral mouth, and a posterior anus. The developing Hemichordata pass through stages very similar to the dipleurula larva, and the tornaria larvae of the hemichordate tongue worms are so similar to the bipinnaria larvae of the starfishes that they were originally described as starfish larvae (Fig. 13-4). These larvae and their mode of development are so different from the trochophore larva characteristic of the mollusk-annelid line that the larval traits have served as the basis for the diphyletic system of evolution described here. Although larval resemblances and differences may be misleading because the larvae themselves may evolve in adapting to their environments, the differences between dipleurula and trochophore larvae appear to be more fundamental than can be accounted for by differing adaptive responses. Finally, it should be noted that the larvae of these and other forms are best interpreted as recapitulating the larvae of the ancestral forms rather than as being representative of the adult ancestor.

Adult echinoderms have unsegmented bodies usually with five arms (or multiples of five) bearing tube feet. The water vascular system, of which the

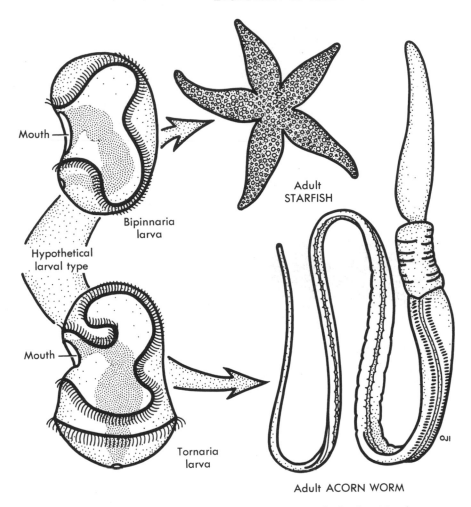

Mouth

Bipinnaria
larva

Hypothetical
larval type

Adult
STARFISH

Mouth

Tornaria
larva

Adult ACORN WORM

Fig. 13-4. Larval homology in the echinoderms and the hemichordates.

tube feet form a part, is a unique system for locomotion, respiration, and food handling. The digestive system is complete though the anus is small (in some it is lacking), and the coelom is well developed. Nervous and circulatory systems, though present, are reduced. Among all the invertebrates, the starfish and its kin seem very unlikely candidates as relatives to the phylum that we, at least, tend to regard so highly, the chordates.

Hemichordata

The hemichordates have sometimes been classified as a subphylum of the Chordata, but more recently the trend has been to call them a separate phylum. Small wormlike animals, they have indications of the three chordate traits—notochord, pharyngeal gill slits, and dorsal nerve cord—but in each case some doubt exists as to their homology. The body is composed of a proboscis, a collar, and a trunk, each region having separate coelomic cavities. The mouth opens at the anterior margin of the collar into the digestive tract, and just back of the collar numerous gill slits permit excess water to pass out of the tract. There is some question as to whether the gill slits have a respiratory function. The "notochord" or stomocord projects forward into the proboscis as an anterior out-pocketing of the digestive tract and serves as a supporting structure, but whether it is truly homologous to the notochord is doubtful. Since the ventral nerve cord is more extensive than the dorsal one that is limited to the collar, again the homologies are not clear. Thus, although the acorn worms are clearly more like the chordates than like any other group, they are still sufficiently different to be considered as a separate phylum.

An extinct group known as the graptolites has recently been included among the Hemichordata, but the evidence for this relationship is rather tenu-ous, and further information seems necessary before any well-founded conclu-sions can be drawn.

Chordata

The phylum Chordata has three subphyla:

1. Urochordata or Tunicata—the tunicates or sea squirts or ascidians
2. Cephalochordata—amphioxus or the lancelets
3. Vertebrata—the back-boned animals or vertebrates

The sessile adult tunicate shows little to suggest its affinity to the other chordates, but the free-living larvae clearly show chordate characteristics. The notochord of the larva is confined to the tail (whence the name Urochordata). The dorsal hollow nerve cord terminates anteriorly in a "brain" and a median eye. Gill slits are found in a region comparable to the pharynx in the higher chordates, and thus all three traits are clearly present. Upon settling down, the larva has its tail reabsorbed, the notochord disappears, and the nervous system is reduced to a ganglion. The gill slits are incorporated into a large branchial sac, and a test or tunic is secreted over the outer surface.

In the cephalochordates the three distinctive chordate traits are seen in simple form in the adults. The notochord and dorsal nerve cord extend the length of the body up into the anterior tip (hence the name Cephalochordata, even though they have no distinct head). Numerous gill arches associated with the circulatory system are found in the pharyngeal region. Amphioxus is a fre-quent subject of study in zoology, for the circulatory, muscular, nervous, and other systems are thought to be representative of the ancestral chordate condi-tion. The presence of nephridia that appear to resemble those of certain poly-chaete annelid worms constitutes something of a phylogenetic puzzle.

The vertebrates, whose evolution has already been discussed, are the dominant animals on the earth at present, for to this group belong the fishes of the sea, the mammals on the land, and the birds of the air. Although many species as adults lack gills and a notochord, nevertheless at some stage in the life cycle the basic chordate traits appear and the relationship of all of these groups to one another is clearly evident.

Confronted by the great diversity of species, one well can wonder whether it is possible to decipher any sort of orderly relationship among so many thousands of kinds of animals. The surprising thing perhaps is not that so few well-defined relationships have been pinned down, but rather that the phylogeny of the animal kingdom is as well known as it is. When the great gaps in our knowledge of the past are realized, it is easier to appreciate the problems involved. One other factor that is almost impossible for the human mind to encompass is the vast stretch of time available in the past during which some of the otherwise almost unbelievable evolutionary changes took place. If the magnitude of the evolutionary changes of just the past ten million years can be appreciated, it becomes perhaps somewhat easier to comprehend the magnitude of changes possible during periods ranging up to hundreds of millions of years.

▶ **SUMMARY**

Any survey of the animal kingdom tends to stress the means of distinguishing the different kinds of animals from one another, but it must be remembered that all animals share many traits in common. Furthermore, despite many questionable or dubious points, it is possible to work out a phylogeny of the animal kingdom based on the similarities among the different groups. Although such a phylogeny is based on the assumption of evolution, the very fact that the phylogeny, when constructed, forms a branching system is in itself an argument favoring evolution.

SUGGESTED READING

Berrill, N. J., 1955. *The origin of vertebrates.* Oxford: Clarendon Press.

Borradaile, L. A., and F. A. Potts, 1958. *The Invertebrata,* 3d ed. New York: Macmillan.

Buchsbaum, R., 1948. *Animals without backbones,* 2d ed. Chicago: University of Chicago Press.

de Beer, G. R., 1954. *The evolution of metazoa. Evolution as a process.* J. Huxley, A. C. Hardy, and E. B. Ford, eds. London: Allen and Unwin.

Hyman, L. H., 1940-1959. *The invertebrates,* Vols. 1-5. New York: McGraw-Hill.

Marcus, E., 1958. "On the evolution of animal phyla," *Quart. Rev. Biol.,* 33:24-58.

Storer, T. I., and R. L. Usinger, 1957. *General zoology,* 3d ed. New York: McGraw-Hill.

Young, J. Z., 1950. *The life of vertebrates.* Oxford: Clarendon Press.

CHAPTER 14

Evolution in Plants

In the plant kingdom as in the animal kingdom classification has been attempted in a way that conforms with the postulated phylogeny of the various groups. This effort has been only partially successful, for again in many cases the relationships are difficult to decipher and arbitrary decisions have been necessary. However, because additional research seemed to indicate that the existing classification did not accurately reflect the relationships among the various plants, a major revision in classification of the plant kingdom was recently made. The classical classification was as follows:

Kingdom Plantae

DIVISION THALLOPHYTA
    SUBDIVISION ALGAE—seaweeds, kelps, pond scum, etc.
    SUBDIVISION FUNGI—molds, yeasts, bacteria, mushrooms, etc.
DIVISION BRYOPHYTA
    CLASS HEPATICAE—liverworts
    CLASS MUSCI—mosses
DIVISION PTERIDOPHYTA
    CLASS FILICINEAE—ferns
    CLASS EQUISETINEAE—horsetails
    CLASS LYCOPODINEAE—club mosses
DIVISION SPERMATOPHYTA
    SUBDIVISION GYMNOSPERMAE—conifers
    SUBDIVISION ANGIOSPERMAE—flowering plants
        CLASS DICOTYLEDONEAE
        CLASS MONOCOTYLEDONEAE

The more modern classification, which has been based on recent morphological and paleobotanical work and is believed to be a more natural system, is as follows:

Kingdom Plantae

	PHYLUM* CYANOPHYTA—blue-green algae
	PHYLUM EUGLENOPHYTA—euglenoids
	PHYLUM CHLOROPHYTA—green algae
formerly ALGAE	PHYLUM CHRYSOPHYTA—yellow-green and golden brown algae and diatoms
	PHYLUM PYRROPHYTA—cryptomonads and dinoflagellates
	PHYLUM PHAEOPHYTA—brown algae
	PHYLUM RHODOPHYTA—red algae
formerly FUNGI	PHYLUM SCHIZOMYCOPHYTA—bacteria
	PHYLUM MYXOMYCOPHYTA—slime molds
	PHYLUM EUMYCOPHYTA—true fungi
	PHYLUM BRYOPHYTA—mosses, liverworts, and hornworts
	PHYLUM TRACHEOPHYTA—vascular plants
formerly PTERIDOPHYTA	SUBPHYLUM PSILOPSIDA
	SUBPHYLUM LYCOPSIDA—club mosses
	SUBPHYLUM SPHENOPSIDA—horsetails
formerly PTERIDOPHYTA	SUBPHYLUM PTEROPSIDA
	CLASS FILICINEAE—ferns
formerly SPERMATOPHYTA	CLASS GYMNOSPERMAE—conifers
	CLASS ANGIOSPERMAE—flowering plants

The major changes can be seen to be an upgrading in the systematic rank of the various algae, reflecting the belief that these groups are not at all closely related, and a rearrangement in the classification of the different groups of higher plants. The latter change seemed necessary because recent evidence has tended to break down some of the former distinctions between the pteridophytes and the spermatophytes.

The terms thallophyte, algae, and fungi are, however, useful ones and undoubtedly will continue to be used even though it is recognized that they represent artificial groupings. The phyla considered as thallophytes are plants that lack true roots, stems, and leaves (or to be more specific, the vascular tissues, xylem and phloem), and in which the zygote does not form a multicellular

---

* The Botanical Rules of Nomenclature recognize "Divisions" rather than "Phyla," but the latter term is used here to parallel zoological usage.

embryo while still in the female sex organs. The algae are thallophytes possessing chlorophyll; the fungi are thallophytes lacking chlorophyll. The postulated relationships among the different plant phyla are shown in Fig. 14-1.

Cyanophyta

The phylum Cyanophyta (or blue-green algae) is an extremely primitive group. The plant is a single cell, occasionally grouped in loose aggregations. There apparently is no definite nucleus, for the chromatin appears scattered in the center of the cell. The chlorophyll is diffused rather than being organized into plastids. The blue color is due to another pigment, phycocyanin, and a red pigment may also be present. The only known method of reproduction is by asexual fission, and none of the cells of the blue-greens has flagella. The Cyanophyta have been described from Precambrian rocks estimated to be a billion years old and are, therefore, among the oldest known fossil plants.

Rhodophyta

The phylum Rhodophyta (or red algae) takes its name from the red pigment phycoerythrin associated in the plastids with chlorophyll and also in some species with phycocyanin. The thallus is ordinarily multicellular, composed of nucleated cells. The life cycle may be complex, with both sexual and asexual reproduction, but an unusual feature of these algae is the absence of any type of flagellated reproductive cell. The red algae have a fossil record going back to the Ordovician and show little resemblance to any other algal group except the blue-greens. Both groups lack flagellated cells and have in common, in at least some species of both groups, the red and blue pigments, phycoerythrin and phycocyanin.

Pyrrophyta and Chrysophyta

The cryptomonads and dinoflagellates have been placed by botanists in the phylum Pyrrophyta. Most members of this phylum are unicellular with two unlike flagella, yellow-green to golden-brown plastids, no cell walls, and reserve food in the form of starches or oils.

The Chrysophyta include the yellow-green algae, the golden brown algae, and the diatoms. The name *chrysos*, "golden," stems from the fact that there are more yellow or brown carotenoid pigments than there is chlorophyll, with both pigments being found in plastids. The food reserves are oils and leucosin, an insoluble carbohydrate. The cell walls are usually formed of overlapping halves, frequently silica impregnated. The three classes of this phylum, in some ways quite different, are thought to be related because of the similar

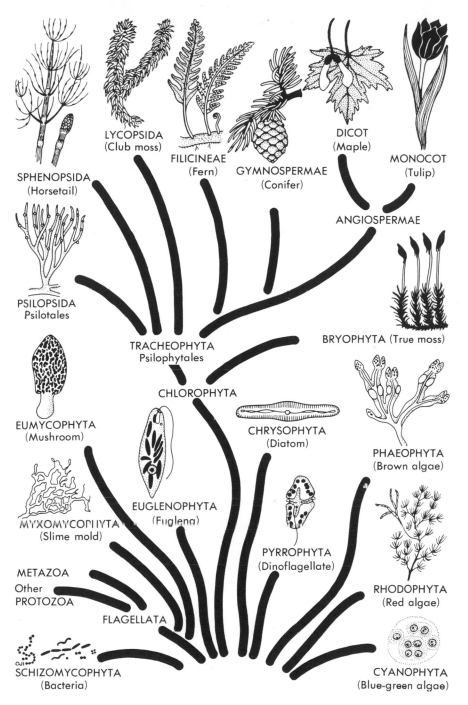

SPHENOPSIDA
(Horsetail)

LYCOPSIDA
(Club moss)

FILICINEAE
(Fern)

GYMNOSPERMAE
(Conifer)

DICOT
(Maple)

MONOCOT
(Tulip)

ANGIOSPERMAE

PSILOPSIDA
Psilotales

BRYOPHYTA (True moss)

TRACHEOPHYTA
Psilophytales

CHLOROPHYTA

EUMYCOPHYTA
(Mushroom)

EUGLENOPHYTA
(Euglena)

CHRYSOPHYTA
(Diatom)

PHAEOPHYTA
(Brown algae)

MYXOMYCOPHYTA
(Slime mold)

PYRROPHYTA
(Dinoflagellate)

RHODOPHYTA
(Red algae)

METAZOA
Other
PROTOZOA

FLAGELLATA

SCHIZOMYCOPHYTA
(Bacteria)

CYANOPHYTA
(Blue-green algae)

Fig. 14-1. The phylogeny of the plant kingdom.

types of reserve food and the silicified bipartite cell walls. The Pyrrophyta and Chrysophyta show some affinities, but the phylogenetic relationships of these two groups are still far from clear.

Phaeophyta

The brown algae or Phaeophyta have their photosynthetic pigments masked by the brown pigment, fucoxanthin. The plants are multicellular, ranging in size from a few cells to the giant kelps over 100 feet in length, and are vegetatively the most highly specialized group among all of the algae. Not only may the plant bodies be highly differentiated, but a variety of methods of reproduction have evolved, and there is commonly an alternation of generations. Although the brown algae have become the most advanced in structure among the algae, resembling in some respects the primitive vascular plants, they are not thought to have given rise to any higher groups of plants nor are they considered to be very closely related to any other group of algae.

Euglenophyta and Chlorophyta

Almost all of the Euglenophyta are naked unicellular flagellates with the chlorophyll not associated with any other pigments except the usual carotinoids (carotene and xanthophyll) found in the green algae and the higher plants. They differ from the blue-green algae in having the reserve food in the form of the carbohydrate, paramylum, and fats.

The green algae or Chlorophyta have chlorophyll and the associated carotenoids in the same proportions as the higher plants. The cells have definite nuclei and chloroplasts, are often flagellated, and the thallus may be unicellular, multicellular, or colonial. The reserve food is starch, and cellulose cell walls are present; in these respects the green algae differ from the euglenoids. However, the green algae are clearly rather similar to the euglenophytes and are thought to have been derived from them. Furthermore, both the bryophytes and the vascular plants are considered to have evolved from filamentous green algae.

Schizomycophyta

Although the bacteria (Schizomycophyta) show some structural and reproductive similarities to the blue-green algae and to some of the true fungi, their exact phylogenetic position is unknown and will probably remain a matter of speculation. They are extremely small (up to 5 microns) and structurally simple unicellular organisms. Bacteria are generally believed to have been among the first living organisms on earth. Most bacteria are parasites or saprophytes (obtaining food from nonliving organic matter), and are called heterotrophic. However, some bacteria, such as iron and sulfur bacteria, are autotrophic—that is, capable of synthesizing organic compounds from simple inorganic substances. Some of the rich iron ore deposits of the earth are extremely old and are thought to have been formed by the action of iron bacteria, which obtain the necessary energy for organic syntheses from the oxidation of ferrous compounds in iron-bearing waters. Thus, these autotrophic chemosynthetic bacteria could have existed even before the photosynthetic process had evolved. Furthermore, since evidence is accumulating as to ways in which organic compounds could have been synthesized by nonliving systems under different environmental conditions in the distant past, it is conceivable that heterotrophic bacteria could also have preceded photosynthetic organisms. Some bacteria are photosynthetic, and the bacteria have been suggested as possible progenitors for both the algae and the fungi. However, this hypothesis is by no means well established, and it has also been suggested that the three groups have evolved in parallel from an unknown common ancestor or even that the bacteria are a degenerate rather than a primitive group. The latter hypothesis seems to have less evidence in its favor, and the current tendency is to regard the bacteria as truly primitive plants, but their exact relationships to other microorganisms and plant groups are likely to remain obscure.

Myxomycophyta and Eumycophyta

The slime molds or Myxomycophyta are typically saprophytes with an unusual life cycle that includes both animal and plantlike features. The organism consists of a naked multinucleate protoplasmic mass or plasmodium, which creeps slowly about in an amoeboid fashion and is capable of ingesting solid food particles. Under favorable conditions, the plasmodium ceases to move and forms spore-bearing fruiting bodies or sporangia, characteristic of plants. The affinities of the slime molds are uncertain, for they appear to be transitional forms between the plant and animal kingdoms. In some respects they seem more closely related to certain protozoa than to any other groups, yet they also show similarities to the more primitive true fungi or Eumycophyta.

The true fungi are quite a diverse group. Common to all of the Eumycophyta is their heterotrophic nutrition and their ability to produce spores, and most of them have plant bodies consisting of masses of filaments or hyphae. Three suggestions have been made as to the origin of the true fungi. They show some resemblance to the Myxomycophyta, to certain Protozoa, and also to some of the algae, from which they might have arisen through loss of chlorophyll. However, again the exact phylogeny is unknown.

Overlapping Systems of Classification

At this point it may be well to stop and reassess some of the material just covered, for there is a fundamental inconsistency that needs to be brought out in further detail. The systems of classification for the plant and animal kingdoms that have been outlined above are rather generally used and are widely accepted by botanists and by zoologists. However, in some respects, these groupings into plant and animal phyla are deceptively clear-cut. For example, most zoologists classify the groups known as cryptomonads, chrysomonads, phytomonads, chloromonads, euglenoids, and dinoflagellates in the class Flagellata of the phylum Protozoa. Most botanists, on the other hand, regard cryptomonads and dinoflagellates as members of the algal phylum Pyrrophyta, chrysomonads as members of the phylum Chrysophyta, euglenoids as Euglenophyta, and phytomonads (or Volvocales) and chloromonads as Chlorophyta. Furthermore, some zoologists consider the slime molds, which botanists classify as the phylum Myxomycophyta, to be an order, the Mycetozoa, of the class Sarcodina (or Rhizopoda) of the phylum Protozoa. These differences are not altogether the result of chauvinistic tendencies of the two groups of scientists, but rather reflect the fact that it is virtually impossible to draw a well-defined line between animals and plants. Clearly, since the zone of overlap is so broad, all living things belong to one great interrelated system, and the separation into plant and animal kingdoms must be regarded as a convenient but artificial device.

Another approach to this problem has been the creation of a third kingdom, the Protista, in addition to Animalia and Plantae. Included in the Protista are such groups as the bacteria, the protozoa, and the slime molds. Although this system has some merit, in that some of the duplication can be avoided, it has the drawback that two artificial lines are required rather than one. However, it is to be hoped that in time the historical barriers between botany and zoology will gradually erode, and a generally accepted biological system of classification for the lower organisms will emerge, which will lack some of the difficulties of the system now in use. At the present time there is no generally accepted system of classification covering all living things. Although this discovery may be disconcerting to the beginning biology student who likes to have things neatly packaged with no loose ends, to the student of evolution it should come as no surprise, for it tends to confirm the validity of the theory of evolution.

No mention of the phylogenetic position of the viruses has been made thus far, simply because there is virtually nothing to say. The viruses consist of the hereditary material, DNA (deoxyribonucleic acid, or in some cases RNA, ribonucleic acid) covered by a protein sheath, and are so simple in structure that it has been impossible to relate them to any other living group. Indeed, the question of whether they can properly be called "living," since they can be crystallized, has even been raised. Here, too, as with the bacteria, it has been suggested that they are degenerate rather than primitive.

Bryophyta

The so-called higher plants are now placed in the subkingdom Embryophyta and have the following traits in common: terrestrial plants, multicellular embryos that are retained in the female sex organs, and an alternation of a multicellular gametophyte generation with a multicellular sporophyte generation. Both phyla in the Embryophyta—that is, the Bryophyta (mosses, liverworts, and hornworts) and the Tracheophyta (vascular plants)—are thought to be descended from the green algae (Chlorophyta). The category Embryophyta, like Thallophyta, is an artificial one because the bryophytes and the vascular plants appear to have originated independently from the green algae. Although it was formerly believed that the bryophytes gave rise to the vascular plants, the first fossils of vascular plants come from Devonian and Silurian deposits whereas fossil bryophytes have not been found until millions of years later in the Carboniferous. Thus, the present belief is that the bryophytes appear to represent an evolutionary dead end because they became adapted, without complete success, to terrestrial life, but have never given rise to any further better adapted groups of plants.

The bryophytes are small in size, lack true roots, stems, and leaves as well as vascular tissue (xylem and phloem), and have a rather small sporophyte generation that is dependent or parasitic on the larger, independent gametophyte to which it remains attached. They depend on water for fertilization, since the motile sperm swim to the egg, and in this they can be compared to the Amphibia, a group that also has become largely terrestrial but in which breeding still ordinarily must take place in the water. In fact, only the gymnosperms and angiosperms do not require "environmental" water for fertilization.

Tracheophyta

In contrast to the bryophytes, the sporophyte is the predominant independent generation in the tracheophyte life cycle. The Tracheophyta or vascular plants are characterized by the presence of some type of tracheary element and a vascular system made up of xylem and phloem, and all are land plants except a few that have secondarily returned to water. In the tracheophytes the root system is adapted for the absorption of water and salts that are transported to the shoot system, which is adapted for photosynthesis. The manufactured food is carried throughout the plant by the vascular system. The shoot, exposed to the air, is protected against water loss by a cuticle, but openings or stomata permit the exchange of gases with the atmosphere.

Origin of Vascular Plants

The exact origin of the vascular plants is still a mystery, but they are now generally thought to have been derived from the green algae through the differentiation of the thallus into root and shoot. The discovery of a very ancient order of fossil plants, the Psilophytales, has tended to support this theory, for they are of extremely simple structure and can be thought of as a group, yet various members show indications of having given rise separately to the Lycopsida (club mosses or ground pines), the Sphenopsida (horsetails), and the Pteropsida (ferns, conifers, and flowering plants). See Fig. 14-2.

Some of the Psilophytales resemble algae because they have dichotomous branching but no leaves or roots. However, they differ in having a cuticle, stomata, a vascular system, and cutinized spores. Furthermore, certain psilophytes have very small leaves suggesting the club mosses, while others indicate leaf formation of a different type, by the flattening and broadening of the branch system. In this case the leaves are comparable to those of broad-leaved plants such as the ferns. Still another type shows the whorled pattern characteristic of the horsetails. Thus, within this one group are found fossil types suggestive of all of the other subphyla of vascular plants. The subphylum Psilopsida, well represented as fossils in the Silurian and Devonian some 350 to 380 million years ago, are now represented by just two genera of the order Psilotales.

The Lycopsida are another group that appear to have had their heyday in the Paleozoic and have persisted in a few genera as a relatively insignificant part of the present-day flora. In the Carboniferous, the coal that was formed came from the remains of these and other plants. Their leaves are structurally simple and spirally arranged, branching is dichotomous, and unlike the psilopsids they have distinct roots, stems, and leaves.

The horsetails, like the Lycopsida, arose in the Devonian, flourished in the Carboniferous, and have since dwindled into insignificance. Perhaps their most striking character is the arrangement of the small leaves in whorls, but they also have roots and jointed stems.

The dominant living plants belong to the Pteropsida. Of these, the ferns appear to be the oldest group and are thought to have given rise to the seed plants. The ancient ferns, along with the horsetails and the club mosses, formed the dominant vegetation of the Carboniferous. The ferns also appear to have evolved directly from the Psilophytales.

The gymnosperms, to which the conifers belong, seem to have evolved from the ferns through the seed ferns (Cycadofilicales), fossil seed plants with many fern like traits. All of the gymnosperms are woody plants with naked seeds.

The angiosperms or flowering plants, which are dominant in the present flora, present a complete mystery with respect to their origin. They are generally considered to have evolved from one of the groups of gymnosperms, but even though the Cycadofilicales, the Bennettitales, the Gnetales, and the Caytoniales have all been suggested as progenitors of the angiosperms, there is no reliable evidence at present in support of any one of these gymnosperm groups or of any other. The fossil record is of little help, for many fossils of flowering plants are found in Cretaceous deposits, but no older, possibly transitional forms have yet been discovered. Within the angiosperms, it is thought that the Ranales (buttercups and magnolias) are the most primitive. These plants belong to the dicoty-

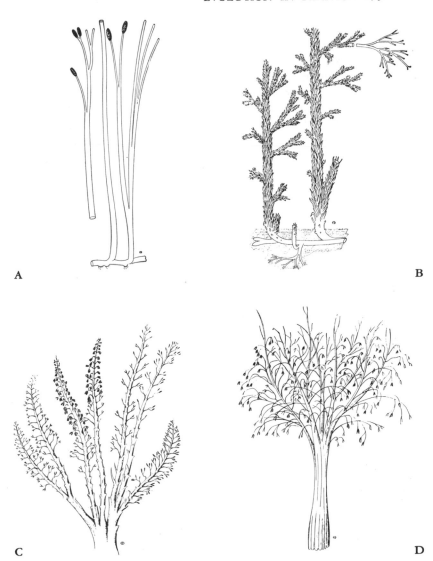

A

B

C

D

Fig. 14-2. Representatives of the primitive order of vascular plants, the Psilophytales. *A, Rhynia*—simple member of group. *B, Asteroxylon*—possibly related to the ancestors of the Lycopsida (the club mosses). *C, Hyenia*—possibly related to the ancestors of the Sphenopsida (the horse tails). *D, Pseudosporochnus*—possibly related to the ancestors of the Pteropsida (the broad-leafed plants). (With permission of Fuller and Tippo.)

ledons (mustards, poppies, roses, peas, composites, etc.), which have two seed leaves serving as storage organs for food. The monocotyledons (grasses, lilies, palms, etc.) used to be considered more primitive but are now thought to have been derived from the dicots.

In plants as in animals, many phylogenetic questions remain to be answered. Although it is not unreasonable to suppose that answers will be found to some—for example, the origin of the angiosperms—on the other hand, completely satisfactory answers to others may never be forthcoming. However, new discoveries continue to be made and new insights gained, so that in time the relationships among living things will be much better understood than they are at present.

SUMMARY ◄─────────────────────────────────────

The classification of the plant kingdom has recently been rather extensively revised. This revision was designed to bring the system into better accord with current thought on phylogenetic relationships among plants. The general effect has been to separate the algae into distinct phyla, thus emphasizing the differences among them, while grouping the higher vascular plants into a single phylum, Tracheophyta. Studies in paleobotany as well as plant anatomy are making the history of evolution within the plant kingdom increasingly well understood. Although many details remain to be learned, the record, even as it stands, is a clear-cut case for evolution.

SUGGESTED READING

Arnold, C. A., 1947. *An introduction to paleobotany.* New York: McGraw-Hill.

Axelrod, D. I., 1960. "The evolution of flowering plants," *Evolution after Darwin,* Vol. I, *The evolution of life.* S. Tax, ed. Chicago: University of Chicago Press.

Bold, H. C., 1957. *Morphology of plants.* New York: Harper.

Fuller, H. J., and O. Tippo, 1954. *College botany,* 2d ed. New York: Holt.

Stebbins, G. L., 1950. *Variation and evolution in plants.* New York: Columbia University Press.

Walton, J., 1953. *An introduction to the study of fossil plants.* London: Black.

CHAPTER 15

Genetic Evidence

Hybridization

A matched team of mules is a sight rapidly passing from the American scene. The proverbial stubbornness and hardiness of the mule are no doubt responsible for developing the equally renowned vocabulary of the muleskinner. To the question, "What is a mule?" several answers can be given in addition to what a muleskinner might have to say about their character and personality. A mule is a species hybrid, the offspring of a jackass (*Equus asinus*) and a mare (*Equus caballus*), and as such is a prime example of hybrid vigor or heterosis, a phenomenon frequently observed in the progeny of two genetically dissimilar individuals (see Fig. 15-1). A mule is also an evolutionary dead end, for with very rare exceptions mules are sterile. By their very existence mules pose the question, "Why can two clearly distinct species hybridize?" and still another, "Since they can form viable, vigorous offspring, why are these offspring sterile?" The answers to the enigma of the mule are wrapped up in the theory of evolution. The hereditary material of the two species is quite evidently sufficiently similar for fertilization to occur and for normal development to proceed under the joint control of the genes from both species. The formation of normal gametes (or sperm and egg cells) requires, however, the pairing of similar or homologous chromosomes. Since the chromosomes of these two species differ in both number and composition, normal pairing or synapsis cannot take place. From that point on, normal gamete formation is disrupted. The interpretation is that these species trace back to a

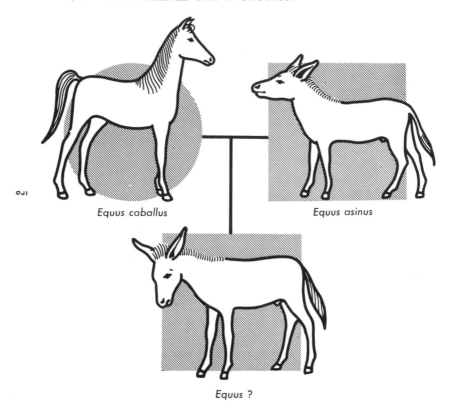

Equus caballus

Equus asinus

Equus ?

Fig. 15-1. The existence of the mule, sterile offspring of the cross between mare and jack, is readily explained by the theory of evolution. These two species, descended from a common equine ancestry, are still enough alike genetically to produce a viable hybrid when crossed, but their chromosomal and genetic differences are too great to permit normal meiosis and gamete formation in the mule.

common ancestor in the not too distant past, and that their genetic materials are still sufficiently similar to permit normal fertilization and development. However, during the course of evolution their chromosomes and genes have diverged to such a degree that they no longer are enough alike to permit normal gamete formation. Other theories leave unanswered the question of why hybridization is possible at all in two clearly distinct species such as these.

Man has attempted many other crosses between different species, and long lists have been compiled of the results of these crosses, many of which have been successful. In general, the greater the similarity between the species, the greater the likelihood of success in hybridizing them. Each successful cross raises once again the question of why such crosses are possible if each species had a separate, independent origin.

In addition to the artificial hybrids many naturally occurring hybrids have also been observed, especially in plants. Relatively little work has been done with the nonvascular plants—algae, fungi, mosses, etc.—but in vascular plants, hybridization has been found with unexpected frequency in a variety of different groups. Natural hybrids have been reported in ferns and in a number of genera of conifers or gymnosperms such as pine, juniper, and fir. Among the flowering plants or angiosperms the number of known natural hybrids continues to increase as further study brings to light more and more instances of hybridization. Some groups of woody plants such as the oaks and willows seem especially likely to form natural hybrid swarms. Certain other groups have been so disrupted by natural hybridization and its after-effects that their taxonomy is almost a hopeless mess. Among them are the blackberries (*Rubus*), the hawthorns (*Crataegus*), the dandelions (*Taraxacum*), the hawkweeds (*Hieracium*), and many genera of grasses.

Though less common than in plants, natural hybrids in animals are by no means unknown. Among the invertebrates only a few phyla have been carefully studied for natural hybrids. However, despite rather careful study in the insects, relatively few natural hybrids have been reported, the best known cases being among the crickets and the butterflies and moths. Among the vertebrates quite a number of natural hybrids have been reported in the fresh-water fishes such as the sunfish, suckers, and trout. Hybrid swarms of toads of the genus *Bufo* are examples from the amphibians, and quite a few hybrids between different species of birds, particularly the ducks, have been recorded. Hybridization in the reptiles and in the mammals is apparently quite rare. It seems probable that ethological or "psychological" isolation, not a factor in plants, contributes in a significant way to the rarity of natural hybrids in animals. However, these few examples should suffice to show that even without man's intervention, hybridization does occur in both plants and animals. The theory of evolution gives a reasonable explanation for this capability.

Not only have many casual or accidental hybrids been reported, but many species of plants have actually arisen subsequent to hybridization. Amphiploidy (also called allopolyploidy; a more detailed discussion of polyploidy will be given later) is the result of the doubling of the chromosome number of a sterile, interspecific hybrid and gives rise to a stable, fertile, true-breeding new species at a single step. It is one of the commonest ways in which new species of plants have arisen, and approximately a third of the species of flowering plants are estimated to have originated in this manner. Many of our most useful crops such as cotton, wheat, oats, tobacco, and potatoes are now known to be amphiploids. In the case of wheat, cotton, and tobacco, good evidence as to the actual parental species is available. The cultivated tobacco, *Nicotiana digluta*, was the first species to be artificially resynthesized from its parent species, *N. tabaccum* and *N. glutinosa*. The first Linnaean species to be artificially recreated was

Galeopsis tetrahit, which was derived from a hybrid between *G. pubescens* and *G. speciosa. Spartina townsendii* and two amphiploids in the goats beard (*Tragopogon*), the latter two known to have arisen in the last 30 years, are examples of species that have originated in nature in recent times under human observation. Since the discovery of the colchicine technique for doubling chromosome numbers, a number of experimental amphiploids have been formed that must, by all the criteria commonly used, be regarded as new species. Some forty years ago, Bateson objected that despite all the discussion about the origin of species, no one had yet observed this event. Although the origin of species by polyploidy may be a special case, rather than what Bateson had in mind, the fact remains that man has now observed the origin of species in nature and has also synthesized his own new species.

Domesticated Species

Darwin opened his book *The Origin of Species* with a chapter on "Variation under domestication" and later summarized his studies in this area in the book entitled *The Variation of Animals and Plants under Domestication.* Domesticated species are still of considerable interest, for they give us a magnified although somewhat distorted view of evolution. Darwin's work, though significant even today, was marred by the lack of knowledge of the causes of variations and of their mode of inheritance. He recognized, however, the relevance of this type of study to the problem of the origin of species. A more sophisticated discussion couched in modern genetic terms is now possible, but the conclusions relating to the significance of domesticated species as evidence for evolution are little different.

In brief, these conclusions are that domestic animals and plants are descended from wild species. In most cases they appear to have been derived from a single species, but some may have originated from species crosses. The numerous breeds or varieties have arisen as the result of both conscious and unconscious artificial selection by man, and also, it must be added, by natural selection operating in the new environments provided by man. The origins of many domesticated species are obscured in the mists of antiquity or of prehistoric times. The dog, the horse, the pig, wheat, rice, and corn—these and many others were domesticated during times for which no historical records are available. In other cases, domestication is so recent that virtually a complete history of the process can be given. For example, fox and mink breeding are less than a century old yet already a number of varieties have been developed, and the fruit fly, *Drosophila melanogaster,* from which so much of our knowledge of heredity has been gained, also must be included in any list of recently domesticated species. Furthermore, new breeds or varieties of the older domesticated species continue to be created, such as the Santa Gertrudis cattle, the Minnesota No. 1, No. 2, and No. 3 hogs, and Thatcher wheat.

The breeds of dogs range from Chihuahuas and Schnauzers to Great Danes and St. Bernards; of horses, from Shetland ponies to Percherons—yet despite their great differences in size and other traits, all dogs are regarded as belonging to one species, as are all horses. The dogs belong to a single species because all the many breeds are capable of hybridizing except where extreme size differences intervene, and even then indirect exchange of genes takes place through intermediate breeds. Since the differences between some of the breeds of domestic animals appear to be much greater than those between some well-defined and reproductively isolated wild species, it may be wondered why these breeds have not become reproductively isolated also. Although no definitive answer can be given, a guess may be hazarded that even the oldest breeds have been established but a very short time, a matter of a few thousand years at most, and that this period has not been long enough for the numerous genetic differences leading to reproductive isolation to have accumulated in the separate breeds. In other words, the differences, great as they appear to be, may still be controlled by comparatively few of the many genes in the species.

The significance of domesticated species as evidence for evolution lies in the fact that they show that species have changed and can be changed. The numerous breeds exemplify on a small scale divergence or descent with modification—in other words, evolution.

Gene and Chromosome Homology

Another type of genetic evidence for the relationship between species is drawn from a comparison of their chromosomes. In every individual, a set of maternal chromosomes is matched by a corresponding set from the father, and pairing or synapsis only occurs between the similar or homologous chromosomes of each set. Furthermore, these maternal and paternal chromosomes pair only in a very specific "gene by gene" fashion. Hence, if pairing occurs between the maternal and paternal chromosomes of a hybrid from a species cross, it is a reasonable assumption that the paired regions are homologous, containing similar genetic material. The best studies of this type have been conducted with species with giant salivary gland chromosomes belonging to the order Diptera and including fruit flies (*Drosophila*), midges (*Chironomus*), mosquitos (*Anopheles*), and gnats (*Sciara*). The large size and banded structure of the salivary gland chromosomes permit the specific identification of given regions. Since somatic pairing occurs, the band by band pairing of homologous regions can be seen in great detail. In hybrids from the cross between *Drosophila melanogaster* and *D. simulans,* two morphologically similar species, most regions of the chromosomes can be seen to be alike and to be paired. Only a few regions show differences in the banding structure, and these remain unpaired. Furthermore, genetic studies have shown that there are similarities in genetic behavior in the synapsed regions whereas the unpaired regions differ in their genetic contents. In general, species less alike morphologically than these two produce hybrids that have fewer homologous paired regions. The most obvious interpretation of these facts is that during the course of evolutionary divergence, the chromosomes, as well as the gross morphology, have been restructured and repatterned. Moreover, because of the specificity of chromosome pairing, chromosomal homologies are even more sensitive and reliable than anatomical homologies.

Above, in passing, we mentioned the similarities in genetic behavior between homologous chromosome regions. This material constitutes still another link in the chain of evidence for evolution. In brief, it has been possible to show that similar mutant types in different species represent mutations of homologous genes. In some cases, these gene homologies have been established by crossing mutant types of each species and obtaining mutant hybrid offspring in the first generation. This result would not be obtained with nonhomologous recessive mutants (that is, mutants expressed only when present in double dose), for the hybrids would then be normal or wild type in appearance. In other cases, where hybridization is impossible, the evidence of necessity is less direct. However, the demonstration of the homology of individual genes in different species represents one of the most precise bits of evidence for their common ancestry yet available.

The Hereditary Material

The study of the chemical nature of the chromosomes from species ranging from viruses and bacteria to higher plants and animals has shown that they are composed of nucleoprotein, a combination of protein and nucleic acid. Nucleic acids are of two kinds: DNA or deoxyribonucleic acid and RNA or ribonucleic acid. DNA is found in the nucleus of cells while RNA may be found in both nucleus and cytoplasm. Chemically very similar, both have a backbone of a long chain of alternate sugar and phosphate molecules with purine and pyrimidine bases attached to the sugars as side groups. The differences lie in the sugars, deoxyribose in DNA and ribose in RNA, and in one of the four bases. Both have the purines, adenine and guanine, and the pyrimidine, cytosine, in common, but in DNA the other pyrimidine base is thymine; in RNA it is uracil. All of the available evidence indicates that the nucleic acids carry the hereditary blueprint from one generation to the next. In all but a few cases (for example, some plant viruses) DNA is the hereditary material while the RNA ordinarily seems to mediate protein synthesis.

One type of evidence for the hereditary role of DNA comes from the discovery that the "transforming principle," which can produce inherited changes when added to bacterial cells, is DNA. Hereditary changes in the type of polysaccharide capsule in pneumococci, for example, are induced by DNA from a related strain rather than by its polysaccharide. Furthermore, when a bacterial cell is infected by a bacterial virus, the DNA from the virus penetrates the bacterium and initiates virus reproduction there, but the protein coat of the virus is left outside of the cell.

DNA has been shown to be composed of two long strands coiled around each other to form a double helix (Fig. 15-2). The bases of one strand pair very precisely with the bases on the other. In fact, adenine pairs only with thymine, and guanine only with cytosine. Hence, the sequence of bases on one strand determines the sequence on the other, a fact that appears related to their power of self-duplication. It might seem that DNA, limited to just four bases, a single, simple type of sugar, and phosphate groups, would lack the complexity necessary to control the great variety of hereditary traits in hundreds of thousands of

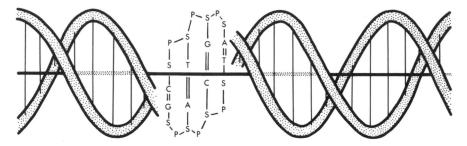

Fig. 15-2. Watson-Crick double helix model of the DNA molecule. S = sugar (deoxyribose). P = phosphate. Purine bases: A = adenine and G = guanine. Pyrimidine bases: T = thymine and C = cytosine. A always pairs with T, and G with C.

species. However, the order of the bases in the DNA molecule is not regular or repetitive, and the specificity and function of the genes appear to be determined by the sequence of the bases along the DNA chain. In this way an enormous variety of specifications can be encoded or spelled out. The picture now emerging is that DNA specificity is conferred on RNA, which moves into the cytoplasm where it controls protein synthesis. Thus, the DNA code is eventually imprinted on the enzymes, the protein compounds that carry on the bulk of the metabolic activities of the cell.

The simple fact that the ultimate genetic material in nearly all species can be represented as variations on a theme in a single type of compound, DNA, makes evolution in all its ramifications more readily comprehensible. This fact points up the fundamental similarity among all living things, and the problem eventually will be to discover how DNA patterns have changed in the course of time to give rise to the great diversity of living species.

SUMMARY ◄──────────────────────────────────────

The discovery of genetic principles has led not only to an understanding of the mechanism of evolution but also to further evidence for evolution. Hybridization between distinct species has been repeatedly observed in plants and animals, and in the case of polyploids has led to the formation of new species. The creation of new species is, in itself, an insurmountable argument against a static-species concept. The development of new breeds and varieties under domestication is still further evidence that species under selection pressure can and do change. The study of the genetic material itself has revealed homologies between different species at all levels of organization, from chromosomal rearrangements to DNA structure. Since DNA is the stuff of heredity, the basic question in the study of evolution is to determine how in the course of time DNA patterns have changed.

SUGGESTED READING

Darwin, C., 1868. *The variation of animals and plants under domestication.* London.

Davidson, J. N., 1957. *The biochemistry of the nucleic acids,* 3d ed. New York: Wiley.

McElroy, W. D., and B. Glass, eds., 1957. *The chemical basis of heredity.* Baltimore: Johns Hopkins Press.

Müntzing, A., 1959. "Darwin's views on variation under domestication in the light of present-day knowledge," *Proc. Amer. Philosophical Society, 103:*190-220.

Stebbins, G. L., 1959. "The role of hybridization in evolution," *Proc. Amer. Philosophical Society, 103:*231-251.

White, M. J. D., 1954. *Animal cytology and evolution,* 2d ed. New York: Cambridge University Press.

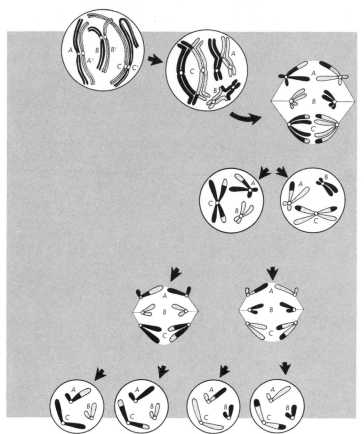

PART *III*

The Mechanism of Evolution

The remainder of the book, which is devoted to the mechanism of evolution, may be regarded as a more extensive genetic argument for evolution even though it has not been written from that point of view. Before the mechanism of evolution is considered in detail, it may be helpful to state, rather briefly and without too many qualifications, the essential points in the current concept of evolution. The theoretical basis of modern evolutionary theory was developed primarily by R. A. Fisher, J. B. S. Haldane, and S. Wright.

Darwin believed that a cross between two unlike individuals resulted in a blending of their heredity and hence in a loss of variability. Mendel, however, demonstrated that heredity is particulate in nature rather than blending. Mendel's results led to the realization in 1908 by Hardy and Weinberg that random mating in a population where all types are equally favored does not result in a loss of variability, but that the variability remains constant from one generation to the next. This concept has come to be known as the Hardy-Weinberg law.

If evolutionary change is to occur, new kinds of hereditary variation must appear. These changes in the hereditary material, known as mutations, have been shown to occur spontaneously at a very low frequency, which can be raised by various forms of radiant energy and by some chemical substances. Mutations are essentially random within the existing genetic system, and form the raw material of evolution. The knowledge of mutations, both genic and chromosomal, and of the mutation process is considerably greater today than it was a few decades ago.

Natural selection determines the fate of new mutations and of the new gene combinations resulting from Mendelian recombination. Only the adaptively favorable genes or combinations of genes will persist and become incorporated into the breeding population.

Evolution is a phenomenon occurring in populations, not in individuals. The evolving unit is a breeding population. If the size of the population is small, random loss or fixation of genes may occur, quite apart from the operation of natural selection. As a result of this "genetic drift," and also because of the greater likelihood of inbreeding, small populations are apt to be more homozygous than large, and consequently less able to adapt to changing environmental conditions.

A species may consist of one large randomly mating population or, more often, of a number of more or less isolated breeding populations. A single large population remains quite variable and evolves as a unit. If each of a number of breeding populations is completely isolated from the others, evolution will proceed independently in each, the resultant of the pressures of mutation and selection and of the random effects of genetic drift. Between the extremes of complete isolation on the one hand and random mating on the other, all degrees of partial isolation are possible. Each population will then serve as an evolutionary experiment, which, if successful, may spread its influence to other populations through the gene flow made possible by migration. If gene flow is too restricted, the more successful population may supplant others as the result of intergroup selection. Thus, the course of evolution may be influenced by the structure of the species population, the way in which it is subdivided into breeding populations, and the degree of isolation and gene flow among them.

The great achievement of the population geneticists is that they have incorporated the four major factors causing gene frequency changes in populations (mutation, selection, genetic drift, and migration) into a mathematical model that permits the consideration of the simultaneous effects of all of these factors. Even though these factors are as biologically diverse as mutation, viability, mating preferences, isolation, differential fertility and fecundity, and migration, they have all been evaluated in terms of their effects on gene frequencies. Evolution, therefore, is now considered to be essentially a series of changes in the kinds or frequencies of genes in populations, or more briefly, a shift in the Hardy-Weinberg equilibrium. Since this is the case, it is essential, if we are to understand the mechanism of evolution, that we gain some grasp of the genetics of populations. But first, we must understand the basic principles of genetics.

CHAPTER *16*

Mendel's Laws

Thus far, we have considered the nature of the biological world and the theory that explains how it has achieved its present state—namely, the theory of evolution. The nature of the evidence in support of the theory of evolution has been reviewed, and some idea of the evolutionary changes that have occurred has been presented. The clearer it has become that evolution is a fact, the more urgent has become the need to explain how one species can evolve into another, and what forces operate to make evolutionary change possible.

Darwin's proposed mechanism for evolution was the theory of natural selection. A major weakness of his theory, which he clearly recognized, was his lack of knowledge about the inheritance of variations. Darwin based his theory of natural selection on the differential survival and transmission of hereditary variations. Though Darwin studied heredity and variation intensively, as others did before and after him, he failed to find the key to the problem. The advent of the science of genetics has supplied some of the missing knowledge, and in the process has broadened and strengthened the theory of natural selection.

The first steps toward an understanding of heredity were made by an obscure monk, Gregor Mendel, who experimented with the common garden pea in a small monastery garden. Alone, without a research team or even a grant for a research project, he worked out with beautiful simplicity and in detail the fundamental laws governing the transmission of characters from parent to offspring in sexually reproducing plants and animals. A prob-

166

lem that had intrigued and puzzled men for centuries was solved by a man who had twice failed his examinations to gain a teaching certificate. Yet his discoveries were apparently neither understood nor appreciated by the recognized scientists of the day, and their significance was not realized until 1900, some 35 years after the work had been completed and published. The study of heredity, or genetics, as it came to be called, is thus a science that, perhaps more than any other, belongs to the twentieth century. During its brief career, it has not only contributed to our basic understanding of the mechanism of heredity, with ramifications in every area of biological thought; it has transformed the face of the earth and added incalculable riches to the resources of the world through the widespread use of new and improved varieties of plants and animals developed through genetic research.

The basic questions that Mendel answered were very simple. If a father and mother and their child are seen together, the resemblances of the youngster to his parents can be readily observed. But all children do not show the same degree of resemblance to each parent. Some appear to be the "spitting images" of their fathers; others, of their mothers. Most show some of the traits of both while some seem to show little resemblance to either parent. This strange and varying assortment of similarities and differences between parents and offspring had been the stumbling block to all who had previously attempted to study heredity. Any adequate theory of heredity must not only explain how father passes on his big brown eyes to junior, and mother contributes her widow's peak, but also where in the world he got that flaming red hair, the like of which has "never" been seen in either family. Genetics, then, is the study of the way in which these resemblances are passed from one generation to the next and of the mode of origin of the variations.

Careful examination and observation of any group of organisms will show that each individual within the group is unique and clearly different from all the rest. Hence, any attempt to study heredity in a group is almost hopelessly complex if an effort is made to study simultaneously all of the distinguishing characters of each individual. It is like trying to pitch a tent in a tornado—impossible to keep track of everything at once. Mendel's success, in large part, was due to the fact that, rather than trying to follow the great multiplicity of characters, he sought to answer the question of how a single trait with two well-defined alternative conditions, such as yellow or green peas, was transmitted from generation to generation. In this way, he reduced the problem to its simplest terms. Although knowledge of the physical basis of heredity was virtually nonexistent at the time, Mendel realized that yellow or green seeds were not transmitted as such from one generation to the next, but that somewhere within the pollen and the ovule there were factors that controlled the tendency to develop one color or the other. Over the narrow physical bridge of pollen and ovule in plants, sperm and egg in animals, must pass all of the factors that determine not only the color of the seeds but also that a pea plant will never become a rose bush; not only the color of junior's hair and eyes but also that he develops into a man and not a mouse.

Since every individual is the product of a developmental sequence controlled and influenced by both heredity and environment, the observed variations may be primarily due to heredity, or environment, or both. The old nature-nurture or heredity vs. environment controversy is virtually meaningless. Without heredity, there is no organism at all, and it therefore must play a role in all that an organism is and does. Yet every organism develops in an environment of some sort, which is always present and whose role must always be considered in any assessment of the individual organism. However, all traits are not equally influenced by heredity and environment, for some are more subject to environmental modification than others.

As Darwin pointed out, only the hereditary variations are important to evolution. We shall therefore not be concerned here with environmental variation, although from the experimental and practical standpoint it is always a factor to be reckoned with. Our problem is to account for the inheritance of both similarities and differences. Actual traits, of course, are not inherited as such. Your eyes are the result of a period of embryological development from the fertilized egg, which has no eyes at all; therefore, they cannot be transmitted directly. We want to know what is transmitted and how it is transmitted from one generation to the next.

Segregation

Mendel studied, in all, seven traits in the garden pea, each with two well-defined alternative conditions. As in much biological research, a good deal of his success can be laid to his choice of a suitable experimental organism. The pea was extensively cultivated, and many varieties with different hereditary traits were readily available. The pea is normally self-fertilized, so that the danger of contamination by foreign pollen was negligible, yet it is fully fertile when crossed. Furthermore, he kept accurate records of the pedigrees of each of his plants, and classified and counted all of the progeny from his crosses. This arithmetic approach gave him more insight into the hereditary process than was possible for those who merely classified without counting. Finally, as is also often the case in research, there was an element of luck involved. Although this is getting ahead of the story somewhat, there are only seven pairs of chromosomes in the pea, and each of the traits Mendel chose happened to be controlled by a different pair. If any two traits had been controlled by the same chromosome pair, the seemingly anomalous results he then would have obtained might have prevented him from breaking through to the generalizations known as Mendel's laws. The chance of such a choice of traits is, roughly, only 1 in 200.

What were the results Mendel obtained when he crossed two pure lines differing in a single trait? One of his crosses was made between a line that produced only full, round peas and another that produced only wrinkled peas (Fig. 16-1). From this cross, all of the progeny, known as the first filial or F_1 generation, were like the round parent. For each of the other characters, Mendel

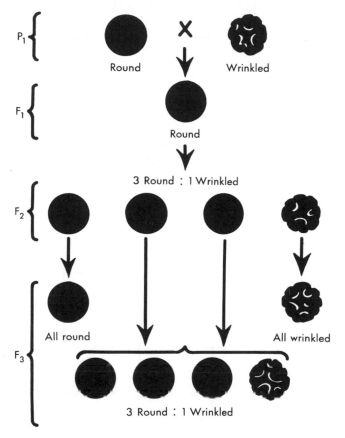

Fig. 16-1. Mendel's results with a monohybrid cross involving round and wrinkled peas.

found that the F_1 progeny from crosses between pure lines were also all like one of the parents. He therefore called *dominant* those traits that were expressed in the F_1, and *recessive* those traits not appearing in the F_1.

The F_1 progeny were then self-fertilized to produce the F_2 generation. In the F_2, a ratio of 3 round plants to 1 wrinkled was obtained. The F_2 wrinkled plants all bred true for wrinkled, but of the F_2 round plants, one-third bred true while two-thirds behaved like the F_1, giving 3 round to 1 wrinkled offspring.

From these results, Mendel drew certain inferences. Since wrinkled was present in one of the parents but was not observed at all in the F_1, some sort of a factor for it must have been present but not expressed in the F_1 generation. Therefore, the F_1 carried a factor for wrinkled as well as for round, and hence was a *hybrid*. Since the wrinkled trait appeared unchanged in the F_2, passage of the factor for wrinkled through the F_1 hybrid did not affect its nature or purity. See Fig. 16-2.

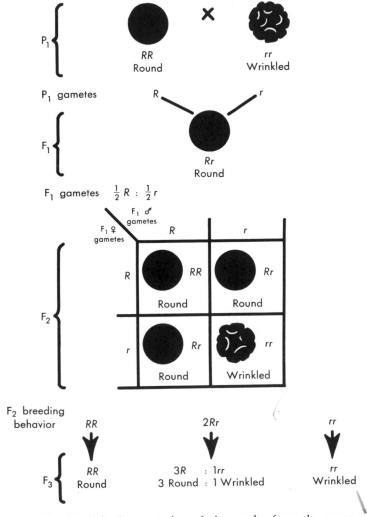

Fig. 16-2. Mendel's interpretation of the results from the mono-hybrid cross with round and wrinkled peas.

Furthermore, the reappearance of the pure-breeding wrinkled and pure-breeding round plants in the F_2 meant that the factors for round and wrinkled, which were present together in the F_1 hybrids, must have been separated or segregated before the formation of the F_2. Therefore, although the F_1 plants were hybrids, their gametes, or sex cells, must have been pure. The gametes must carry either the dominant round factor or the recessive wrinkled factor, and must be of two kinds. The 3:1 ratio could easily be explained if the two kinds of gametes were produced in equal numbers and union of the gametes at fertilization occurred at random. These results and conclusions led to the formulation of what is now known as Mendel's first law, the *principle of segregation*. It can be stated as follows: When a hybrid reproduces, it transmits with equal frequency either the dominant character of one parent or the recessive character of the other, but not both.

These concepts can be more readily visualized and handled if they are written out in a convenient short form.

Let R = factor for round

r = factor for wrinkled

Then a pure plant for round would be RR, and for wrinkled, rr. A cross between the two, known as a *monohybrid* cross, can be outlined as follows, where P_1 is the first parental generation:

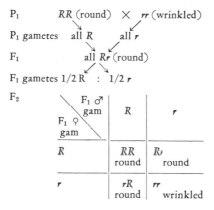

From the checkerboard used to get the F_2, it is readily seen why a 3:1 F_2 ratio is obtained, and also why 2 of the 3 round individuals must be hybrids.

At this point it may be well to introduce a few more terms and concepts. A true-breeding organism, such as an RR round pea plant or an rr wrinkled plant, is said to be *homozygous;* a hybrid plant, such as an Rr plant, which produces two kinds of gametes, is said to be *heterozygous.* The term "factor" used by Mendel has been to a large extent supplanted by the word "*gene.*" Learning genetics is much like learning a new language, and just to show how the jargon is used, the cross outlined above is said to be between a line that is homozygous for the gene for round and one homozygous for wrinkled to give a heterozygous round F_1. When inbred, the F_1 produces an F_2 consisting of 1 homozygous wrinkled and 3 round, of which ⅓ are homozygous and ⅔ heterozygous.

The concepts of genotype and phenotype are related to each other and are fundamental. The sum total of all the traits *expressed* by the individual—morphological, physiological, psychological, biochemical, etc.—is said to comprise his *phenotype*. The sum total of all of the genes an individual carries, received from his parents and transmissable to his offspring, is said to be his *genotype*. The phenotype is the product of the genes in the genotype acting within a particular environment. The same genotype placed in different environments—for example, cuttings from a single plant reared under different climatic conditions—will give different phenotypes. Yet the same phenotype may be produced by different genotypes, as for example the *RR* and *Rr* round peas.

Dominance is not a universal phenomenon. The *Rr* peas, for example, are as round as the *RR* seeds, but microscopic examination of the starch grains shows them to be intermediate in form between those from *RR* and *rr* seeds. Also, a cross between a red variety and a white variety of zinnias gives a pink F_1 hybrid, and an F_2 of 1 red, 2 pink, and 1 white. Such examples can be multiplied many times to show that all degrees of dominance exist; it may be complete, partial, or lacking.

A human trait inherited in accordance with the simple rules outlined above is albinism. Albinos in man are characterized by a deficiency in pigmentation and, frequently, eye defects, in addition to other anomalies. Albinism is due to a recessive gene in the homozygous condition. Although it is a rare condition, there are many normally pigmented people who carry this gene in the heterozygous condition. A simple method for determining what proportion are carriers is to discover what proportion of the marriages of albinos to unrelated normally pigmented people result in the production of albino children. Such matings are known as "test crosses," since crosses to the homozygous recessive quickly reveal the genotype of the normally pigmented parent. If the normal parent is homozygous, all of the children will be pigmented.

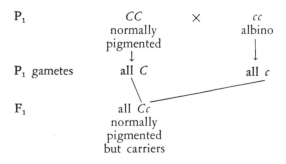

If the normal parent is a heterozygous carrier of the albino gene, however, half of the children, on the average, will be albino.

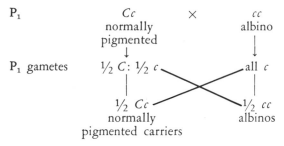

P_1 Cc × cc
normally   albino
pigmented

P_1 gametes   ½ C: ½ c all c

½ Cc ½ cc
normally   albinos
pigmented carriers

Such studies have shown that although only about 1 European in 20,000 is an albino, approximately 1 in 70 is a heterozygous carrier of the gene for albinism. Thus, the test cross, or the *back cross* to the recessive, as it is also called, is the most direct method of ascertaining the genotype of an individual whose genotype is unknown.

Independent Assortment

After Mendel had established the way in which single traits were transmitted from generation to generation, his next question became: What happens if individuals differing in two traits are crossed? In one such cross, for example, one of the parents had wrinkled and yellow seeds while the other bred true for round, green seeds. This cross produced a uniform F_1, all having round and yellow seeds, these being the dominants. In the F_2, however, four phenotypes appeared, two like the original parents plus the other two possible combinations, round yellow and green wrinkled. Furthermore, they occurred in a definite ratio of 9:3:3:1. Mendel inferred from these results that the segregations of the factors governing these two traits were independent of each other. The 3:1 segregation of one factor pair (green-yellow) was completely independent of the 3:1 segregation of the other factor pair (round-wrinkled). The 9:3:3:1 ratio then occurs because, of the ¾ of the seeds which are round, ¾ are yellow and ¼ green; of the ¼ which are wrinkled, ¾ will also be yellow and ¼ green. Hence,

$$¾ × ¾ = \frac{9}{16} \quad \text{round yellow}$$
$$¾ × ¼ = \frac{3}{16} \quad \text{round green}$$
$$¼ × ¾ = \frac{3}{16} \quad \text{wrinkled yellow}$$
$$¼ × ¼ = \frac{1}{16} \quad \text{wrinkled green}$$

These results formed the basis of Mendel's second law, the *principle of independent assortment.* The law, stated briefly, is that the segregation of one factor pair occurs independently of any other factor pair.

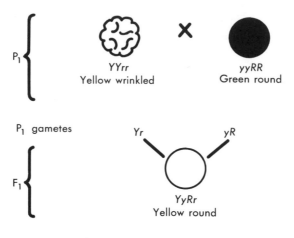

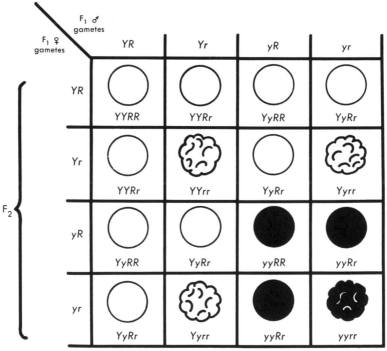

9 Yellow round : 3 Yellow wrinkled : 3 Green round : 1 Green wrinkled

Fig. 16-3. A dihybrid cross in peas.

This *dihybrid* cross, as it is called, can be outlined as follows:

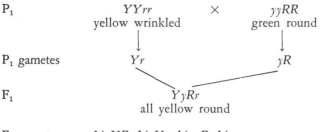

P₁   *YYrr*   ×   *yyRR*
                  yellow wrinkled   green round

P₁ gametes   *Yr*   *yR*

F₁   *YyRr*
                         all yellow round

F₁ gametes   ¼ *YR*: ¼ *Yr*: ¼ *yR*: ¼ *yr*

Since the segregations are independent of each other, all possible combinations of the dominant and recessive genes are formed with equal frequency in the F₁ male and female gametes. See Fig. 16-3.

F₂ F₁ ♀ gam \ F₁ ♂ gam	YR	Yr	yR	yr
YR	YYRR	YYRr	YyRR	YyRr
Yr	YYRr	YYrr	YyRr	Yyrr
yR	YyRR	YyRr	yyRR	yyRr
yr	YyRr	Yyrr	yyRr	yyrr

The checkerboard should be examined carefully. The origin of the four phenotypes and their ratio will then be obvious: ⁹⁄₁₆ of the individuals have at least one dominant *Y* and one dominant *R*; ³⁄₁₆ are homozygous *yy* but carry dominant *R*; ³⁄₁₆ are *rr* but carry dominant *Y*; and only ¹⁄₁₆ of the plants are homozygous for both recessives. Furthermore, though there are only four phenotypes, they result from nine distinct and different genotypes, four of which will breed true. It should be noted that the same results in the F₂ would have been obtained if the original cross had been

P₁   *YYRR*   ×   *yyrr*
      yellow round   green wrinkled

──────────────────────────────────── ▶ *SUMMARY*

Variation is the working material of evolution, but not all variations are inherited; only the hereditary variations are of significance in evolution. Therefore, the distinction between phenotype and genotype is fundamental. Every individual carries two complete sets of genes, one set coming from the mother, the other from the father. Each gamete carries only one complete set of genes. Mendel discovered the orderly way in which these genes are transmitted from one generation to the next. Each pair of factors or genes segregates prior to gamete formation and then combines at random while the different pairs of genes segregate and recombine independently of one another. These principles form the genetic basis of variation through the recombination of genes. Even though the expression of some genes may at times be masked due to dominance, they are not lost but may reappear in subsequent generations. Through genetic recombination an almost infinite number of new genotypes can be formed on which natural selection can act.

SUGGESTED READING

The birth of genetics. Mendel-de Vries-Correns-Tschermak. Supplement to *Genetics* 35(5), Part 2.

Colin, E. C., 1956. *Elements of genetics,* 3d ed. New York: McGraw-Hill.

Sinnott, E. W., L. C. Dunn, and Th. Dobzhansky, 1958. *Principles of genetics,* 5th ed. New York: McGraw-Hill. Appendix contains English translation of Mendel's original paper.

Snyder, L. H. and P. R. David, 1957. *The principles of heredity,* 5th ed. Boston: Heath.

Srb, A. and R. D. Owen, 1952. *General genetics.* San Francisco: Freeman.

Stern, C., 1960. *Principles of human genetics,* 2d ed. San Francisco: Freeman.

Waddington, C. H., 1939. An introduction to modern genetics. London: Allen and Unwin.

CHAPTER 17

Variation Due to Recombination

Multiple Alleles

Mendelian inheritance is particulate, the particulate genes retaining their identity in crosses. Segregation and recombination form the basis of much of the variability in a species population. Thus far, we have considered alternative forms, or alleles, of the same gene to be of just two kinds, exemplified by the dominant yellow (Y) and its recessive allele (y), or the dominant round (R) and its recessive allele wrinkled (r). Numerous studies have shown, however, that a given gene can exist in a number of different alternative conditions; hence a whole set of alleles may exist rather than only a dominant and a recessive. In some cases, there may be as many as forty of these *multiple alleles,* as they are called, in a single set—that is, forty different forms of the same gene, each with its own distinguishable phenotypic effects. However, any diploid individual can carry in the cells of his body only two of these alleles at the most, while each of his gametes can carry but one.

Multiple alleles open up new ranges in the possibilities for genetic recombination. In the ABO blood groups in man, for example, three major alleles determine the blood types, the genes being I^A, I^B, and I^O. The blood types and the genic combinations producing them are as follows:

177

blood type (phenotype)	genotype
O	$I^O I^O$
A	$I^A I^A$ or $I^A I^O$
B	$I^B I^B$ or $I^B I^O$
AB	$I^A I^B$

One added allele increases the number of possible genotypes from 3 to 6, and increases the phenotypes to 4 from the two seen in the F_2 of a monohybrid cross with dominance. Note that I^A and I^B are both dominant to I^O, but not to each other.

Another example may be taken from the C gene in the rabbit. Four alleles at this locus are the following:

$$C = \text{full color}$$
$$c^{ch} = \text{Chinchilla}$$
$$c^h = \text{Himalayan}$$
$$c = \text{albino}$$

The C gene produces the familiar coat of the wild rabbit; c^{ch}, a pearly gray animal; c^h, a white rabbit with black extremities; and c, a pure white rabbit with pink eyes. See Fig. 17-1.

With four alleles, 10 distinct genotypes but only four color phenotypes are possible, since the dominance relations show $C > c^{ch} > c^h > c$. The number of different genotypes possible with n alleles can be shown to equal $\dfrac{n^2+n}{2}$. Hence, the variability due to multiple alleles is by no means trivial and increases very rapidly as the number of alleles increases.

number of alleles (n)	number of possible genotypes
1	1
2	3
3	6
4	10
5	15
6	21
10	55
20	210
40	820

These possibilities are restricted to just one kind of gene. When it is remembered that the total number of genes in the genotype must be in the thousands, and that each gene may have several forms, then the number of combinations possible among these different sets of multiple alleles becomes simply enormous —far greater than the number of individuals in the species. The wonder, perhaps, is not that two individuals in a species never look exactly alike, but that they resemble each other as much as they do.

One further aspect of multiple allelism warrants mention. Each of the four C genes has a distinctly different effect on the phenotype. Yet in specially studied cases, it has been demonstrated that genes of different origin producing the same gross phenotypes, which cannot be distinguished from one another by

Fig. 17-1. Variation in rabbits due to multiple alleles. Top: left, full color; right, chinchilla. Bottom: left, Himalayan; right, albino. (Courtesy of Snyder and David.)

inspection, nevertheless have subtly different effects, either physiologically or in their interaction with other genes in the genotype, and hence must be regarded as alleles rather than one and the same gene. These genes with equivalent gross phenotypic effects that are nonetheless demonstrably different are known as isoalleles. For example, in the fruit fly, a mutant type with an interrupted wing vein, known as *cubitus interruptus (ci)*, has been crossed to various flies of different origin, all with normal wing venation, and hence carrying wild-type alleles of the ci gene. However, since the expression of these wild-type genes in heterozygous combination with ci showed different degrees of effect on the cubitus vein, these wild-type genes are therefore isoalleles, and were designated as $+_1$, $+_2$, and $+_3$. Because of the difficulties of detection, the amount of isoallelism is not easily determined, but it is probably quite common, and contributes to the available variability in a more subtle way.

Background Effects

Thus far we have considered the gene to act independently in producing a trait, with a one-to-one relation between gene and character. Actually, any trait is produced by the action of many different genes plus the effects of the environment. Hence, not only the numbers of combinations of genes, but the possibilities for interaction between them and between the genes and the environment must also be considered, for genes do not act in a vacuum. In the snapdragon an ivory variety (*rr*) and a red variety (*RR*) are known. The F_1 hybrid (*Rr*), if grown in bright light at a low temperature, is red; if grown in the shade at a high temperature, it is ivory. Thus the same genotype in different environments gives different phenotypes, and the dominance relations can only be defined by specifying the environmental conditions. Brachyury, a short-tail mutation in the mouse, behaves as a dominant in the European house mouse, *Mus musculus,* but as a recessive in the Asiatic house mouse, *Mus bactrianus,* when the same mutant male is crossed to females of both species. In this case the same gene placed on different genetic backgrounds rather than in different environments produces different phenotypes.

Recombination and Interaction

To illustrate the point that the combined action of many genes is responsible for a single trait, let us consider the coat color in mink, *Mustela vison.* The rich, dark brown coat of the wild mink is the product of the genotype, *PP IpIp AlAl BB BgBg BiBi CC OO ss ff eb eb cm cm.* These genes are known to affect coat color because mutant forms of each have been discovered; undoubtedly still others will be identified when mutant forms of them are found. It is one of the peculiarities of Mendelian genetics that the individual gene can be identified only when two alternative forms of the gene exist. Thus, in a sense, the wild-type gene is an inference from the mutant allele. The mutant alleles of the genes listed above are as follows:

genotype	name	genotype	name
pp	—Platinum	$c^H\ c^H$	—Albino
ip ip	—Imperial platinum	*oo*	—Goofus
al al	—Aleutian	*S*	—Black cross
bb	—Brown-eyed pastel	*F*	—Blue frost
bg bg	—Green-eyed pastel	*Eb*	—Ebony
bi bi	—Imperial pastel	*Cm*	—Colmira

Imagine, if you will, the possible color combinations that could be produced by suitable crosses. Some of these combinations have already been produced, with spectacular results, especially in the names they have received.

Ffpp   —Breath of spring platinum
Ffbb   —Breath of spring pastel
al al ip ip—Sapphire
bbpp   —Platinum blond

Although this particular type has not been synthesized, it would be most interesting to see an animal of genotype, *bg bg oo,* which should probably be called a green-eyed goofus.

When different genes affect different traits, it is relatively simple to predict the outcome of crosses involving these genes. However, when different genes affect the same trait, prediction is more difficult because of the interactions between the genes. Even the simplest such cross, involving just two gene pairs, can illustrate the complexities. In chickens, for example, the following results have been obtained in comb shape (see Fig. 17-2):

P_1 rose   ×   pea
                               ↓
F_1 walnut
                             ↓
F_2 9 walnut : 3 rose : 3 pea : 1 single

This cross is obviously of the dihybrid type because a 9:3:3:1 ratio is obtained. The relationships are shown below:

phenotype	genotype
Walnut	*R– P–*
Rose	*R– pp*
Pea	*rr P–*
Single	*rr pp*

A somewhat more complex example of interaction can be drawn from the mouse:

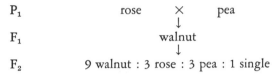

P_1 black   ×   albino
                            ↓
F_1 agouti (wild type)
                            ↓
F_2 9 agouti : 3 black : 4 albino

The F_1 agouti appears to be a throw-back to the ancestral wild-type mouse. However, the black and albino reappear in the F_2, which again suggests a two-factor or dihybrid cross, but with a somewhat aberrant 9:3:4 ratio. The explanation:

phenotype	genotype
Agouti	*C– A–*
Black	*C– aa*
Albino	*cc A–,* and *cc aa*

Fig. 17-2. Variation in comb shape in fowl due to the interactions between two pairs of alleles. *A*, rose. *B*, pea. *C*, walnut. *D*, single. (With permission of Srb and Owen.)

The difference from the previous cross lies in the fact that individuals homozygous for *cc* have no pigment whatever, no matter what other genes for pigment production may be present. In this case, then, the recessive c gene masks the expression of both the *A* and the *a* genes. In a sense, this phenomenon is like dominance in that one type of gene suppresses another, but since it involves different gene pairs rather than alleles, it has been called *epistasis*.

One last example may serve to illustrate still another ratio and give some insight into the mechanism of action of these genes. Certain varieties of white clover produce fairly high amounts of cyanide while others have a low cyanide content. A cross between two low-cyanide varieties gave the following results:

P₁   low strain *A*   ×   low strain *B*

$$P_1 \qquad \text{low strain } A \qquad \times \qquad \text{low strain } B$$
$$\downarrow$$
$$F_1 \qquad \qquad \text{high in cyanide}$$
$$\downarrow$$
$$F_2 \qquad \qquad \text{9 high : 7 low}$$

The chemistry of cyanide production in clover is fairly well understood, and may be outlined as follows:

	gene L			gene H	
	↓			↓	
precursor substance	enzyme L ——————→	substrate (cyanogenic glucoside)	enzyme H ——————→	cyanide	

Thus strains A and B are both low but for different reasons. Strain A with genotype *LLhh* lacks enzyme H; B of genotype *llHH* cannot form enzyme L. The proof of these statements comes from testing the F_2 for cyanide in the manner shown below.

proportion of F_2	leaf extract alone	leaf extract + substrate	leaf extract + enzyme H	genotype
9	+	+	+	*L–H–*
3	0	+	0	*llH–*
3	0	0	+	*L–hh*
1	0	0	0	*llhh*

Here the nature of the interaction is quite clear. A chain of synthesis is involved that, if broken at any point, produces the same phenotype, low cyanide content. Each step in the chain depends on the preceding steps. If the phenotypes differed for each type of interruption—for example, if the substances accumulated at the blockage points differed in color—then further genotypes could be detected phenotypically.

This material on recombination brings out one of the main advantages of sexual reproduction; namely, the formation of gametes with a random sample of one allele from each of the thousands of allelic pairs makes possible a variability or plasticity that is impossible without sex. Individuals reproducing asexually leave descendants with the same genotype as their own, but with sexual reproduction, new gene combinations are always produced at fertilization. These new genotypes do not simply involve new ways of adding old traits together. Through the interactions of the genes in these combinations, very different new types of individuals may emerge, some of which may have real advantages over their parents. Hence in both natural evolution and controlled evolution or plant and animal breeding, segregation, independent assortment, recombination, and interaction of genes provide a potent means of progress toward better adapted or more useful plants and animals.

SUMMARY ◀────────────────────────────────

Genes at a given locus are not necessarily confined to just two alternatives, the dominant and recessive alleles, but may consist of a whole series of multiple alleles. Though each diploid individual will have, at most, only two alleles and each gamete only one, the possibilities for variability within a population are greatly extended by multiple alellism. The genetic variation of a population is further enhanced and diversified by the variety of interactions among genes at different loci. These epistatic interactions add still another dimension to the possibilities for genetic variation stemming from the recombination of genes. Since evolutionary change is dependent upon the available genetic variability, the variation arising from recombination plays a significant role in the evolution of sexually reproducing species.

SUGGESTED READING

Demerec, M., ed., 1958. "Exchange of genetic material: Mechanisms and consequences," *Cold Spring Harbor Symp. Quant. Biol.*, Vol. 23. Long Island Biological Ass'n.

See also references at the end of Chapter 16.

CHAPTER 18

The Physical Basis
of Evolution

The hereditary mechanism elucidated by Mendel accounted for the transmission of similarities and the origin of changes from one generation to the next. Since evolution involves change over successive generations, it obviously is related to the hereditary mechanism. In fact, the mechanism of heredity is the mechanism of evolution as well. Both heredity and evolution have the same physical basis, and it is time now that we consider the physical basis of evolution. The factors of Mendel were merely symbols or abstractions. He had no idea of where they were or of what they were, but postulated their existence in order to explain his data.

In the interval between the publication of Mendel's results and their rediscovery, the study of cells, or cytology, progressed tremendously. The cell theory had been formulated only a few decades before Mendel's time, and the cells were then recognized as the basic structural units in both animals and plants, but little was known of the details of their structure or function. The chromosomes in the nucleus were not even named until 1888, long after Mendel's work. That nuclei came from existing nuclei was only recognized about 1875 by Strasburger. The process by which new nuclei are formed was called *mitosis*.

Mitosis

Mitosis is a continuous process, which, for descriptive purposes, has been divided into phases or stages known as

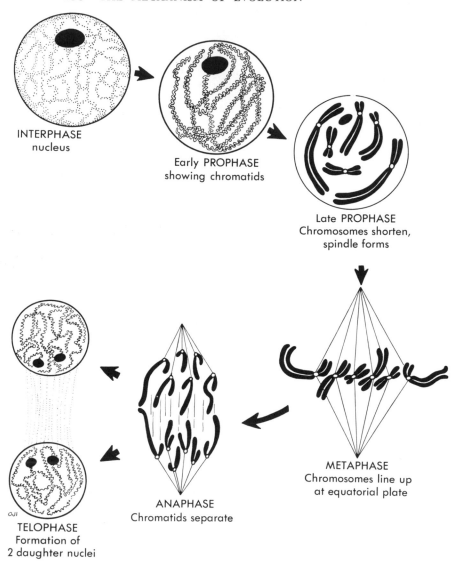

INTERPHASE
nucleus

Early PROPHASE
showing chromatids

Late PROPHASE
Chromosomes shorten,
spindle forms

METAPHASE
Chromosomes line up
at equatorial plate

ANAPHASE
Chromatids separate

TELOPHASE
Formation of
2 daughter nuclei

Fig. 18-1. Mitosis in nucleus with three pairs of chromosomes.

prophase, metaphase, anaphase, and *telophase.* The interphase between successive mitoses has been called the resting stage, but a more suitable term perhaps is the metabolic stage. During mitosis each of the chromosomes in the nucleus undergoes a longitudinal doubling to form two chromatids (see Fig. 18-1). The chromatids of each chromosome separate during anaphase and move as chromosomes to the opposite ends of the cell where they form two similar groups that

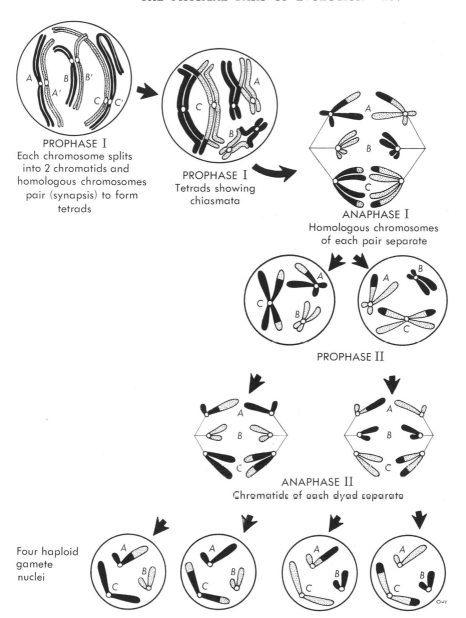

PROPHASE I
Each chromosome splits
into 2 chromatids and
homologous chromosomes
pair (synapsis) to form
tetrads

PROPHASE I
Tetrads showing
chiasmata

ANAPHASE I
Homologous chromosomes
of each pair separate

PROPHASE II

ANAPHASE II
Chromatids of each dyad separate

Four haploid
gamete
nuclei

Fig. 18-2. Meiosis in gametocyte with three pairs of chromosomes.

then reconstitute two new daughter nuclei. These nuclei become the centers of two new cells when a new cell membrane forms between them. The chromosome material in the new cells is similar and is also like that of the original mother cell. Mitosis is thus a precise means of self-duplication of the chromosomes, and all of the cells in the body produced by this process should have the same chromosome content.

Life Cycle in Animals

Each of us was formed by the fertilization of an egg or ovum by a sperm cell. The egg carries a set of chromosomes from the mother; the sperm, a similar set from the father. The fertilized egg or zygote and all the cells derived by mitosis from it thus carry two sets of chromosomes. If no reduction in number occurred prior to the next fertilization, the number of sets of chromosomes would double in each generation. However, a reduction in number does occur during the process of meiosis (Fig. 18-2), which may be regarded as a modification of mitosis. Thus the gametes, sperm and egg, carry a single set of chromosomes, one of each type, and are said to be $1n$ or haploid. The body or somatic cells with two sets or a pair of each type of chromosome are said to be $2n$ or diploid.

In the formation of sperm and egg cells in animals, a process known as gametogenesis, nuclear behavior is basically similar in males and females but in other ways spermatogenesis and oögenesis differ. In the testis, stem cells known as spermatogonia divide mitotically. Some of these cells continue to function as stem cells, while others enlarge somewhat to form primary spermatocytes. The first meiotic division of a primary spermatocyte then gives rise to two secondary spermatocytes. With the second meiotic division, four spermatids are formed. Metamorphosis of the spermatids, during which much of the cytoplasm is lost and a flagellum or tail is formed, leads to the formation of four functional spermatozoa.

The oögonia in the ovary are fewer in number than the spermatogonia. An oögonium, through the accumulation of cytoplasmic material, enlarges greatly to form a primary oöcyte. The first meiotic division is equal with respect to the nuclei, but the great bulk of the cytoplasm goes to one cell, and the other nucleus with very little cytoplasm is pinched off as the first polar body. The second meiotic division is also unequal cytoplasmically, so that an egg and the second polar body result. Thus oögenesis gives rise to only one functional egg cell even though as in spermatogenesis four cells result from the meiotic divisions. In higher animals the haploid condition is confined to the gametes themselves. There is an alternation between haploid and diploid conditions each generation, but the diploid condition restored at fertilization prevails during virtually all of the life cycle.

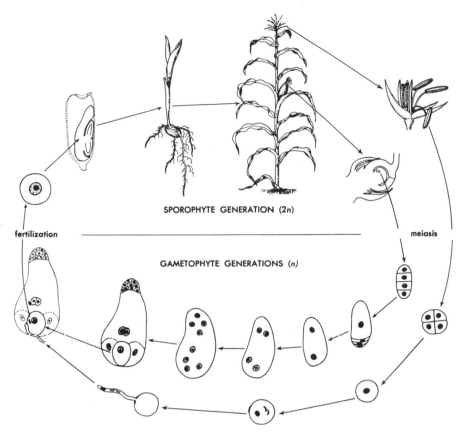

SPOROPHYTE GENERATION (2n)

fertilization ——————————————————————————— meiosis

GAMETOPHYTE GENERATIONS (n)

Fig. 18-3. The life cycle of an angiosperm (corn). (With permission of Wilson and Loomis.)

Life Cycle in Plants

Among higher plants an alternation of generations also exists in the life cycle. Two distinct stages are found, a diploid sporophyte and a haploid gametophyte. The gametophyte in mosses and ferns is quite prominent, but in the flowering plants it consists of just a few cells, and the plant body is the sporophyte generation.

The meiotic divisions occur during the formation of haploid spores by the sporophyte. The spores, by a series of mitotic divisions, produce the haploid male and female gametophytes, which in turn produce haploid gametes. Union of the gametes forms a zygote that then develops into the diploid sporophyte.

In angiosperms (see Fig. 18-3), the sporophyte or plant bears two kinds of spores, usually within the same flower. The male spores or microspores are formed in the anthers of the flower; the female spores or megaspores develop in the ovules of the pistil of the flower. The stamens and pistil are surrounded by accessory flower parts, the petals and sepals.

In the anther, microspore mother cells enlarge and undergo two meiotic divisions to form a tetrad of male spores. The haploid unicellular male spore then undergoes a mitotic division to form a tube nucleus and a generative nucleus. This binucleate structure, the pollen grain, is the male gametophyte.

The female spores form from megaspore mother cells. Each ovule contains a megaspore mother cell that divides meiotically to form a row of four cells. Three of these cells degenerate, but the fourth enlarges to form a functional female spore. The haploid nucleus divides mitotically to form a two-, four-, and finally eight-nucleate embryo sac. Three nuclei collect at each end, and one of the cells at one end becomes the egg. The mature embryo sac at this stage is the female gametophyte, consisting of the egg nucleus plus two synergid nuclei at one end, two polar nuclei at the center, and three antipodals at the other end.

The pollen grain, after landing on the end of the pistil, breaks open, and the pollen tube grows down through the tissues of the pistil toward the ovule. As the tube, containing both tube and generative nuclei, approaches the ovule, the generative nucleus divides by mitosis to form two sperm nuclei. When the pollen tube enters the embryo sac, the tube nucleus disintegrates and a double fertilization occurs. One sperm nucleus fertilizes the egg to form the diploid zygote; the other unites with the two polar nuclei at the center of the embryo sac to form the $3n$ or triploid endosperm, a tissue for food storage. The zygote then develops into the new diploid sporophyte generation.

Meiosis

Meiosis, in the simplest terms, consists of two nuclear divisions during which the chromosomes divide only once. Most of the unique features in meiosis occur during the prophase of the first division. During this time, the two members of each pair of chromosomes come to lie side by side. Since by the time of this synapsis each chromosome has duplicated into two halves or *chromatids,* a tetrad of four chromatids is formed. Exact reciprocal exchanges between two nonsister chromatids frequently occur. In this way a portion of a maternal chromatid is transferred to a paternal chromatid and vice versa. These exchanges are detected cytologically as *chiasmata* in late prophase.

At anaphase the homologous chromosomes of each pair separate to form dyads of sister chromatids, except in regions where exchanges have occurred. In these regions both maternal and paternal segments are present. At the second anaphase the centromere holding sister chromatids together divides and the chromatids of each dyad go to opposite poles, no further duplication of the chromosomes having occurred. Hence each chromatid in a tetrad comes to lie in a different nucleus. A quartet of cells is formed, each cell with one complete set of chromosomes rather than the two present in the original cell.

Sex Determination

The precision observed in the distribution of the chromosomes at mitosis and meiosis suggested to the German biologist Weismann toward the close of the nineteenth century that the chromosomes must in some way be involved in the transmission of hereditary characteristics. The proof for this idea came years later, and grew out of the discovery of the way in which sex is determined. For centuries it was believed that sex was determined by environmental forces acting on the embryo during its development. It would be difficult to assess the abuses to which mothers were subjected to ensure the production of a child of the desired sex, usually male. However, in the early 1900's it was discovered that males had an unequal pair of chromosomes not observed in females. The males, therefore, produced two kinds of sperm, one bearing a large or X chromosome plus one each of the other chromosome types, the other bearing a small or Y chromosome plus a set of the other chromosomes known as the *autosomes*. Females were found to carry two X's and two sets of autosomes, and their eggs after meiosis, one X and one set of autosomes. The X and Y chromosomes were called *sex chromosomes* because fertilization of an X-bearing egg by an X-bearing sperm produced a female whereas fertilization of an X-bearing egg by a Y-type sperm resulted in a male. Thus the cytological facts developed rapidly, but independently of the development of knowledge about heredity. Of course cytology flowered late in the nineteenth century before genetics as a science even had its start, but even after 1900 and the rediscovery of Mendel's laws, the two sciences pursued independent courses.

Sex Linkage

Then, among the many red-eyed fruit flies in Thomas Hunt Morgan's laboratory at Columbia, a single white-eyed male was discovered. When crossed to red-eyed females, all of the F_1 were red-eyed. Inbreeding the F_1 gave a 3 red to 1 white ratio in the F_2. This result seems perfectly normal, except for the fact that all of the F_2 white-eyed flies were males. This unusual result, it was seen, could be explained if the gene causing white eyes were located on the X chromosome. The pattern of inheritance then would be:

P_1

$$
\begin{array}{ccccc}
X & X & & X & Y \\
W & \big| \ \big| & W & \times \quad w & \big| \ \big| \\
\end{array}
$$

red-eyed female   white-eyed male

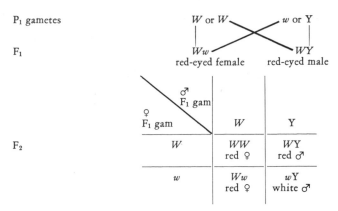

If this assumption is correct, it should be possible to predict the results of the reciprocal cross, white female with red male, as follows:

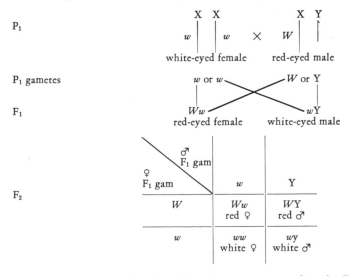

White-eyed males and red-eyed females were expected in the F_1, with a 1:1 ratio of red and white in the F_2, and this was the result obtained. Thus, it seemed clear that the gene for white eyes must be on the X chromosome, and this unusual type of inheritance, intimately associated with sex, came to be called sex linked. It marked the first step toward proving that all of the genes are located on the chromosomes, the autosomes as well as the sex chromosomes. Mendel's factors, then, are not mere abstractions but are physical entities borne by the chromosomes in the nucleus of the cell. The chromosomes are therefore the physical basis of heredity *and* of evolution.

Though a great deal still remains to be learned, the chromosomes are now known to be formed of nucleoprotein, a combination of protein and deoxyribonucleic acid, with the latter in all probability the vehicle of hereditary information. These small bodies, measured in thousandths of millimeters, carry the factors that in large measure determine not only man's outward appearance—his build and height, his skin, eye, and hair color—but also less obvious traits, such as disease resistance, intelligence, and personality.

The discovery that the genes were located on the chromosomes opened up entire new areas to exploration in the search for knowledge about heredity, and also gave new insight into the mechanism underlying Mendel's laws. The separation of maternal from paternal chromosomes at meiosis is the basis of Mendel's first law of segregation. The random alignment of chromosome pairs at metaphase is the basis of Mendel's second law of independent assortment. In other words, the position on the metaphase plate of the maternal and paternal chromosomes of one chromosome pair is independent of their position in any other pair; hence the gametes contain random combinations of maternal and paternal chromosomes. As the number of chromosome pairs increases, the number of possible kinds of gametes grows, the number of kinds doubling with each added pair. In man, for example, with 23 pairs of chromosomes, 2^{23} different combinations of maternal and paternal chromosomes are possible in the gametes of a single individual. Small wonder that even brothers and sisters are never alike.

The number of genes in any species far exceeds the number of chromosome pairs. Obviously some of the different genes must reside on the same chromosome. In such cases, Mendel's law of independent assortment does not hold, for genes on the same chromosome tend to stay together in crosses, and are said to be *linked*. The discovery that the genes are on the chromosomes was the basis of the third major principle of heredity, the principle of linkage. However, this linkage is not complete, for crossing over or recombination between genes on the same chromosome sometimes occurs. The chiasmata formed in first meiotic prophase are the visible evidence of the exchange of segments of chromatids between maternal and paternal chromosomes, which forms the basis for crossing over. Hence, recombinations occur within as well as between maternal and paternal chromosomes, and the amount of possible recombination is increased far beyond 2^{23}.

► **SUMMARY**

The chromosome mechanism is the physical basis not only of heredity but of evolution. The factors discovered by Mendel are located in the chromosomes. The behavior of the chromosomes is responsible for Mendelian segregation and independent assortment. However, genes on the same chromosome tend to be inherited as a linked group, occasionally broken up by crossing over. A favorable combination of genes within a chromosome tends to be held together and not broken up completely in the next generation. Natural selection preserves favorable gene combinations, but could not very well do so if completely independent assortment of genes occurred each generation. Hence, even the organization of genes into chromosomes can be regarded as adaptive, a means of preserving favorable gene combinations; recombination and crossing over give rise to variations, which make possible adaptations to new or changing environmental situations.

SUGGESTED READING

Darlington, C. D., 1937. *Recent advances in cytology,* 2d ed. Philadelphia: Blakiston.

Riley, H. P., 1948. *Introduction to genetics and cytogenetics.* New York: Wiley.

Swanson, C. P., 1957. *Cytology and cytogenetics.* Englewood Cliffs, N. J., Prentice-Hall.

White, M. J. D., 1954. *Animal cytology and evolution,* 2d ed. Cambridge University Press.

CHAPTER 19

Linkage

Linkage and Crossing Over

Even though genes on the same chromosome tend to be inherited as a group, recombination or crossing over between linked genes does occur. The mechanism of crossing over is a reciprocal exchange of segments between two nonsister chromatids, which occurs in the four-strand tetrad stage of first meiotic prophase, and is observable cytologically as a chiasma and genetically as a recombinant or crossover phenotype. The phenomenon of crossing over has made it possible to map out the relationships between the genes on the same chromosome pair.

Let us first examine a cross involving two pairs of linked genes. The first work in which linkage was recognized was carried out by Bateson and Punnett with the sweet pea in 1906. The traits were long (L) versus round (l) pollen and purple or blue (B) versus red (b) flowers. Crosses involving these traits gave the following results:

$$P_1 \qquad \frac{Bl}{Bl} \qquad \times \qquad \frac{bL}{bL}$$
$$\text{blue round} \qquad\qquad \text{red long}$$

$$P_1 \text{ gam} \qquad \underline{Bl} \qquad\qquad \underline{bL}$$

$$F_1 \qquad \frac{Bl}{bL} \quad \text{back} \qquad \frac{bl}{bl}$$
$$\text{blue long} \quad \text{cross} \quad \text{to} \qquad \text{red round}$$

F₁ gam \ F₁ gam	bl	phenotype	n obs.	percent obs.	
Bl	$\dfrac{Bl}{bl}$	blue round	153	43.5	non C.O.
bL	$\dfrac{bL}{bl}$	red long	155	44.1	non C.O.
BL	$\dfrac{BL}{bl}$	blue long	23	6.5	C.O.
bl	$\dfrac{bl}{bl}$	red round	21	6.0	C.O.

12.5 percent

In this instance, instead of 25 percent of the total in each of the F₂ categories expected with independent assortment, there was a great excess of the original parental types and a deficiency of the recombinant or crossover types. Rather than 50 percent new types, only 12.5 percent crossing over occurred. This frequency of crossing over is remarkably constant between any given pair of gene loci.

Linear Order of the Genes

Next let us consider an example involving three pairs of linked genes. Echinus (*ec*) is a recessive mutant in the fruit fly (*Drosophila melanogaster*) causing rough eyes; scute (*sc*), a recessive causing some bristles to be missing; and crossveinless (*cv*) eliminates the crossveins of the wings. The wild-type genes for all three mutants can be designated by a plus, a convention that makes the following cross somewhat easier to follow:

P₁ $\qquad \dfrac{+\ ec\ +}{+\ ec\ +} \times \dfrac{sc\ +\ cv}{sc\ +\ cv}$

P₁ gam $\qquad +\ ec\ + \qquad sc\ +\ cv$

F₁ $\qquad$ ♀♀ $\dfrac{+\ ec\ +}{sc\ +\ cv}$ back cross to $\dfrac{sc\ ec\ cv}{sc\ ec\ cv}$ ♂♂

F₁ ♀ gam \ F₁ ♂ gam	sc ec cv	individuals observed
+ ec +	$\dfrac{+\ ec\ +}{sc\ ec\ cv}$	810
sc + cv	$\dfrac{sc\ +\ cv}{sc\ ec\ cv}$	828

non C.O. gametes

C.O. gametes		
sc ec +	$\dfrac{sc\ ec\ +}{sc\ ec\ cv}$	62
+ + cv	$\dfrac{+ + cv}{sc\ ec\ cv}$	88
sc + +	$\dfrac{sc + +}{sc\ ec\ cv}$	89
+ ec cv	$\dfrac{+ ec\ cv}{sc\ ec\ cv}$	103
+ + +	$\dfrac{+ + +}{sc\ ec\ cv}$	0
sc ec cv	$\dfrac{sc\ ec\ cv}{sc\ ec\ cv}$	0
	total	1980

If each gene pair were on a different pair of chromosomes, equal numbers of flies would have been observed in each of the eight phenotypic classes. However, independent assortment obviously did not occur, for the numbers range from 0 to 828. The crossover percentage between two linked gene loci is determined by dividing the number of individuals showing recombination between these two loci by the total number of individuals of all types and multiplying by 100.

$$\text{percent C.O.} = \frac{\text{C.O.}}{\text{total}} \times 100$$

$$\text{percent C.O. between } sc \text{ and } ec = \frac{62 + 88 + 0 + 0}{1980} \times 100 = 7.6 \text{ percent}$$

$$\text{percent C.O. between } ec \text{ and } cv = \frac{89 + 103 + 0 + 0}{1980} \times 100 = 9.7 \text{ percent}$$

$$\text{percent C.O. between } sc \text{ and } cv = \frac{62 + 88 + 89 + 103}{1980} \times 100 = 17.3 \text{ percent}$$

Crossover percentages between linked genes may range anywhere from very close to 0 percent up to 50 percent, depending on which two genes are chosen. These crossover frequencies not only indicate that these genes are linked, but they also make it possible to arrange them in a definite linear order. This line, with the genes marked off at intervals determined by the crossover frequencies, is known as a chromosome map. From the above data, the following map can be constructed:

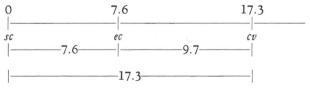

No individuals appeared at all in the two double crossover classes, +++ and *sc ec cv.* If crossovers in the two regions *sc-ec* and *ec-cv* were independent events, the expected probability of simultaneous or double crossovers in these regions would be 7.6 percent × 9.7 percent = 0.7 percent. In other words, about 14 double crossover individuals would have been expected in this cross, but none was observed. Therefore, it appears that if one crossover occurs, the probability of another crossover in adjacent regions of the same chromosome is reduced. This phenomenon, known as *interference,* indicates that crossing over must involve segments of the chromatids rather than individual gene loci. Interference is complete, as in this case, within a certain distance from the first crossover, and becomes progressively less the farther away the second crossover is from the first. The proportion of expected double crossovers that actually occur is called the *coincidence,* which thus serves as an indication of the amount of interference.

Actually, the only satisfactory way to represent the relationships of linked genes graphically is to show the genes as points on a line. In numerous linkage tests made with a variety of species, if the crossover frequencies, say for three gene loci *a, b,* and *c,* are *ab* and *bc,* then the frequency of *ac* is either *ab* plus *bc,* as in the example above, or *ab* minus *bc* if *c* lies between *a* and *b.* Results such as these form the basis of the fourth and final major principle of genetics, the linear order of the genes. Of the four principles, Mendel was responsible for segregation and independent assortment, and Morgan and his co-workers for linkage and the linear order of the genes.

Extending these test crosses makes possible a complete mapping of each chromosome. There are only as many linkage groups as there are chromosome pairs, and each gene can be located with respect to all of the others. The greater the physical distance between two genes on the same chromosome, the greater the chance of recombination between them, and the farther apart they will appear on the map.

SUMMARY ◄─────────────────────────────────────

The genes, the basic units of evolution, are located on the chromosomes and are arranged in a linear order that can be mapped with considerable precision. Evolution, therefore, occurs within the limits imposed by the chromosome mechanism of heredity.

SUGGESTED READING

See references at the end of Chapter 16.

CHAPTER 20

Chromosomal Variation

Linkage studies and chromosome mapping are possible because the structure of the chromosomes is very stable. On rare occasions, however, chromosome rearrangements may occur. These rearrangements can usually be detected both cytologically and genetically, for the linkage relationships of the genes are changed by any restructuring of the chromosomes. In order for rearrangements to occur, the chromosomes must break. Chromosome breakage may be "spontaneous," but it can also be induced by such agents as ionizing radiation and certain chemical compounds. In many cases the breaks heal or restitute with no detectable cytological or genetic effect. However, if the broken ends fail to unite or else reunite in new combinations, they then can be detected.

Duplication and Deficiency

A number of types of rearrangements have been recognized (see Fig. 20-1). A *deficiency* or *deletion* may arise as follows:

A B C   D E F G H → A B C   D E + F G H

breakage point	deficiency for FGH region	acentric fragment

A deficiency is often lethal when homozygous, or even, if large enough, when heterozygous, and is therefore not apt to play a role in evolution.

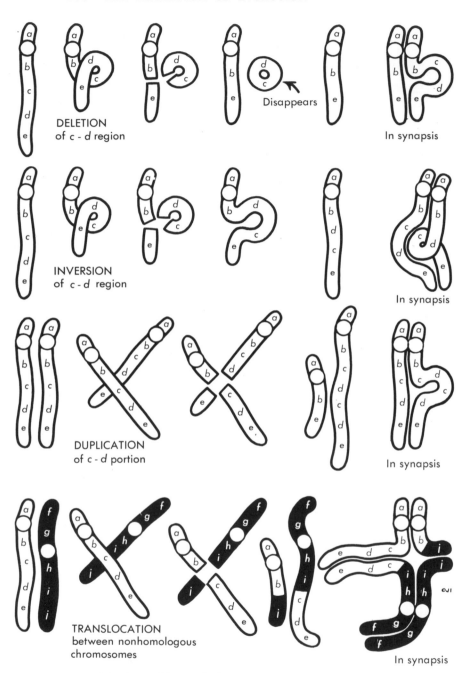

DELETION
of c - d region

In synapsis

INVERSION
of c - d region

In synapsis

DUPLICATION
of c - d portion

In synapsis

TRANSLOCATION
between nonhomologous
chromosomes

In synapsis

Fig. 20-1. Types of chromosome rearrangements.

A *duplication* of a chromosome segment may arise in the following way:

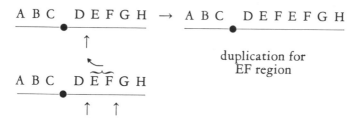

duplication for
EF region

The addition of the extra EF segment gives rise to a duplication or repeat of that region. Duplications are generally viable and represent a way of adding additional gene loci to the genotype. Furthermore, it has been suggested that mutation can then produce genes of divergent function as follows:

$$E \xrightarrow{\text{duplication}} \begin{vmatrix} E & \longrightarrow & E \\ & \text{mutation} & \\ E & \longrightarrow & E' \end{vmatrix}$$

In this way, during the course of evolution the total number of genes could be increased with a corresponding diversity of function.

Inversion

An *inversion* results when two breaks in a chromosome rejoin after the fragment has rotated 180 degrees.

$$\text{A B C} \quad \text{D E F G H} \rightarrow \text{A B C} \quad \text{D G F E H}$$

inversion

The linkage relations are changed with G, for example, now closely linked with D rather than H. Inversions that include the centromere are *pericentric;* those not including the centromere are *paracentric*. Individuals may be either homozygous or heterozygous for an inversion. In inversion heterozygotes, the synapsis of homologous chromosomes at meiosis is somewhat abnormal, for homologous genes continue to pair wherever possible despite their different linkage relations in the two homologues. As a result of these pairing forces the chromosomes are thrown into easily recognized, characteristic loops. If pairing and crossing over do occur, abnormal chromosomes and fragments are frequently produced that are usually unviable. Hence, the inversions act essentially as crossover suppressors, preventing recombination within chromosomes since the crossover products give rise to gametes with aberrant haploid sets of chromosomes for the most part. Thus in an evolutionary sense inversions are conservative because ordinarily only the old gene combinations give rise to viable organisms.

Translocation

A *reciprocal translocation* arises when breaks in two chromosomes are followed by reunion with the fragments interchanged.

Genes in the exchanged fragments now belong to new linkage groups, but the genes will still pair with their old allelic partners so that in a translocation heterozygote four chromosomes will form a single synaptic figure.

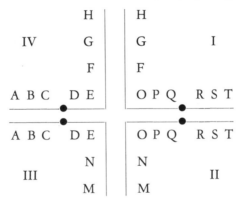

A little study will show that if chromosomes I and IV go to the same pole, the gametes will be deficient for the genes in the region MN while those in region FGH will be duplicated. The reverse is true if chromosomes II and III go to the same pole. Because of the deficiencies, sterility will ensue. Only combinations of I and III or II and IV can be expected to be fertile. Furthermore, crossing over may lead to additional sterility. If several translocations are present, rings of chromosomes, chains of chromosomes, or other unusual synaptic configurations will be observed in meiotic prophase because of the specificity of the pairing reaction. Crosses between populations having different gene arrangements, whether inversions or translocations, will not ordinarily be selectively advantageous since there is partial sterility in the resulting progeny. In some species, however, inversions (for example, *Drosophila*) and translocations (for example, *Oenothera*) have become a part of the normal genetic system within breeding populations, apparently having an adaptive function.

Position Effect and Pseudoallelism

In addition to changing the linkage relationships, in some cases rearranging the relationships of the genes to each other changes their effects on the phenotype though the genes themselves are apparently unchanged. This phenomenon is known as *position effect*. The classical example of position effect involves Bar eye in the fruit fly. The Bar-eye condition is due to the duplication of a small segment of the chromosome and can be diagramed as follows:

1. wild type   2. Bar eye   3. double Bar   4. double Bar/
                                                      wild heterozygote

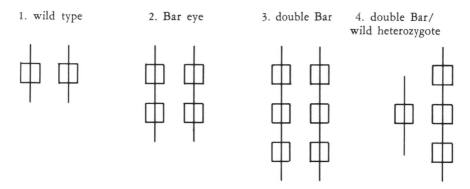

The genic contents of types 2 and 4 are identical, but the heterozygote has significantly smaller eyes than the homozygous type. Hence, the phenotypic difference must be due to the genes' arrangement, and the expression of a gene is dependent not only on its intrinsic effects but also on its position with respect to the other genes in the genotype.

Position effect has also been found to be the rule with pseudoalleles. The term pseudoallele was coined to describe cases originally thought to involve a single locus with multiple alleles but that turned out to be two or more very closely linked loci with all the genes affecting the same trait. One interpretation currently favored is that these loci arose by duplication (hence their similarity in action) followed by mutation to divergent functions as suggested above. The white-apricot case in *Drosophila melanogaster* will serve as an example of position pseudoallelism. The eye-color mutants, white and apricot, were originally thought to be members of a multiple allelic series at the white locus, and were designated w and w^a. The discovery of rare crossovers (approximately 0.01 percent) between white and apricot indicated that separate closely linked loci were involved, and the mutants were designated w and *apr*. Position effect was revealed when the phenotypes of the two kinds of double heterozygotes were compared. In the *cis* condition both mutant genes are on one chromosome, both wild-type genes on the other. The *trans* state has one mutant and one wild-type gene on each homologue.

$$\frac{apr \quad w}{+ \quad +}$$
cis

$$\frac{apr \quad +}{+ \quad w}$$
trans

The *cis* phase has phenotypically wild-type red eyes whereas the *trans* has a light apricot eye color. Since both types of double heterozygotes have exactly the same genes, position effect is obviously involved. The discovery of position effect and of pseudoallelism has led to a considerable revision in the gene concept.

Heteroploidy

Let us now consider chromosomal variations involving changes in the numbers of whole chromosomes rather than rearrangements involving chromosome fragments. Two general types of change have been found. *Polyploids* (or euploids) are individuals with one or more complete haploid sets of chromosomes added to the usual diploid number. *Heteroploids* (or aneuploids) have some number of chromosomes other than an exact multiple of the haploid number.

A heteroploid, for example, may have an extra chromosome from one pair, or $2n + 1$ chromosomes, and is then known as a simple *trisomic*. If a chromosome from one pair is lacking $(2n - 1)$, it is known as a simple *monosomic*. These and more complex heteroploids tend to lead to sterility or deficient gametes, and hence are generally of little evolutionary significance.

Polyploidy

The changes involving whole haploid sets of chromosomes, however, have been of considerable evolutionary significance, especially in plants. These polyploids may be of several kinds, among the more common being triploids ($3n$), tetraploids ($4n$), hexaploids ($6n$), and octoploids ($8n$). Many domesticated plant species are polyploid (wheat, cotton, apples, etc.), and it is now possible for plant breeders to induce polyploidy with colchicine, a chemical substance that inhibits the formation of the mitotic spindle. The polyploids frequently have more vigorous vegetative growth and larger and more intensely colored flowers, and hence are especially desirable as new horticultural varieties.

Polyploidy arises in two distinctly different ways. A multiplication of the chromosome sets from a single species gives rise to *autopolyploidy*. If A, for instance, represents a single haploid set of chromosomes, the diploid will be AA, and an autotetraploid, AAAA. Though vegetative vigor is usually good, sterility is high in autopolyploids due to abnormal synapsis at meiosis when more than two homologous chromosomes form a synaptic figure.

Allopolyploids or amphiploids are formed when hybridization between two different species is followed by a doubling of the chromosome number in the diploid hybrid or by the formation of unreduced gametes:

P_1	AA	×	BB
P_1 gametes	A		B
F_1		AB	
	chromosome doubling		
F_1 gametes	AB	×	AB
F_2		AA BB	allotetraploid

The F_1 AB hybrid is generally quite sterile due to the lack of pairing between the chromosomes of the A and B genomes. The F_2 allotetraploid, on the other hand, is fertile, acting as a functional diploid, since each type of A and B chromosome is represented twice, and pairing at meiosis is normal between these homologues. In some cases polyploids more or less intermediate to the auto- and allopolyploids have been formed, which are known as segmental allopolyploids.

More than one third of all species of higher plants, the angiosperms, are polyploid, and thus polyploidy has been of considerable importance to plant evolution. With the discovery of means of inducing polyploidy, new horizons have been opened to the plant breeders. An early and classical example of a synthetic allotetraploid was *Raphanobrassica,* formed from the radish (*Raphanus*) and the cabbage (*Brassica*). Such a plant obviously had considerable potential since the edible portions are the root in one parent, the shoot in the other. Briefly, the details of the cross are as follows:

P_1	radish	×	cabbage
	$2n_1 = 18$		$2n_2 = 18$
P_1 gametes	$n_1 = 9$		$n_2 = 9$
F_1		$n_1 + n_2 = 18$	
		sterile diploid	
		chromosome doubling	
F_1 gametes	$(n_1 + n_2)$	×	$(n_1 + n_2)$
F_2		$n_1\ n_1\ n_2\ n_2$	
		fertile allotetraploid	

One difficulty emerged when these sturdy, fertile F_2 plants were examined; they had a root like a cabbage and a head like a radish.

SUMMARY ◄──

Chromosomal variation as well as genic variation can be observed in natural populations. These variations include rearrangements involving chromosome fragments such as duplications and deficiencies, inversions, and translocations. The addition or loss of whole chromosomes gives rise to heteroploidy, in which the number of chromosomes does not equal an exact multiple of the haploid number. Polyploids, with additional complete haploid sets of chromosomes, may arise within a single species or subsequent to hybridization between different species. Chromosomal rearrangements may, on occasion, lead to position effects when the gene, in a new location with respect to the rest of the genes, has a changed effect on the phenotype even though the gene itself is apparently unchanged.

SUGGESTED READING

See references at the end of Chapter 18.

CHAPTER 21

Mutation

Over a century ago a short-legged ram unlike any of the other sheep was born into the flock of a New England farmer named Seth Wright. This ram transmitted the short legs to his progeny, and from him was thus derived the Ancon breed of sheep (see Fig. 21-1), valued by New Englanders because these sheep were unable to jump the stone fences so common there. Apparently they were not prized for very long, since the breed became extinct about eighty years ago. However, more recently a Norwegian lamb with short legs appeared, and from this animal a new strain has been developed. The sudden appearance of a new hereditary trait in a population is said to be due to a mutation, a change in the hereditary material. In this case, the trait behaved as a simple recessive in crosses, and presumably had its origin by mutation and not by the recombination of existing genes. A great variety of mutations has been observed in a number of different species. The valuable platinum mutation in the fox, streptomycin resistance in bacteria, and the hemophilia mutation ("bleeder's disease") that Queen Victoria bestowed so liberally among her descendants are cases in point.

Types of Mutations

In a broad sense a mutation is any hereditary change not due to the simple recombination of genes. Included in this sense are gene or point mutations, chromosomal changes, either structural or numerical, and position effects. In a narrower sense, muta-

207

tion is used to refer to a self-duplicating change at a single gene locus. Gene mutations are of fundamental importance to evolution because they form the raw material of evolution. Only by mutation can truly new kinds of genetic variation appear, and all evolutionary change is based, ultimately, on mutation. Mutation alone, however, cannot account for evolution, for the sporadic mutants must in some way become a part of the genotype of the population.

There is no simple method of classifying mutations, for they may affect all kinds of traits in the organism, from its pigmentation to its psychoses, and

Fig. 21-1. Normal ewe on left. Short-legged Ancon ewe in the center and ram on the right are homozygous for the recessive Ancon mutation.

they are therefore of an almost bewildering variety. One method of classification frequently used takes only the effect on viability into consideration, and the mutants are then classified as lethal, semilethal, subvital, normal, and supervital. Another common approach is to group the mutations according to their visible effects on the phenotype, and mutants are described as wing mutants, eye-color mutants, body-color mutants, bristle mutants, etc. However, the so-called "white-eye" mutant in the fruit fly also causes transparency of the testicular envelope, a change in spermatheca shape, and a lowered viability, longevity, and fertility.

Hence, to call white an eye-color mutant scarcely indicates the entire story. These genes with a multiplicity of effects are said to be *pleiotropic,* but the apparent variety of effects may be traceable to a single primary change in gene function. The observed phenotypic effects are generally far removed from the primary action of the gene. The biochemical mutants in microorganisms may be somewhat closer to the primary gene action. These mutant types usually fail to form a particular biochemical substance such as an amino acid or a vitamin because of the absence or inactivation of an enzyme needed to mediate the synthesis. Study of mutants of this type may in time do away with the need for the more or less arbitrary classifications of mutants currently in use.

Induced Mutation

"Spontaneous" mutations occur all the time, but they are called "spontaneous" simply because the exact causes are not as yet well understood. The mutation rate can be raised well above this "spontaneous" rate by various experimental techniques that have provided some insight into the mechanisms of mutation. Temperature shocks were one of the first methods used to raise the mutation rates; in flies, exposures for short periods to both low and high temperature extremes outside the normal range were found to be effective. Within the normal temperature range of the organism, mutation rates will be higher at the higher temperatures.

The discovery that x-rays and other ionizing radiations (α, β, and γ rays, protons, neutrons) induced mutations and caused chromosome breakage marked a milestone in the study of mutation. The number of mutations is directly proportional to the dose of radiation and is independent of intensity. In other words, a dose of 500 roentgens (a roentgen or r unit produces two ionizations per cubic micron of tissue) will cause the same number of mutations whether received over a period of 20 minutes or 20 months, and the effect is cumulative. Chromosome breaks are presumed to be proportional to dose also. However, two-hit chromosomal aberrations (for example, translocations, whose formation depends on the simultaneous occurrence of two open breaks) show an intensity effect, since at low intensities one break usually reunites before another break occurs. Ultraviolet light, essentially a nonionizing radiation, is also mutagenic though relatively less effective at breaking chromosomes than the ionizing radiations.

The mutagenic properties of the mustard gases were discovered during World War II, and since then a variety of chemical substances has been shown capable of raising rates of mutation and chromosome breakage. As yet, no pattern is apparent in the types of effective compounds, which include peroxides, formaldehyde, urethane, triazine, diepoxide, caffeine, phenol, and also cancer-producing compounds such as dibenzanthracene and methyl-cholanthrene.

Study of the effects of mutagenic agents in combination with each other or with other agents has shown a variety of modifying effects. Infrared alone is not mutagenic, but pretreatment with infrared followed by x-radiation raises the yield of aberrations above that of the same dose of x-rays alone. On the other hand, exposure of cells to ionizing radiations under conditions of anoxia generally reduces the yield of aberrations as compared to radiation with oxygen present. The mutagenic effects of ultraviolet light can be counteracted by subsequent exposure to visible white light. Chemical substances such as reducing compounds, British anti-Lewisite (BAL), and alcohol have been shown to protect cells against radiation damage. However, even though such findings offer the hope that some protective measures can eventually be developed against the physiological and genetic damage caused by atomic warfare or other radiation hazards, the therapeutic consumption of large quantities of alcohol in the event of an atomic war has not yet been recommended.

Mutation Rates

A most interesting aspect of the mutation process was revealed by the discovery of the so-called mutation-rate genes, which affect the mutation rates of genes at other loci. In corn, for example, the recessive a_1 gene (the A_1 locus controlling anthocyanin production) is stable in the presence of the recessive dt allele at the dotted locus. The dominant Dt, however, induces instability in the a_1 allele, causing it to mutate to A_1 at a high rate, so high, in fact, that it is called an "ever-sporting" gene. (New mutant types used to be called "sports" before the term mutation came into general use. It seems a pity, almost, that the more colorful word was not retained.) Another instance is the "hi" mutant in *Drosophila*, which differs from Dt in that it raises mutation rates at many loci rather than just one, and also induces chromosome breakage. The existence of these mutation-rate genes raises the intriguing possibility that the mutation rates in natural populations can be controlled by natural selection by either favoring or eliminating these genes.

Mutation is essentially a random process in that it is not possible to predict when a given gene will mutate, nor do mutations occur as an adaptive response to an environmental stimulus. However, it is not completely random, for the mutations occur within the framework of the existing genotype. Furthermore, the same mutation tends to recur, time and again, but different rates of mutation prevail at different loci and for different mutational changes at the same locus. Hence, all types of mutations do not have the same probability of occurrence and some genes are more stable than others, but all of them, except the ever-sporting variety, are exceedingly stable. In man, for instance, the mutation rate to the dominant gene causing aniridia, absence of the iris, has been estimated at 10 per million gametes or 1/100,000. One way to consider this fact is that a single normal allele would be expected to go through 100,000 generations, on the average, before it mutated. Another way, however, equally valid, is to state that a single ejaculate containing 100,000,000 spermatozoa would be expected to contain approximately 1000 sperm cells carrying new aniridia mutants. The mutation rate from the normal condition to the sex-linked recessive gene causing hemophilia has been estimated at one in 31,000 gametes; that to the autosomal dominant causing achondroplastic dwarfism is approximately one in 24,000.

In corn, more precise studies than in the human material have shown a wide range of spontaneous mutation rates, as given below:

trait	mutation	gametes tested	number of mutations	average per million gametes
colored → noncolored aleurone and plant	$R \rightarrow r$	554,786	273	492
inhibitor → noninhibitor of aleurone color	$I \rightarrow i$	265,391	28	106
purple → red aleurone	$Pr \rightarrow pr$	647,102	7	11
starchy → sugary endosperm	$Su \rightarrow su$	1,678,736	4	2.4
yellow → white starch in endosperm	$Y \rightarrow y$	1,745,280	4	2.2
full → shrunken endosperm	$Sh \rightarrow sh$	2,469,285	3	1.2
nonwaxy → waxy endosperm	$Wx \rightarrow wx$	1,503,744	0	0

These figures may be compared with those given above for man:

trait	average per million gametes
achondroplasia	42
hemophilia	32
aniridia	10

It will be seen that the rates per generation are roughly of the same order of magnitude even though the generation lengths are quite different. The same is true of bacteria and *Drosophila* with even shorter generation lengths. The fact that species with generation lengths ranging from about half an hour to thirty years have comparable average mutation rates per locus per generation of roughly 10^{-5} to 10^{-6} seems to bear out the earlier suggestion that mutation rates are to some extent under the control of natural selection. If, on an absolute time basis, the bacterial mutation rates prevailed in man, the human load of mutations would be enormous.

Most of the mutations that occur are deleterious and recessive to the prevailing types of genes. These genes, the "wild type," are the favorable mutations of the past, which have been preserved by natural selection and have increased in frequency until they have become the most frequent type. Thus, any random change affecting these favorable genes has a much greater probability of being deleterious than it has of being more favorable than the existing genes.

Though Bateson and Punnett at first visualized recessive mutations as complete losses or deficiencies of the gene loci, the discovery of back mutations has made this idea untenable. Even though many apparent reverse mutations have turned out, on careful genetic analysis, to be due to mutations at entirely different loci, nevertheless, careful analyses such as those of Giles with *Neurospora* have established the existence of true reverse mutations.

Controlled Genetic Changes

None of the mutagenic agents discussed thus far can be used to induce a predictable specific mutation. Present techniques, both radiation and chemical, involve essentially a shotgun treatment, with the geneticist examining the pieces for whatever mutations may have occurred. This method, of course, must be regarded as very crude, and it would be highly desirable, especially for the practical breeder, if he were able to control the mutation process and to induce specific kinds of mutations at will. At least one type of experiment has given reason for hope that controlled mutations may one day be possible.

In the *Pneumococcus* bacteria various types have been identified that differ in the type of polysaccharide capsule enclosing the cell. The encapsulated bacteria form a smooth colony when cultured. By mutation, the ability to form the polysaccharide capsule may be lost, and the unencapsulated cells then form a rough colony. Back mutation will give rise to encapsulated cells, but the capsule always has the same type of polysaccharide as the original type. For example,

$$\text{smooth Type I} \xrightarrow{\text{mutation}} \text{rough Type I} \xrightarrow{\text{mutation}} \text{smooth Type I}$$

However, the addition of an extract from killed bacteria with a different capsular type produced the following result:

$$\text{smooth Type I} \xrightarrow{\text{mutation}} \text{rough Type I} \xrightarrow{\text{extract from Type III}} \text{smooth Type III}$$

In this case, a predictable change was induced, but the active inducing agent was not the Type III polysaccharide itself, but rather the DNA (desoxyribonucleic acid) from the Type III bacteria. Bacterial *transformation,* as this phenomenon is called, may not represent a true induced mutation, but it is an induced directed hereditary change, and hence is extremely significant as a step toward directed mutation.

In a somewhat similar case known as *transduction,* genetic material can be transferred from one bacterial strain to another via a bacterial virus. The virus apparently transports the genes or a small chromosome segment from one bacterial host to another where it becomes incorporated into the genotype of the new host.

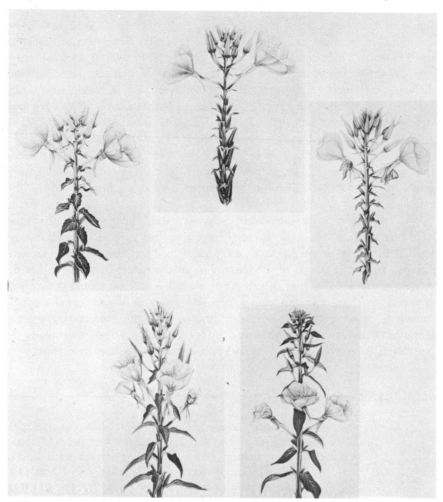

Fig. 21-2. Some "mutants" of the evening primrose, *Oenothera lamarckiana,* on which de Vries based his mutation theory. *Oenothera lamarckiana* above. The "mutants" from the left counterclockwise are: *O. gigas, O. albida, O. scintillans,* and *O. oblonga.* (From de Vries.)

The Mutation Theory of de Vries

In the very early days of genetics de Vries (1902) proposed the mutation theory of evolution as an alternative to the theory of natural selection. de Vries had been working with the evening primrose, *Oenothera lamarckiana,* in which new and strikingly different types of plants occasionally appeared, breeding true to the new type (see Fig. 21-2). On the basis of this work, de Vries suggested that new species originate as a result of these large discontinuous variations or mutations rather than from the gradual accumulation of numerous small hereditary differences in size, shape, color, etc., by natural selection. However, his theory turned out to be based on a variety of changes, stemming from the unique features of the genome of *Oenothera,* and including tetraploidy, trisomics, reciprocal translocations, and balanced lethal systems. With a few possible exceptions, these hereditary changes did not represent genic mutations at all even though they bred true and remained distinct from the parental types; rather, they were actually the result of recombination of chromosomes or genes. These spurious mutants in *Oenothera* are the result of a unique situation not to be found in all species, and therefore they cannot serve as a general mechanism for evolution.

As the knowledge of heredity has increased, mutations of all degrees have been studied. Their effects may be great, or they may be so small that refined statistical or genetic methods are needed to detect the difference between different mutant types. As an understanding of the nature of mutation has developed, it has become clear that de Vries, though basing his mutation theory of evolution on changes that were not genic mutations at all, was fundamentally correct in stressing the significance of mutation to the evolutionary process. However, mutation alone cannot account for evolution; rather it furnishes the raw materials on which other forces act to bring about evolutionary change.

SUMMARY ◄────────────────────────────────

In a broad sense mutation implies a change that takes place in the hereditary material and does not arise as a consequence of recombination. In a narrower sense mutation is used to refer to a self-duplicating change at a specific locus. Mutations form the raw working material of evolution, for the mutation process is the only one giving rise to entirely new kinds of hereditary variation. Because spontaneous mutations are typically recurrent, it is possible to estimate mutation rates. These rates may be increased by various treatments such as temperature shock, ionizing radiations, and chemical mutagens, and by the effects of mutation-rate genes. Mutation is a random process in the sense that it is impossible to predict when a given gene will mutate and that mutations do not occur as adaptive responses to environmental stimuli. However, they can only occur within the framework imposed by the existing genotype. Most new mutants are deleterious, presumably because the prevailing "wild types" are the favorable mutations of the past, preserved by natural selection, and any random change in these favorable genes has a greater chance of being harmful than of having increased adaptive value.

The mutation theory of evolution, suggested by de Vries as an alternative to natural selection, is not sufficient alone to account for evolution, but mutation and natural selection together are major factors in evolution.

SUGGESTED READING

Demerec, M., ed., 1951. "Genes and mutations," *Cold Spring Harbor Symp. Quant. Biol.,* Vol. 16. Long Island Biological Ass'n, New York.

Muller, H. J., 1959. "The mutation theory re-examined," *Proc. X International Congress of Genetics, 1:*306-317.

Stadler, L. J., 1954. "The gene," *Science, 120:*811-819.

CHAPTER 22

Quantitative Inheritance

Thus far, the traits we have considered have been discontinuous, and the differences have been qualitative and could be easily determined. A person is either red-haired or he is not. Classifying people according to height or weight is something else, for they are not just tall or short, thin or fat; they fall into a continuous pattern from tall to short, thin to fat. In fact, more people fall into the intermediate height and weight ranges than at the extremes. They must be measured rather than classified, and the frequency distribution of these measurements takes the form of a bell-shaped normal curve. When, for example, the height of a group of college men was measured, the frequency distribution had the form shown in Fig. 22-1.

Such a population can be described in terms of the mean and the standard deviation. The mean or average falls at the center of the normal curve, and is estimated from the sample as

$$\bar{x} = \frac{S(x)}{n}$$

where
$\bar{x}$ = mean
S = the sum of
x = the measurement on one individual
n = the number of individuals measured

The standard deviation (s) is a measure of the variability of the group and is computed as

$$s = \sqrt{\frac{S(x - \bar{x})^2}{n - 1}}$$

More than 99 percent of the individuals in the population should fall within plus or minus three standard deviations from the mean. The standard deviation thus provides a way of comparing an individual with the population of which he is a part. The square of the standard deviation (s^2) is of considerable theoretical importance in the study of variability and is known as the *variance*.

The standard error of the mean ($s_{\bar{x}}$) is estimated as

$$ s_{\bar{x}} = \frac{s}{\sqrt{n}} $$

and is useful as an estimate of the variability of sample means in much the same way that the standard deviation is an estimate of the variability of individuals in a sample.

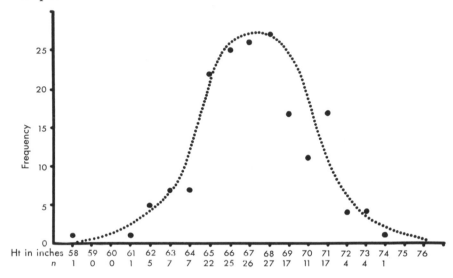

Ht in inches	58	59	60	61	62	63	64	65	66	67	68	69	70	71	72	73	74	75	76
n	1	0	0	1	5	7	7	22	25	26	27	17	11	17	4	4	1		

Fig. 22-1. The normal curve. Height in man. (Data from Blakeslee.)

For the data from Fig. 22-1

$\bar{x} = 67.31$ inches

$s = 3.09 \qquad\qquad\qquad s^2 = 9.56$

$s_{\bar{x}} = 0.23$

Thus, more than 99 percent of the individuals in the sample would be expected to have heights lying within the limits $67.31 \pm 3s$ or from 58.04 to 76.58 inches, and actually only 1 in 175 lies just outside this range. Similarly, more than 99 percent of the means of comparable samples would be expected to fall within the limits $67.31 \pm 3s_{\bar{x}}$ or from 66.62 to 68.00 inches.

From the normal curve, it can be seen that small deviations from the mean are more frequent than large, that negative deviations are as frequent as positive, and that very large deviations are not due to chance alone. An excessively fat boy, then, may be suffering from thyroid trouble, or simply, like Mr. Pickwick's Joe, from overeating. Thus, quantitative traits are subject to environmental modification, much more so than qualitative traits such as red hair.

Genetics of Quantitative Traits

The genetic analysis of quantitative traits is difficult because of their continuous nature and the effects of the environment, and for some time it was felt that a Mendelian explanation was inadequate to account for the results from crosses involving such traits. In a classical cross by East, for example, between Black Mexican sweet corn and Tom Thumb popcorn, the F_1 mean was intermediate between the means of the parents. The F_2 mean was similar to the F_1 mean, but the F_2 was considerably more variable than either the F_1 or the parents, the more extreme F_2 individuals overlapping the parents (Fig. 22-2).

East and Nilsson-Ehle independently arrived at a Mendelian explanation for such results. The intermediacy of the F_1 had long been interpreted to indicate some type of blending inheritance, but blending failed to account for the increased variability of the F_2. The multiple factor hypothesis postulated that quantitative traits were due to the action of a number of different gene pairs, each cumulative but of small effect as compared to environmental influences. The intermediate F_1 was due to a partial or complete lack of dominance. The increased variability of the F_2 was due to the segregation and recombination of the many gene pairs. For instance, the above cross can be outlined as follows:

P_1 *AABBCCDD* $\times$ *aabbccdd*

         Black Mexican   Tom Thumb

F_1 $\downarrow$

               AaBbCcDd

	plus genes		frequency (possible distinct genotypes and phenotypes)
F_2	8	*AABBCCDD*	1
	7	*AABBCCDd, AABBCcDD,* etc.	4
	6	*AABBCCdd, AABBCcDd,* etc.	10
	5	*AABBCcdd, AABbCcDd,* etc.	16
	4	*AABBccdd, AaBbCcDd,* etc.	19
	3	*AABbccdd, AaBbCcdd,* etc.	16
	2	*AAbbccdd, AaBbccdd,* etc.	10
	1	*Aabbccdd, aaBbccdd,* etc.	4
	0	*aabbccdd*	1

This theory, though simplified, has been very serviceable for work with quantitative traits. Some of the more obvious oversimplifications are that the genes have

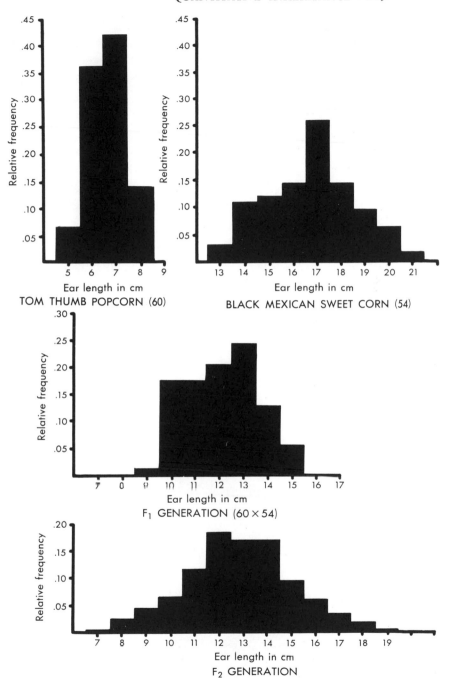

Fig. 22-2. Quantitative inheritance in maize. Ear length in parents, F_1 and F_2 generations of a cross between Tom Thumb popcorn and Black Mexican sweet corn. (Data from East and Hayes.)

equal and additive effects. Evidence is available that multiple factors, also called polygenes, are not all equivalent in their effects on a given trait and that the effect of a given genic substitution will vary with different genetic backgrounds rather than being simply additive. Hence, contrary to the multiple factor hypothesis, these genes are neither equal nor additive in their effects. The genetic situation is obviously complex, and the environmental influences on quantitative traits also make this type of trait difficult to study. However, such studies are very significant both to the student of evolution and to the practical breeder, for the more important economic traits and species differences have both turned out to be of this type. The radish, of the genus *Raphanus,* and the cabbage, of the genus *Brassica,* are not only distinct species but belong to different genera. When they have been crossed, the leaves, flowers, seed pods, etc., are intermediate between those of the parent species, indicating differences at many gene loci of the multiple factor type. Sumner obtained similar results in work with two subspecies of the deer mouse, *Peromyscus polionotus.* The extent of the pigmented area varies considerably between the subspecies *leucocephalus* as compared to *polionotus,* and crosses revealed the following situation:

P_1 *leucocephalus* $\times$ *polionotus*

          45.5 $\downarrow$ 93.0

F_1 68.3

              $\downarrow$

F_2 69.1

The F_2 was more variable than the F_1, the typical result in multiple factor crosses. These few examples, to·which the mule could be added, illustrate a principle that is generally true: where crosses between members of different taxonomic groups are possible, the progeny are intermediate for most traits—an indication that evolution has proceeded by the gradual accumulation of numerous genetic differences.

Multiple factors play a somewhat different type of role when they modify the expression of a gene of major effect. In the familiar black and white spotted Holstein dairy cattle, one gene locus controls spotting. SS and Ss individuals are self-colored; ss are spotted. However, the amount of spotting is influenced by numerous other modifying factors. These genes are detectable only in ss individuals and have no other known effect than their ability to modify the expression of the ss genotype. They are so numerous that they cannot be individually identified or handled genetically, yet selection by the breeder can either increase or decrease the amount of spotting.

Heterosis

The American farmer in recent years has planted hybrid corn almost exclusively. This hybrid corn, because of its greater sturdiness, size, and yield, is of greater economic value than the varieties grown forty years ago. Hybrids frequently show such hybrid vigor, or *heterosis,* which in some way is related to their increased heterozygosity. Hybrid vigor is now being exploited in hogs, chickens, and other species of plants and animals. In addition to its importance in breeding, the heterosis phenomenon, which is a special aspect of quantitative inheritance, plays a role in evolution. See Fig. 22-3.

Let us consider a representative case of heterosis. Corn, which is usually cross-pollinated, can be self-fertilized to produce inbred lines, each very uniform, of poor quality, and distinct from the others. A cross of two inbreds gives an F_1 hybrid of greatly increased size and yield. The F_1, rather than being intermediate between the inbred parents, has a considerably greater yield because of the larger plants with more ears per stalk, more rows per ear, and more kernels of larger size per row. However, this heterosis cannot be perpetuated, for the yield in the F_2, F_3, and subsequent generations becomes progressively less with the inbreeding of each generation until, by the F_7 or F_8, the vigor is down to the level of the original inbred parents.

Two major theories have been proposed to explain the origin of heterosis. Both are Mendelian, variations of the multiple factor hypothesis; one is known briefly as the dominance theory, the other as overdominance. In 1917, D. F. Jones proposed the theory of linked favorable dominant genes to account for heterosis. He assumed that the genes favoring increased vigor, yield, size, etc., are dominant while the more deleterious alleles are recessive, and that each line or variety has some unfavorable as well as favorable genes. The hybrid between two varieties then has favorable dominants at the maximum number of loci since the different varieties will tend to carry different favorable and unfavorable genes.

inbred A $\times$ inbred B

P_1 $\qquad$ *aaBBccDDeeff* $\qquad$ *AAbbCCddEEFF*

F_1 $\qquad\qquad$ *AaBbCcDdEeFf*

However, the segregation at inbreeding of the F_1 will restore the homozygous recessive condition at one or more of the various loci, and in subsequent generations more and more loci will become homozygous recessive and the vigor will accordingly decline. It might seem possible to develop a line carrying only favorable dominants in the homozygous condition with vigor as great as that of the F_1 hybrid, but linkage of favorable and unfavorable genes on the same chromosome makes this virtually impossible. Even without linkage, if 20 or 30 gene pairs are involved in heterosis—probably a low estimate—it would be almost impossible to recover such a type from a population of manageable size.

It should be noted in passing that inbreeding itself is not harmful. Cleopatra, the product of generations of inbreeding among the Ptolemies, is almost sufficient by herself to confirm this statement. The only effect of inbreed-

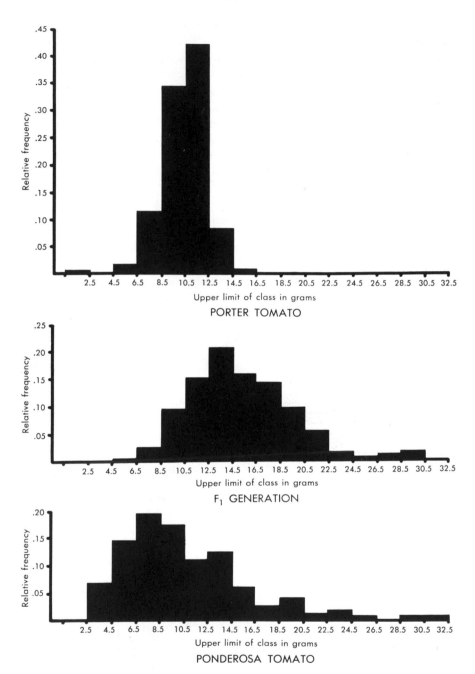

Fig. 22-3. Heterosis in tomatoes. Weight per locule in grams in Porter and Ponderosa varieties of tomatoes and in their F_1 hybrid. (Data from Powers.)

ing is to increase homozygosity. However, since it brings to light otherwise hidden deleterious recessives, the effect is generally harmful. It is highly possible that the superstitions, religious taboos, and legal restrictions about incest stem originally from its frequently dire biological consequences rather than from the more abstruse psychological damage, the latter due to fears that may well have developed after the taboos were established.

The theory of interaction of alleles, later termed overdominance, was developed by Fisher and East. The two theories may be compared as shown below:

dominance $\qquad AA \cong Aa > aa$

overdominance $\quad A_1A_1 < A_1A_2 > A_2A_2$

In the latter, the heterozygote is superior to both homozygotes. Neither A_1 nor A_2 is necessarily deleterious, but the heterozygote with two kinds of alleles is metabolically superior to either homozygote with only a single allele represented. Under this theory, heterosis is directly dependent on heterozygosity; the greater the number of heterozygous loci, the greater the heterosis. With the dominance theory, the heterosis is not directly dependent on heterozygosity, for it is possible, theoretically at least, for the homozygote to be as vigorous as the heterozygote. These two theories are not mutually exclusive, and some evidence has been adduced in support of both of them. Furthermore, it should be pointed out that a considerable portion of the observed hybrid vigor may be attributable to the complementary action of genes at different loci, brought together in favorable combinations by crossing.

In conclusion, since wild populations of all sorts are generally highly heterozygous, it is not surprising to find heterosis as a normal situation in many wild populations. Furthermore, quantitative inheritance is of particular importance in evolutionary studies because crosses between subspecies and species typically reveal polygenically controlled differences between them. Evolutionary divergence has, therefore, proceeded by means of the gradual accumulation of numerous genetic differences.

▶ *SUMMARY*

Quantitative traits such as size or weight must be measured rather than classified, and typically the frequency distribution for such a trait in a population takes the form of a normal curve. The variability is thus best described in terms of the mean and the standard deviation, but does not lend itself to simple Mendelian analysis. However, the multiple factor hypothesis, which postulates a number of genes, each of small effect, has furnished a Mendelian explanation for the behavior of quantitative traits in crosses. Hybrid vigor, or heterosis, a special aspect of quantitative inheritance, is frequently observed in the hybrid offspring of relatively inbred parents. The dominance and overdominance theories of heterosis explain heterosis as the result of the masking of deleterious recessives or of the favorable interaction of alleles, respectively. These complementary theories give a genetic explanation to the heterosis phenomenon. Quantitative traits and heterosis assume particular importance in the study of evolution since both have been shown to play a significant role in natural populations.

SUGGESTED READING

Falconer, D. S., 1960. *Introduction to quantitative genetics.* New York: Ronald.

Gowen, J. W., ed., 1952. *Heterosis.* Ames: Iowa State College Press.

Mather, K., 1949. *Biometrical genetics.* New York: Dover.

CHAPTER 23

Variation in Natural Populations

Some of the more fundamental aspects of genetics have now been discussed. Our next problem is to relate this information to natural populations and through natural populations to the question of the origin and evolution of species. Many students of evolution, ecology, paleontology, and taxonomy have long felt that the geneticist, cooped up in his laboratory with curtains drawn, raising abnormal flies in bottles, or x-raying them to produce mutations and chromosomal aberrations, could contribute very little to the understanding of phenomena in nature. The assortment of freaks that the geneticist worked with seemed to have little resemblance to the collections of individuals from natural populations that these other workers studied. Only recently has this viewpoint started to shift, as closer genetic analysis of wild populations has begun to reveal the extent of their genetic variability. Most of this variability is concealed in the form of heterozygous recessive genes, but it is, nevertheless, much greater in extent than had previously been suspected.

You would hardly need to be convinced that the human species is extremely variable, for people obviously differ in eye color, shade of hair, ear size and shape, and so on and on. However, you may hesitate before accepting the statement that natural populations, whether of mice, lice, or rice, tiger lilies or tigers, are also quite variable. Yet, wherever adequate genetic analyses have been made, natural populations have been shown to be genetically highly variable. Phenotypically, wild populations are usually quite uniform, although I have felt it necessary to qualify this last statement ever since I saw, like an apparition, an albino "gray" squirrel crossing my yard, and, while trout fishing one day on the North Shore of Lake Superior, a purple millefoil growing in the midst of a patch of the usual white type, and later, white bluebells growing in the same crevice with blue bluebells. These unusual variants, quite clearly, were genetic, and a careful survey of a wild population of any species will reveal a number of individuals phenotypically distinguishable from the usual "wild type." Since *Drosophila* is so well known genetically, it is not surprising that some of the best information of this type is derived from wild *Drosophila* populations. In *Drosophila melanogaster,* for instance, two percent of several thousand flies showed visible differences from the wild type; these affected the size, shape, or number of bristles, size, shape, or color of the eyes, wing shape or venation, and shape of the legs. On genetic testing, not all were due to mutations, but the majority were.

Genetic Analysis of Natural Populations

A more thorough analysis of the genetic variability is possible by extracting a single chromosome from a wild population and making it homozygous in order to reveal its genetic contents (see Fig. 23-1). The general method used in *Drosophila* consists of crossing a single wild male with females from a tester stock (for example, A/B) carrying a dominant mutant A to mark one chromosome and a different dominant B to mark its homologue. These dominant genes are usually lethal when homozygous. The marked chromosomes carry inversions that tend to lead to the elimination of almost all crossovers. A single male showing A and carrying only one of the two chromosomes from his wild father is selected from the F_1 and crossed again with A/B females. From among the progeny of this cross the A males and A females are taken and interbred. In all of them the homologue of the A chromosome is identical, descended from a single original wild chromosome without crossing over. In the next generation the A/A type die while of the remaining flies, $\frac{2}{3}$ will be expected to be A and $\frac{1}{3}$ wild type. However, if the chromosome being tested carries a recessive lethal, no wild-type flies will appear. Reduced viability or visible effects produced by the chromosome are readily detected. In this manner genetic analyses of individual chromosomes from wild populations have been conducted.

The analysis of a series of second chromosomes from *Drosophila* in New England, Ohio, and Florida showed that 55 percent of these chromosomes contained lethal or deleterious recessive genes, most of them at different gene loci and hence of independent origin. Many surveys of other species of *Drosophila* have produced similar results, and one such study led to the conclusion that in less than 3 percent of the flies studied was there no harmful mutation in either the second or third chromosomes. When the other three pairs of chromo-

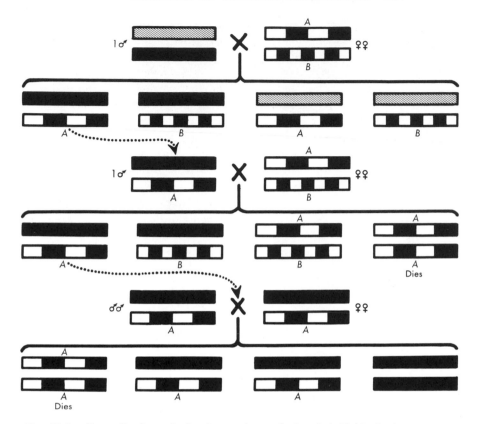

Fig. 23-1. Generalized method of genetic analysis of individual chromosomes from wild populations.

somes are taken into account, it is clear that there are practically no individuals who do not carry at least one deleterious recessive mutant gene. Since these deleterious genes are balanced by their dominant wild-type alleles, a given pair of chromosomes may carry several harmful genes that are not expressed. If the mutants are closely linked lethals, a balanced lethal system will be established,

$$\frac{+_1 \quad 1_2 \quad +_3 \quad 1_4}{1_1 \quad +_2 \quad 1_3 \quad +_4}$$

in which only the heterozygotes survive. Unless there is some means of detecting the homozygous lethal zygotes, such a balanced lethal system will appear to be a true-breeding homozygous strain.

Mutations are constantly recurring in both wild and laboratory populations, which replenish the lethals and the deleterious mutants that are being eliminated from the population by natural selection against the homozygotes. However, the harmful effects of these mutants are apparently not confined to the homozygotes, for a study of the viability of individuals heterozygous for lethals showed them on the average to be 4 percent less viable than the homozygous wild-type individuals. Thus, the damage wrought by deleterious genes due to their insidious effects on heterozygotes over a number of generations may be greater than the single genetic death of the homozygote.

One further point to be noted and perhaps emphasized is that the mutations revealed by the genetic analyses of wild populations of *Drosophila* were no different in kind from those studied by the geneticist in the laboratory for many years. Furthermore, *Drosophila* are not unique in carrying large numbers of concealed recessives; they are observed frequently in other species as well. The most striking variant I ever saw was an albino snapping turtle, but adequate sampling of any species will reveal some individuals distinctly different from the so-called "wild type." More careful study will show that the extreme types grade into less extreme types and on into quantitative differences so that the variability is in degree rather than in kind.

The phenotypic variation in wild populations has frequently been ascribed to environmental effects, and without doubt this is often true. A comparison of the growth of a field of corn during a wet summer and a dry one will reveal how great an influence the environment can have. Hence, there has been a general tendency to regard all of the differences exhibited between populations of a species living in different habitats to be nongenetic. However, when representatives from different populations are grown together under the same environmental conditions, many of the differences remain. For an example, let us consider a cinquefoil, *Potentilla glandulosa,* which grows in California. As you go inland from the Pacific, this plant is found in a variety of habitats: the Coast Range, with low elevation and a mild climate; the foothills of the Sierra Nevada with both dry slopes and open meadows and a continental climate of hot summers, cold snowy winters, and rainy springs; subalpine and alpine habitats up in the Sierras with a short growing season, cold winters, and abundant precipitation. Reciprocal transplants of individuals from each of these habitats to all of the others showed that the differences between them were hereditary. The populations had become genetically adapted to their own particular habitats, and hence, even though not far removed geographically, they belonged to different races or ecotypes. Furthermore, even though all were members of the same species, none of the lowland races could even survive in the alpine environment. See Fig. 23-2.

When the different races were crossed, no two individuals among some 1600 F_2 progeny were alike, and the minimum number of genes differentiating these races was estimated to be from 60 to 100. Such a burst of recombination indicates clearly that the genes in one race differ from their alleles in other races, and that the observed differences are not due merely to the direct effects of the different environmental forces operating on similar genotypes.

Chromosomal Variation

In addition to the genic variability existing within populations and between populations of the same species, chromosomal rearrangements are found frequently and in some cases regularly in wild populations. The most detailed study of inversions in nature has been made in the genus *Drosophila* with the inversions in the third chromosome of *D. pseudoobscura*. Many inversions, which rearrange the banded structure in the salivary chromosomes, have been identified. The different arrangements can be related to each other by the fact that one pattern can give rise to another by a single inversion. For example,

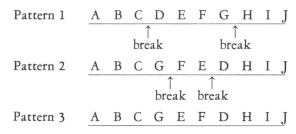

These three patterns are clearly related to each other, though 3 and 1 are not directly related but only through 2. Three sequences for their origin are possible:

$$
\begin{array}{ccc}
1 & \longrightarrow 2 & \longrightarrow 3 \\
1 & \longleftarrow 2 & \longleftarrow 3 \\
1 & \longleftarrow 2 & \longrightarrow 3
\end{array}
$$

In this manner, a phylogeny of these inversion types has been constructed, including more than 20 different inversions and two other species as well, *D. miranda* and *D. persimilis*.

Translocations are also found in natural populations, the best-studied case being the Jimson weed (*Datura stramonium*). *Datura* has 12 pairs of chromosomes, but crosses of different races give rings of 4 or 6 chromosomes rather than 12 bivalents. The cause of these rings, as we have seen, is the synapsis of chromosomes with translocations. At least 7 translocations have been identified from different races of Jimson weed, and translocations have been observed in many other species of plants and animals. The evening primrose is the most spectacular case, having translocations as a regular part of the genetic mechanism of individuals in the same population.

Natural polyploids are especially common among plants, for most genera of plants have polyploid members. In the genus *Solanum* (nightshade, potato, eggplant, and so on) the following numbers have been identified:

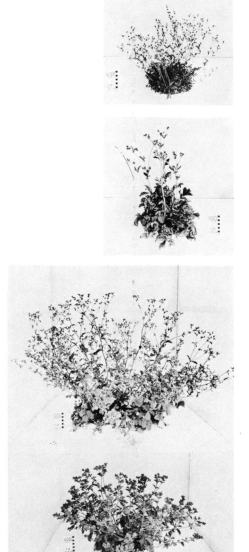

Fig. 23-2. Representatives of four subspecies or ecological races of the cinquefoil, *Potentilla glandulosa,* grown in a uniform garden at Stanford. The different races come from central California along a 200 mile transect from the coast inland into the Sierra Nevada. Races shown from west to east are: bottom row, *typica;* second row, *reflexa;* third row, *hanseni;* top row, *nevadensis.* All to the same scale. (Courtesy of Clausen and Heisey.)

$2n = 24, 36, 48, 60, 72, 96$, and 120. Polyploids are also known in such diverse groups as strawberries, grasses, lilies, spiderworts, cotton, tobacco, iris, mints, willows, and sunflowers. In these cases, the polyploids are higher multiples of some basic haploid number. In some cases, the postulated ancestry of an apparent allopolyploid has been confirmed by the experimental resynthesis of the poly-

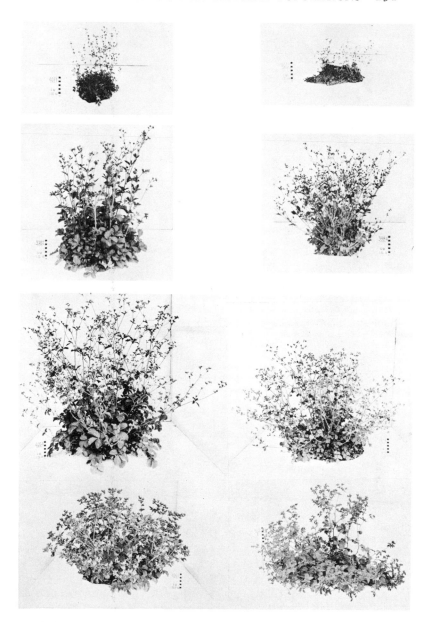

ploid from the diploid ancestors. One such case is the synthesis of the allo-polyploid *Galeopsis tetrahit* from the diploids, *G. pubescens* and *G. speciosa* (Fig. 23-3).

This brief survey should make it clear that the genic and chromosomal changes found during observation and experiment in the laboratory and in ex-

Fig. 23-3. The first successful resynthesis of a naturally occurring species, *Galeopsis tetrahit*. Shown are the ancestral diploid species, *G. speciosa* (left) and *G. pubescens* (right), and the artificial tetraploid (center) derived from them, which is indistinguishable from wild *G. tetrahit*. (Courtesy of Müntzing.)

perimental plots have their counterparts in wild populations. There is no intrinsic difference between the variations seen in the laboratory and in the field. Their nature and their causes are the same, and the study of evolution can safely be based on the knowledge about heredity and variation gained by experimentation.

SUMMARY ◄────────────────────────────────

By means of special techniques, natural populations that usually appear quite uniform can be shown to carry a sizable store of genetic variability in the heterozygous condition. Although much of the variation between individuals and between populations may be environmental, the evidence is clear that in most cases there is a genetic component as well, especially when the populations are living under different ecological conditions. In addition to genic differences, chromosomal variation frequently forms a characteristic part of the hereditary variability of a species. Thus, for example, in many species translocation or inversion heterozygotes are routinely found, and many plants are clearly polyploid in origin.

SUGGESTED READING

Darwin, C., 1872. *The origin of species.* New York: Mentor Books (1958).

Dobzhansky, Th., 1951. *Genetics and the origin of species,* 3d ed. New York: Columbia University Press.

Mayr, E., 1942. *Systematics and the origin of species.* New York: Columbia University Press.

Stebbins, G. L., 1950. *Variation and evolution in plants.* New York: Columbia University Press.

CHAPTER *24*

Genetics of Populations

Evolution has been termed "descent with modification," by Darwin. Further consideration is needed to clarify this concept. The first question to answer is "What is it that evolves?" It is not the individual, for the individual lives and dies with a fixed genotype that does not change; rather, the species is the evolving unit. Even without a formal definition of a species, it is nevertheless clear that a species consists of a number of individuals; it is a population, and evolution is a population phenomenon. For evolutionary change to occur, a population with one set of hereditary characteristics must in some way give rise to a population with a different set of hereditary characteristics. Since inherited traits are controlled by the genes, evolution can be redefined as a change in the kinds or frequencies of genes in populations. The problem then becomes to discover how the frequency of a gene already existing in the population may change, or how new types of genes, originating by mutation, become incorporated into the population. In order to study the genetics of a population, it is necessary to consider it, not as a group of individuals, but rather as a pool of genes from which individuals draw their genotypes and to which they in turn contribute their genes to form the pool for the next generation.

Up to this point we have been concerned with gene effects in individuals and with the results of controlled matings between individuals of specified genotypes. Most knowledge and prediction in genetics is based on this type of experimentation. The problem now, however, is to consider the operation of heredity in a natural variable population of freely interbreeding

234

individuals. How are the genes present in the members of such a Mendelian population transmitted and distributed to succeeding generations? In order to understand an extremely complex situation, it is best to study it in its simplest possible terms. By restricting our attention to the bare essentials of events at a single gene locus, we can discover the underlying principles. Once established, there is no reason to suppose that these basic principles do not hold in the more complex as well as in the simple cases.

The Hardy-Weinberg Equilibrium

Let us consider first what happens in a population in which selection, mutation, and other evolutionary forces are not operating. In man, the ability to taste phenylthiocarbamide (PTC) is inherited as a simple dominant. Tasters of PTC are, then, of two genotypes, TT or Tt; nontasters are homozygous recessive, tt. Since very few persons are aware of either their genotype or phenotype, marriages occur at random with respect to this trait. People do not ask their potential mates whether they like PTC, for they simply do not care. There is, therefore, neither preference nor avoidance of a mate because of his PTC sensitivities, and mating on this score is said to be at random.

There is no simple answer to the question of how frequent tasters and nontasters should be in a human population. There will be no classical 3 : 1 Mendelian ratio, nor will the dominant tasters necessarily be more frequent than the recessive nontasters, for there is no known selective advantage of one type over the other. A population may contain any proportion of tasters and nontasters, depending on the frequencies of the dominant and recessive genes. In a population of 100 people there will be, since they are diploid, 200 genes at the taster locus. Let us suppose that there are 20 TT, 40 Tt, and 40 tt. The frequency of gene T is $p = \dfrac{40+40}{200} = .4$. The frequency of gene t is $q = \dfrac{40+80}{200} = .6$. If there are 10 TT, 60 Tt, and 30 tt, $p = \dfrac{20+60}{200} = .4$ and $q = \dfrac{60+60}{200} = .6$. Hence, even though the distribution of these genes in individual genotypes is different, their frequencies in the two populations are identical. If mating is at random in the former population, the different types of matings will occur in proportion to the frequency of the various genotypes as shown below.

♂ ♀	TT .2	Tt .4	tt .4
TT .2	$TT = .04$	$TT = .04$ $Tt = .04$	$Tt = .08$
Tt .4	$TT = .04$ $Tt = .04$	$TT = .04$ $Tt = .08$ $tt = .04$	$Tt = .08$ $tt = .08$
tt .4	$Tt = .08$	$Tt = .08$ $tt = .08$	$tt = .16$

Summing up, we find $TT = .16$
$Tt = .48$
$tt = .36$
and still $p = .16 + .24 = .4$
and $q = .36 + .24 = .6$

But this method is too cumbersome. If mating is truly random, then the combination of gametes is at random, and it is possible to deal directly with gene frequencies in the gametes to obtain the same result.

♂ ♀	$p = f(T)$ .4	$q = f(t)$ .6
p .4	$p^2 = .16$	$pq = .24$
q .6	$pq = .24$	$q^2 = .36$

$$p^2 + 2pq + q^2 = 1$$
$$.16 + .48 + .36 = 1$$
$$(TT) \quad (Tt) \quad (tt)$$

Furthermore, it should now be clear that even the checkerboard is unnecessary, for the relation between gene frequency and genotype frequency can be expressed as the binominal $(p + q)^2 = 1$. From the binominal expansion, it is clear that in a large random mating population not only the gene frequencies but also the genotype frequencies will remain constant. In a random mating population with $p = .4$ and $q = .6$, the equilibrium frequencies will be $TT = 16$ percent, $Tt = 48$ percent, and $tt = 36$ percent.

It should be noted that if only the frequency of the homozygous recessive class is known, the frequency of the recessive gene can be calculated. For example, if 9 percent of a human population has red hair, then

$$f(rr) = q^2 = 0.09$$
$$f(r) = q = \sqrt{.09} = 0.3$$
$$f(R) = p = 1 - q = 0.7$$
$$f(RR) = p^2 = 0.49$$
$$f(Rr) = 2pq = 2(.3)(.7) = 0.42$$

Also, if $D = f(RR)$

$$H = f(Rr)$$
$$R = f(rr)$$

Then $p = \dfrac{D + \frac{1}{2}H}{D + H + R}$

and $q = \dfrac{R + \frac{1}{2}H}{D + H + R}$

Thus can the entire population be described. Perhaps the most surprising fact to emerge is that 42 percent of a random mating population must be heterozygous carriers of the recessive gene that is expressed homozygously in only 9 percent of the population. This disparity becomes even greater for the less frequent recessives. For instance, if $q^2 = 0.01$, $2pq = 0.18$; if $q^2 = 0.0001$, $2pq = 0.0198$.

This equilibrium is known as the Hardy-Weinberg equilibrium, after the men who independently derived the equation and understood its implications. To state the law more explicitly, in a large, randomly mating population, in the absence of mutation and selection, the relative frequencies of the genes will tend to remain constant from generation to generation. Darwin, because of his belief in blending inheritance, thought that variability decreased each generation and had to be constantly replenished. However, from the Hardy-Weinberg equation, it is clear that so long as TT, Tt, and tt survive and reproduce equally, the variability in the population will be unchanged, and the equilibrium then is a conservative factor in evolution. In fact, evolution can now be redefined quite simply as a shift in the Hardy-Weinberg equilibrium. The factors responsible for bringing about such shifts are mutation, natural selection, migration or gene flow, and random genetic drift, each of which we shall consider in greater detail here and in following chapters.

Mutation

Let us first examine the effects of mutation on gene frequencies. Suppose that T mutates to t at the rate of 1 in 10,000 gametes per generation. Mutation can then be said to be causing an increase in the frequency of t, for the proportions of T and t are changing. In due time, if no other force intervenes, no T genes would be left at all, and the entire population would be tt. Such a change would be very slow and very unlikely, but theoretically mutation pressure alone could bring about evolution, in this case eliminating the taster gene.

However, reverse mutations also can occur, usually at different rates. Suppose that t mutates to T at the rate of 5 per 100,000.

Let
$$u = T \;\rightarrow\; t = 0.00010$$
$$v = t \;\rightarrow\; T = 0.00005$$

Then the change in frequency of T (Δp) will equal the net change brought about by these opposed mutation rates.

$$\text{increase in } T = vq$$
$$\underline{\text{decrease in } T = up}$$
$$\Delta p = vq - up$$

Since the reverse mutations are occurring, the population can never become homozygous for one type of allele. Hence, an equilibrium will be established at the point where the number of mutations from $T{\rightarrow}t$ just equals the number of mutations from $t{\rightarrow}T$; in other words, when $\Delta p = vq - up = 0$. This equation can then be transformed as follows:

$$vq = up$$
$$v(1 - p) = up$$
$$v - vp = up$$
$$up + vp = v$$
$$p(u + v) = v$$
$$\hat{p} = \frac{v}{u + v}$$

It should be noted that the equilibrium value of p is dependent only on the mutation rates and is independent of the initial gene frequencies, which may range anywhere then from $p = 0$ to $p = 1$. For the rates given above,

$$\hat{p} = \frac{0.00005}{0.00010 + 0.00005} = 0.333$$

$$\hat{q} = 0.667$$

Thus, there will be twice as many recessive t genes mutating half as often as the dominant T genes, and the result is an equilibrium since the absolute numbers of mutations are equal.

Even though evolutionary change due to the action of mutation pressure is theoretically possible, the course of evolution is not controlled to any great extent by mutation. Mutation is a limiting factor rather than a controlling factor in evolution.

SUMMARY ◄──

The frequency of a gene may be defined as the proportion that a given allele forms of the total of all the different kinds of alleles at this locus in the population. Random mating occurs when any male in a population has an equal chance of mating with any female. Hardy and Weinberg showed that in a large, randomly mating population, in the absence of mutation and selection, the gene frequencies will remain constant, and the genetic variability thus is conserved. However, if mutations occur, mutation pressure will tend to cause shifts in gene frequency. Where reverse mutations also occur, a new equilibrium will be established that is solely determined by the mutation rates.

SUGGESTED READING

Cold Spring Harbor Symp. Quant. Biol., Vol. 20, 1955. "Population genetics." Long Island Biological Assn., New York.

Haldane, J. B. S., 1932. *The causes of evolution.* New York: Harper.

Lerner, I. M., 1950. *Population genetics and animal improvement.* New York: Cambridge University Press.

Li, C. C., 1955. *Population genetics.* Chicago: University of Chicago Press.

CHAPTER 25

Natural Selection

The primary factor controlling the course of evolution is natural selection. We have already discussed the Darwinian concept of natural selection, which assumed a population more or less stable numerically with a reproductive rate far higher than necessary to ensure the maintenance of the population's size. Because the population is variable, the ensuing deaths occur more frequently among the less well-adapted individuals, and the better adapted types survive. Darwin placed emphasis on predation and on competition, and to many, natural selection came to signify a concept of nature, red in tooth and claw. Another aspect of Darwinism, neglected in recent years, was his concept of sexual selection due either to male competition or female preference.

The modern concept of natural selection involves a subtle change in emphasis from differential survival to differential reproduction. From the standpoint of evolution, it matters little whether an individual survives to the age of 2 or to 102; if he dies without offspring, his genes are lost from the population. Any and all factors that bring about differential reproduction—the production of more progeny by one hereditary type in proportion to its numbers than by the other types—are factors in natural selection. Included among these factors are survival and longevity, fertility and fecundity, competition and cooperation, disease and parasite resistance, food requirements, physiological tolerances, sexual selection, color patterns, behavior patterns, and so on and on. To the extent that any of these factors, trivial or major, affects reproductive fitness, they have adaptive value; and to the extent that the differences are controlled by genes, the favorable genes will increase in frequency while the less favorable genes will decline in frequency each generation. The net effect is the production of organisms well adapted to survive in their particular environments. Since many, many selective pressures operate, it is clear that the organism must make some adjustment to all of them. Hence, the final phenotypes are compromises that permit the organism to make the best possible adjustment to all the various selection pressures, but no one adaptation is apt to be perfect. Natural selection, then, brings about adaptation; it may be to a changing environment, or it may be an improvement in the existing adaptations to a fairly stable environment. Evolution may thus be thought of also as successive or perhaps in some cases progressive adaptation.

A great deal has been written about the theory of natural selection. It has been hailed as a monumental advance, but it has also been severely criticized and even regarded as completely erroneous. We cannot hope to pursue all of the avenues open to discussion, but we can point out that the basis of many of the objections seems to be the difficulty in visualizing how such enormously complex systems as the human eye, the electric organ in fishes, the insect societies, and the adaptively appropriate patterns of instinctive behavior could have arisen as the result of gradual changes emanating from such an apparently simple process as differential reproduction. The fault, however, lies more with the imagination than with the process of natural selection, for selection almost inevitably tends toward the improvement of adaptation, and these examples represent some sort of adaptive pinnacle. Although a detailed history of the origin of many of the more bizarre adaptations is not yet possible, it is by no means impossible that this history may eventually be learned.

That natural selection gave rise to a brutal concept of nature made the theory of natural selection distasteful or even unacceptable to many people. The idea of competition or the struggle for existence was regarded as a threat to any higher concept of man or of nature. Distasteful or not, predation, competition, and parasitism are biological facts of life. Anyone who has spent any time in the field realizes that death is a very casual, commonplace affair among living things. Predators live at the expense of their prey; parasites, though less demanding, at the expense of their hosts. Members of the same species may compete for food, space, light, or other essentials. In fact, intraspecific competition may be even more severe than the competition between different species. In a crowded group of seedlings only a few will survive the competition for light and space. This contest is bloodless but fatal nonetheless to the losers. Similarly, under crowded conditions the growth of small tadpoles is inhibited by the presence of larger tadpoles of the same species, and they eventually die despite the presence of abundant food. We may be repelled by the garter snake that engulfs a living leopard frog inch by inch, or by the leech that drains its blood, leaving it in a moribund condition, but this is their normal way of life. Thus natural selection does involve a struggle for existence, and attempts to gloss over this fact do an injustice to the concept.

On the other hand, to regard selection as nothing more than a bitter struggle to survive is just as erroneous, for biological success depends on many factors in addition to escaping death. Cooperative behavior may also contribute to reproductive fitness, and may increase as the result of natural selection. Care of the young in birds and mammals, division of labor in colonial species such as protozoans, coelenterates, and insects, and the complex group behavior of fishes, birds, and mammals have all arisen during the course of evolution. In most cases they clearly are adaptive and contribute directly or indirectly to reproductive fitness, and therefore must have been favored by and developed under the influence of natural selection. Thus, natural selection must be regarded as being responsible not only for the unending struggle for existence but also for many of the forms of altruistic behavior. In some of these cases, the behavior has dire consequences for the individual—for example, the bee, which dies once it has stung an invader—but if the chances of survival of the colony are thereby improved, this behavior will be favored by selection.

Natural selection in itself does not admit of being judged as good or evil. We may regard its consequences as either good or bad, but they flow from the sole criterion in selection, reproductive fitness. Those factors, whatever their nature, that increase fitness will tend to be favored by natural selection; those decreasing it will tend to be eliminated.

Artificial Selection

Since there are sometimes questions or doubts as to the efficacy of selection, it may be well to consider some examples of the operation of selection. A magnified, if somewhat distorted, view of evolution is obtained from an examination of the results obtained by artificial selection. The changes wrought by man in developing new breeds are, strictly speaking, evolutionary changes, since a population with a new set of hereditary traits is derived from an ancestral population; but they are on a small scale and are directed toward man's benefit or amusement rather than that of the species. Certainly no dachshund or Pekingese would be likely to consider himself especially well equipped to make a go of it on his own. A well-documented history of the development of a new breed of animals is that of the Santa Gertrudis cattle on the fabulous King Ranch in Texas. The ranch is in southern Texas where ordinary beef cattle—such breeds as Shorthorn, Aberdeen Angus, and Hereford—did not thrive in the semitropical rather arid climate, for they were bothered by the heat and ticks and did not grow well on the available grasses. The Brahma cattle of India thrived in this climate, but were of poor quality. Crosses and back-crosses of Shorthorn and

Brahma, accompanied by selection for the desired beef qualities and ability to withstand the climate, ultimately produced a population with approximately $\frac{7}{8}$ of its gene pool derived from the Shorthorns and $\frac{1}{8}$ from the Brahmas (see Fig. 25-1). This new breed is heat and tick resistant and gains better on grass feeding than any other breed. A couple of footnotes may be added to this story. Dissatisfied with the type of grass on their range, the owners of the King Ranch developed new varieties of grass and reseeded vast areas of the ranch with the improved type. Furthermore, their success in selecting and breeding horses for their ability to run faster than other horses has paid off at the Kentucky Derby and elsewhere. The success of breeders in all instances is due basically to changing the frequencies or types of genes and gene combinations in the population of animals or plants with which they are working. These changes, secured by artificial selection, are brought about by the differential reproduction of the favored types.

Selection for Resistance

The Santa Gertrudis cattle have been developed within the past 50 years, and many other evolutionary changes in this interval can be cited. The introduction of chemotherapeutic agents and antibiotics was followed by the origin of strains of bacteria that were resistant to these agents; for instance, strains resistant to the various sulfas, terramycin, aureomycin, penicillin, and streptomycin are known. Moreover, strains of bacteria actually dependent on streptomycin for normal growth have been discovered. These changes are the result of the drug having killed all of the microorganisms except those carrying mutations to resistance, which then become progenitors of the resistant strains. The mutations have been shown to be random and not produced as a specific result of treatment by the antibiotic, for by suitable techniques, mutations to resistance have been isolated in bacteria never exposed to the antibiotic at all. These facts lead to caution in hailing any new wonder drug as the final solution for any particular disease, for the possibility always exists that the disease organism will mutate to resistance. Furthermore, the indiscriminate use of any antibiotic is inadvisable simply because it will increase the frequency of the resistant mutants in the bacterial population and make the disease more difficult to control if most infections are due to resistant rather than susceptible organisms. Therapy has been directed toward using combinations of drugs, since the chances of independent mutations to resistance to two or more antibiotics in a single bacterial cell are vanishingly slight.

Hydrogen cyanide is commonly thought of as one of the deadliest poisons, yet resistant strains of the scale insects attacking citrus fruits have evolved. Similarly, the widespread use of DDT caused in insect populations a selection pressure that led to the development of resistant strains of mosquitos,

Fig. 25-1. The genesis of a new breed of beef cattle. Hybridization between Brahmas (above), Shorthorns (center) followed by selection produced the Santa Gertrudis breed (below). (Courtesy of Snyder and David.)

house flies, and body lice. They have appeared in many different parts of the world, often within two or three years of the introduction of DDT.

Bacteriophages are viruses that attack and destroy bacteria. Bacteria that are resistant to phage can arise by mutation, but the virus can also mutate to forms able to attack the previously resistant bacteria. A similar situation exists in wheat-stem rust. As plant breeders develop new varieties of wheat that are resistant to the currently prevalent strains of rust, new mutant strains able to attack the resistant wheat increase sharply in frequency until a new outbreak of stem rust occurs. The plant breeder must try to keep one jump ahead, but as things stand, he is not likely to work himself out of a job. These situations involving two different species are more complex because both host and pathogen (the disease-causing agent) are capable of evolution, and each exerts a selective pressure on the other.

The Baldwin Effect

A great deal still remains to be learned about the ways in which natural selection operates to bring about adaptation, for it is a subtle as well as a powerful force. Furthermore, the appeal of Lamarckianism has persisted because it has seemed that many of the more remarkable adaptations could have arisen only in direct response to the environment or to the needs of the organism rather than by the operation of natural selection on random mutations. Some recent experiments by Waddington on what is known as the Baldwin effect have been most revealing. A number of wild-type fruit flies were subjected to temperature shock during development. As a result of this treatment some of these flies were crossveinless. The crossveinless condition of the wings was not due to mutations induced by the heat treatment, however, for untreated progeny of these flies were wild type and could be shown not to carry a crossveinless mutation. Such an environmentally induced condition that simulates the phenotype of a genetic mutant is known as a *phenocopy*. Nevertheless, the crossveinless flies were bred together, the offspring given heat shock during development, and the crossveinless offspring again selected and interbred over a period of several generations. After about 15 generations of selection, the heat treatment was discontinued, but crossveinless flies still continued to appear in these stocks.

At first thought, this result seems clearly to indicate Lamarckian inheritance of acquired characteristics. Actually it does not, but it may serve to reconcile to some extent Lamarckianism with the theory of natural selection. In the first place, the initial wild-type stock had not been selected or inbred and was therefore undoubtedly heterozygous. Among this array of genotypes were some that could produce the crossveinless phenotype, but only under the unusual environmental conditions provided by the temperature shock. When these genes were brought to expression, selection then became possible. Experiments with the crossveinless stock resulting from selection showed that the crossveinless condition was controlled by polygenes or multiple factors rather than by a single gene locus. Therefore, selection over a number of generations had simply increased the frequency of these genes in the population to the point where individual genotypes carried enough of them to cause the crossveinless phenotype even in the absence of temperature shock. In other words, it could be said that selection had lowered the threshold for crossveinless. It should be noted that even the ability to produce the so-called phenocopies was not independent of the genotype. In these experiments, a mechanism has been revealed by which the responses of individuals to new environmental pressures have been incorporated through natural selection into the population as a whole. Thus could the transition from individual physiological adaptation to population genetic adaptation be made. The distinction between these two types of adaptation is obviously not clear-cut, because, just as the adaptation of a population to its environment is determined by its genetic composition, the adaptive responses possible to an individual are also controlled by his genotype. Therefore, even though many adaptive changes may appear Lamarckian, they may nevertheless have a completely reasonable explanation under the theory of natural selection.

The Theory of Selection

With these examples in mind, let us now consider the way in which gene frequencies change because of selection. The theory of selection is very simple. Suppose that A and a alleles are present in a population with equal frequency, but that only 99 a genes are transmitted to the next generation for every 100 A. The recessive a gene is therefore at a slight selective disadvantage to the dominant. The selection coefficient, s, is a measure of this disadvantage and is obtained as follows:

$$\frac{1 - s}{1} = \frac{99}{100}$$

$$s = 0.01$$

Most selection pressures operate on the diploid or zygote phase rather than on the haploid or gametic stage. A common type of zygotic selection is that against deleterious recessive homozygotes with the homozygous dominants and the heterozygotes equally viable. For this situation the change in frequency of the dominant A gene is calculated as follows:

genotype	AA	Aa	aa	total
frequency before selection	p^2	$2pq$	q^2	1
frequency after selection	p^2	$2pq$	$q^2(1 - s)$	$1 - sq^2$

Here, s measures the selective disadvantage of the aa type.

$$\Delta p = p_1 - p \qquad\qquad p = f(A) \text{ in generation } 0$$

$$p_1 = \frac{p^2 + pq}{1 - sq^2} \qquad\qquad p_1 = f(A) \text{ in generation } 1$$

$$\Delta p = \frac{p^2 + pq}{1 - sq^2} - p = \frac{spq^2}{1 - sq^2}$$

If sq^2 is small, the denominator is essentially equal to 1, and further simplification is possible to

$$\Delta p = spq^2$$

If s, p, or q is small, selection will act only very slowly. Therefore, selection pressures are most effective at intermediate gene frequencies. From the equation it is clear that selection will have no effect at all if s, p, or q equals zero. In other words, one allele must have a selective advantage and both alleles must be present in the population for selection to operate. Hence, selection is ineffective in a homozygous population, no matter how great the environmental variation may be. As early as 1910, Johannsen showed experimentally the futility of selection on environmental variation. As a result, Darwin's ideas on selection have been modified and clarified, for he did not make a clear distinction between hereditary and environmental variation and believed natural selection could act on both. He was inclined to accept Lamarckian inheritance of acquired characters, though at times he also seemed to have some reservations about the possibility that environmentally induced changes could become hereditary.

If selection is directed against a deleterious dominant, the gene is expressed and exposed to selection in both AA and Aa individuals. If no dominant individual leaves progeny, the gene will be eliminated except for new mutations, in a generation. Even if selection is not complete, it is still very effective, for all of the dominant genes are exposed to selection. It is for this reason that deleterious dominant mutations are so rarely observed in wild populations, and a fair proportion of those seen arise from new mutations.

On the other hand, selection against a harmful recessive gene is considerably less effective. The gene is carried by both Aa and aa, but the full force of selection acts only on the aa individuals. Since the defective homozygotes aa are normally less frequent than the heterozygotes Aa, the frequencies being as q^2 (aa) is to $2pq$ (Aa), a large proportion of the deleterious recessives are not exposed to selection. Furthermore, the less frequent a becomes, the greater the proportion of the recessives carried by the heterozygotes, and hence the less effective selection becomes. Even recessive lethals may be present in a fairly high frequency, for when no recessive homozygotes survive or reproduce, affected individuals will continue to appear as the offspring of heterozygous normal parents.

Selection and Mutation

If selection against an unfavorable recessive were to continue over a long period of time, eventually the recessive might be expected to be eliminated entirely from the population. However, recurrent mutation will periodically add additional recessives to the population before the recessive is completely gone. The forces of selection pressure and mutation pressure will therefore tend to be opposed under these circumstances, and an equilibrium between these opposing forces will be established. Since

$$\Delta p = spq^2 - up$$

where spq^2 is the effect of zygotic selection against the homozygous recessive aa and u is the mutation rate from A to a, then at equilibrium

$$\Delta p = spq^2 - up = 0$$
$$spq^2 = up$$

and
$$\hat{q}^2 = \frac{u}{s}$$

Thus the frequency of appearance of the homozygous recessive type aa ($\hat{q}^2$) is determined by the relationship between the mutation rate and the selection coefficient. In the case of a recessive lethal s equals 1, and $\hat{q}^2 = u$ directly. For example, if one person in 40,000 dies owing to a homozygous recessive lethal condition, the mutation rate to the recessive also equals 1/40,000. Moreover, $q = 1/200$, $p = 199/200$, and $2pq$, the frequency of the heterozygotes (Aa), equals 398/40,000, or approximately 1 percent. Thus even though the gene is lethal, less than 1 percent of these lethal genes are exposed to selection each generation, and their frequency in the population may remain surprisingly high.

Evolutionary change comes about, then, as a result of the joint effects of mutation and natural selection. New kinds of genes originate in a population by mutation and may increase in frequency because of either recurrent mutation or chance events, for selection is relatively ineffective at extremely low gene frequencies. As gene frequencies increase, selection becomes increasingly important in determining the ultimate fate of the genes in the population. Without the genetic variability originally supplied by mutation, natural selection is powerless to operate. Without the sifting and winnowing of natural selection, mutation pressures would soon reduce a population to an array of freaks.

SUMMARY ◄───────────────────────────────────

The essence of natural selection is differential reproduction. Thus, many factors in addition to survival may be significant. Natural selection is the mechanism through which adaptation is achieved, for the better adapted individuals leave proportionately more offspring. The concept of natural selection as a "struggle for existence" or "the survival of the fittest," though correct in many cases, is incomplete, since cooperative behavior or even altruism may also be developed by natural selection if they contribute to reproductive fitness. The efficacy of selection can be demonstrated in domesticated species as well as in natural populations. Perhaps the most unusual example was the work on the Baldwin effect, which demonstrated that an apparently Lamarckian change could be explained within the existing theoretical framework. Selection can be effective only in heterozygous populations, and is thus without effect on environmental variation. Selection against dominant genes will be considerably more successful than against recessives, since the recessives in the heterozygous condition are not exposed to selection. Ordinarily, selection pressures and mutation pressures are opposed, and an equilibrium between the origin of new genes through mutation and their elimination by selection is achieved.

SUGGESTED READING

Darwin, C., 1872. *The origin of species.* New York: Mentor Books (1958).

Dobzhansky, Th., 1951. *Genetics and the origin of species,* 3d ed. New York: Columbia University Press.

Fisher, R. A., 1930. *The genetical theory of natural selection.* Oxford: Clarendon Press. (Also Dover, New York.)

Lerner, I. M., 1958. *The genetic basis of selection.* New York: Wiley.

───, 1959. "The concept of natural selection: a centennial view," *Proc. Amer. Philosophical Society, 103*(2):173-182.

Muller, H. J., 1949. "The Darwinian and modern conceptions of natural selection," *Proc. Amer. Philosophical Society, 93*(6):459-470.

Schmalhausen, I. I., 1949. *Factors of evolution. The theory of stabilizing selection.* (I. Dordick, tr.). Philadelphia: Blakiston.

Sheppard, P. M., 1958. *Natural selection and heredity.* London: Hutchinson.

CHAPTER 26

Polymorphism

If natural selection constantly causes the elimination of the less fit, in time a population might be expected to consist solely of the best adapted type. In reality, such a situation seldom if ever exists, for despite the constant pressure of natural selection, wild populations continue to have considerable genetic variability, a fact already discussed in an earlier chapter. Now we must consider in more detail how this variability is maintained.

A population is said to be *polymorphic* when two or more distinct types of individuals coexist in the same breeding population. Ford has limited this definition further by saying that the forms must exist in such proportions that the rarest is not being retained in the population merely by recurrent mutation. However, this added restriction is not particularly useful, for it presupposes a knowledge of the mutation rates in natural populations that is rarely available, and it cannot easily be applied except by inference. Polymorphism is used with respect to what we have earlier called discontinuous traits rather than for continuous variation. These traits may be morphological, in which case they are generally controlled by two or more alleles of a gene of major effect, and therefore present no difficulty in classification. They may also be chromosomal; the various inversion types in *Drosophila pseudoobscura* mentioned earlier represent a case of chromosomal polymorphism. Furthermore, human populations are not only polymorphic for many morphological traits, but they are also polymorphic for the blood groups. Thus, whether polymorphism is open to study depends to some extent on whether suitable methods for its detection have been devised. Chromosomal and blood group differences are clearly discontinuous, but they became subjects of research only after cytological and serological techniques for their detection had been developéd.

The definition is intended to exclude such differences as are observed between geographical races. The differences between members of the same species that belong to different breeding populations living in separate areas are said to be *polytypic*. Different races of birds may overwinter in the same region and thus coexist for a time, but this situation cannot be termed polymorphism, for the races are still members of separate breeding populations. More will be said later about the origin of polytypic differences in races, but at this point we shall concentrate on polymorphism.

In the chapter on selection we have already seen that an equilibrium may be established between mutation pressure and selection pressure. Thus the polymorphism observed in a population may be due simply to the balance between the forces of mutation and selection. Furthermore, the Hardy-Weinberg equilibrium is established when the various genotypes all have the same selective value or are adaptively neutral. Proof of adaptive neutrality is virtually impossible since a demonstration that no selective advantage exists under one set of genetic and environmental conditions is no proof that it might not exist under somewhat different circumstances. The possible variations in conditions being almost limitless, pursuit of adaptive neutrality is like chasing a will o' the wisp. Nevertheless, it remains a possibility not to be ignored, especially since the genes may be neutral except under quite specific conditions. However, many cases of polymorphism are adaptive and clearly involve more than these relatively simple types of equilibria. For this reason polymorphism has assumed a significant place in evolutionary studies.

Transient Polymorphism

Two additional types of polymorphism have been identified, *transient* and *balanced*. *Transient polymorphism* exists during the period when a new or previously rare mutant becomes advantageous and spreads through the population. During its spread, an obvious but transient polymorphism will exist. It is transient because the new form will eventually (except for mutation) replace the old. *Balanced polymorphism* exists when selection actively maintains more than one type in a population. A variety of types of balanced polymorphism has been discovered. Because of their very nature, balanced polymorphisms will be more common than examples of transient polymorphism.

The most carefully studied case of transient polymorphism is the phenomenon known as *industrial melanism,* which has been observed in at least 70 species of moths in England and on the continent of Europe. Although otherwise they may be quite different, all of these moths normally rest in exposed places, depending for protection on their cryptic coloration, a mottled pattern that blends in with a background of bark or lichen. The industrial revolution of the past century and a half has had a profound effect on the countryside in industrial regions. The smoke and soot from thousands of chimneys have coated trees and shrubs for miles around. As a consequence the background on which the moths now must rest in industrial areas is much darker than it was over a century ago. A remarkable change in these species has led to the replacement of the typical mottled forms by much darker melanic forms in the industrial areas. In some species (for example, the peppered moth, *Biston betularia*) the fre-

Fig. 26-1. Left: dark and light forms of the peppered moth (*Biston betularia*) on the trunk of an oak at the industrial city of Birmingham, England. Right: dark and light forms of the peppered moth on the lichen-coated trunk of an oak in an unpolluted region. (Courtesy of Kettlewell.)

quency of the melanic types has reached over 95 percent in many populations. Kettlewell has shown that in industrial regions the melanic type is much less likely to be taken by birds than the typical mottled moths, but that in unpolluted country the melanic form is quite conspicuous and is subject to heavier predation by birds than are moths with the typical pattern (see Fig. 26-1). There are also indications that the melanic moths may differ in viability or behavior from the typical form.

In virtually all of the species the transition has been due to the increase in frequency of dominant mutant genes for melanism even though recessive mutants and systems of multiple factors are also known to cause increased melanin production in at least some of these species. Since the various kinds of black moths were all rather rare prior to the industrial revolution, it is quite clear that natural selection has operated specifically to bring about this phenotypic transition through the dominant mutants rather than through some other genetic mechanism. Although other reasons for the utilization of dominants have been suggested, the most obvious was given many years ago by Haldane, who showed that in a randomly mating population a rare dominant will increase in frequency when favored by selection much more rapidly than will a rare recessive or a rare polygenic system. The reasons for this fact are quite simple. All of the dominant mutants are exposed to selection and hence when selection pressure shifts to favor the dominants, half of their progeny will carry and express the dominant in the next generation and will again be favored by natural selection. Rare recessive individuals, though also favored by selection because of their phenotype, will seldom leave progeny like themselves since most of their matings will be with wild-type individuals, and the favored recessive mutant will be submerged in the heterozygous condition in the population until by chance in future generations two recessives again combine in a single individual. Selection will ordinarily work even less effectively to increase the frequency of rare favorable polygenic systems, since they are constantly being broken up by genetic recombination. Thus, it is not at all surprising that even though various genetic mechanisms causing melanism must have been available in these species, the one almost invariably selected was the dominant mutant.

Although industrial melanism in moths is probably the most closely studied case of adaptive polymorphism involving dominant mutant genes, many other examples of polymorphism involving dominants to the wild type can be cited. Melanism in the hamster (*Cricetus cricetus*), color patterns in the grouse locust (*Apotettix eurycephalus*), in the platyfish (*Platypoecilus maculatus*), in ladybird beetles (*Coccinellidae*), and in frogs (*burnsi* and *kandiyohi* mutants in *Rana pipiens*) are all controlled by dominant genes and have relatively high frequencies in natural populations. In domesticated plants such as barley, oats, wheat, flax, cotton, cabbage, and tomatoes many cases of disease resistance controlled by simple dominant mutations can be cited. Furthermore, resistance to subtertian malaria in man has been shown to be increased in individuals heterozygous for the sickle cell gene. All of these examples—and more could be cited —suggest that dominant mutations may play a significant role not only in polymorphism but in evolution as well.

The Origin of Dominance

Thus far, we have taken dominance and recessiveness more or less for granted although we have discussed the fact that dominance is not exclusively a property of a particular gene, but may be modified by the rest of the genotype and by both the internal and external environment in which the gene functions.

At this point it seems advisable to raise the question of the origin of dominance. Several hypotheses have been advanced, and it seems likely that no one theory is correct and the others wrong, but rather that each contains some elements of truth.

Bateson and Punnett were the first to suggest a theory of dominance when they proposed that the recessive condition was due to the absence of the dominant. This simple presence-absence concept became untenable after the discovery of dominant effects due to deficiencies, of reverse mutations from recessive to dominant, and of multiple alleles.

Fisher pointed out that the great majority of mutants that occur are deleterious and are recessive to the "normal" or "wild-type" alleles found in natural populations, and he thus framed the question in terms of the origin of dominance of wild-type genes. He further noted that mutations are recurrent and frequent enough so that a given mutant will be regularly reintroduced into a population even though it is deleterious. He assumed that the very first time a particular mutation occurs, the heterozygote will be phenotypically intermediate between the two homozygotes. Dominance will then arise as the result of the selection of modifying factors at other loci that push the expression of the intermediate heterozygote toward that of the homozygous wild type.

Several difficulties in this theory should be pointed out. The assumption of an initially intermediate heterozygote is in a sense gratuitous, for it is actually part of what must be proven. Furthermore, the theory offers no adequate explanation for the appearance of the occasional recurrent deleterious mutant that is dominant to the wild type. Wright has also estimated that heterozygotes will be so infrequent and the selective advantage so slight that the selection pressures will be too small to be a controlling factor in the fixation of modifiers. In addition, the modifiers will have other primary effects of their own, and their ultimate frequency will depend more on the action of selection with respect to these primary effects than it will on their effects on the dominance of some other gene.

As an alternative to Fisher's theory of modifiers Wright suggested a physiological theory of dominance. He noted that the normal or wild-type genes are functional, but deleterious mutants represent a partial or complete inactivation of the gene. Dominance then results because the wild-type allele, which is active, will be expressed in the presence of the deleterious mutant, which is not. The genes are presumed to control the formation of enzymes, which catalyze chemical reactions in living things. The rate of these enzymatic reactions depends on both the concentration of the enzyme and that of the substrate. If a single normal gene in a heterozygote produces enough enzyme for a reaction to proceed at the maximum rate possible, the heterozygote will resemble the homozygote, and dominance will be complete. If, on the other hand, it does not produce enough enzyme, dominance will be incomplete, but the greater the activity of the gene, the more the heterozygote will resemble the homozygote.

Haldane proposed that dominance resulted from the selection of the more efficient wild-type alleles from among a group of different wild-type alleles or isoalleles. Since individuals heterozygous for the more active allele would be more like the normal homozygote, they would have a selective advantage in heterozygotes, and the more active allele would be favored by selection over the less active type. Thus he argued that selection would favor the allele that had a safety factor of at least two in enzyme production so that a single gene could perform the task ordinarily done by two. This theory, like Wright's, is essentially a physiological theory of dominance.

A final theory, developed by Plunkett and Muller, again involves the selection of modifiers. Unlike Fisher's idea, however, selection is directed, not primarily at the infrequent heterozygotes, but at the wild-type homozygotes. Those modifying factors are selected that tend to stabilize the wild-type phenotype under all sorts of environmental and genetic stresses. Under this hypothesis, modifiers are selected not just for their ability to suppress the harmful effects of an occasional deleterious mutant, but rather to build up a safety factor for the wild type.

From the wealth of theories it is clear that the question of the origin of dominance has not yet been finally resolved. Experimental evidence can be cited in support of both the physiological and modifier theories. There is no question, for example, that dominance can be shifted by the selection of suitable modifiers. Nevertheless, it is also true that different wild-type alleles may show different degrees of dominance in heterozygotes. The theories are not mutually exclusive, for it is quite conceivable that mutants may occur that are favorable and dominant from the outset and are immediately favored by selection. However, if such mutants are not available, selection may be forced to work with the genetic materials at hand to increase the dominance of existing mutants through modifiers at other loci.

Balanced Polymorphism

Balanced polymorphism may arise in a number of different ways. If the rarer form were always at a selective advantage, adaptive values would change as frequencies changed. A rare form favored by selection would lose this selective advantage as it became more common, until at high frequencies it would be at a disadvantage. In this way selection would tend to damp any oscillations in gene frequency before they led to the extinction of one allele, and a balanced situation would be maintained. Such a situation might arise as a result of the feeding habits of predators that tend to take the common forms of their polymorphic prey but overlook the rare ones.

In the twin-spot ladybird beetle (*Adalia bipunctata*) changing selection pressures of a somewhat different kind are responsible for still another type of equilibrium. The red phase increases in relative frequency during the winter, but the black phase increases during the summer. As a result of the seasonal shifts in adaptive value, neither type is eliminated. Similar seasonal shifts in the frequency of inversion types in *Drosophila pseudoobscura* indicate that balanced polymorphism is a device by which this species, too, adapts to seasonal changes. Seasonal polymorphism is more apt to be observed in species with a short generation length.

A rather unusual type of polymorphism is exemplified by the *T* locus in mice. A number of distinct alleles have been found in different wild populations that in the homozygous condition cause sterility or even lethality but have no visible effect on the phenotype of heterozygotes. Mendelian segregation in heterozygous females is normal, so that eggs bearing mutant and normal genes are produced in equal numbers. However, in heterozygous males, segregation is highly abnormal, for up to 95 percent of the sperm cells carry the deleterious mutant. Under these circumstances, the increase in frequency of the mutant that would otherwise occur is checked or held in balance by the lethal or sterile effects of the gene. Comparable examples have been described in *Drosophila* under the term "meiotic drive." Many questions remain to be answered about what appear to be most peculiar and anomalous situations.

Any system whereby mating between individuals of unlike genotype is encouraged or enforced leads to the establishment of a stable polymorphism. Incompatibility systems in plants are a case in point. Some species such as red clover (*Trifolium pratense*) have a series of multiple self-sterility alleles, S_1, S_2, S_3, S_4, etc. Pollen that carries any particular allele will fail to fertilize the ovules of any plant carrying the same allele. Thus S_1 pollen will successfully fertilize ovules in S_2S_3, S_2S_4, and S_3S_4 plants but not in S_1S_2, S_1S_3, or S_1S_4 plants. Self-fertilization is therefore impossible, and furthermore no homozygotes can be formed.

The Pin-Thrum situation in the primrose (*Primula vulgaris*) is comparable but differs in some respects. Pin flowers have a long style with the stigma at the mouth of the corolla tube of the flowers and the anthers half-way down the tube. In Thrum flowers the positions of anthers and stigma are reversed as compared to Pin. This difference ordinarily behaves as if controlled by a single locus, with Pin being the homozygous recessive (*pp*) and Thrum the heterozygote (*Pp*). The pollen tube formed by Pin pollen grows only very slowly on Pin, but Thrum pollen on a Thrum stigma forms no pollen tube at all. Since Thrum is a heterozygote, its pollen is of two types. Therefore, the pollen behavior must be determined, not by the genotype of the pollen itself as with the self-sterility alleles, but by the genotype of the Thrum parent, for *p* pollen from a Pin plant will grow down the style of a Thrum (*Pp*) plant, but genetically similar *p* pollen from a Thrum plant will not.

In animals, nonrandom mating has occasionally been reported in which unlike individuals are more apt to mate than individuals of like genotype. If negative assortative mating of this kind actually does occur, it too would result in balanced polymorphism, for individuals of the rarer type would have a greater likelihood of obtaining mates. This case actually represents still another way in which selection intensity would be related to gene frequency.

Although this category is seldom included in discussions of polymorphism, it is worth pointing out that any species with separate sexes is polymorphic in every sense of the word. In most cases this polymorphism is chromosomal as well as phenotypic, and cross fertilization is mandatory. In addition to the primary differences between the sexes, there are many secondary sexual characters. The adaptive value of these traits in many cases seems quite apparent, but much remains to be learned about these adaptive values, their mode of origin by selection, and the genetic mechanisms controlling them.

Heterosis and Polymorphism

The final mechanism of balanced polymorphism to be discussed is the situation in which the heterozygote is more fit than either homozygote. In other words, heterosis may also serve as a means of maintaining balanced polymorphism. The most extreme case of this sort is a balanced lethal system. If linkage is close or crossing over is in some way suppressed, only Ab/aB progeny will result from Ab/aB heterozygous parents, for the Ab/Ab and aB/aB homozygotes will die owing to the homozygous recessive lethals (bb or aa). Individuals of the Ab/aB type will breed true in spite of being heterozygous.

Overdominance will also lead to a balanced heterozygous system. In this case only a single locus need be involved, and the homozygotes may be only slightly inferior to the heterozygote. When the heterozygote (Aa) is superior, selection, rather than tending toward homozygosity for a favored allele, will favor the heterozygotes, and hence will produce a stable equilibrium at the gene frequencies that confer optimum fitness on the entire population. These frequencies are determined by the relative fitness of the two homozygotes. If the fitness of Aa is set equal to 1, of AA equal to $(1 - s_1)$, and of aa equal to $(1 - s_2)$, then

$$\Delta p = \frac{pq(s_2q - s_1p)}{1 - s_1p^2 - s_2q^2}$$

and at equilibrium $\quad \Delta p = 0$ and $s_1p = s_2q$

Solving this equation,

$$\hat{p} = \frac{s_2}{s_1 + s_2}$$

For example, if $Aa = 1$

$$AA = 1 - s_1 = .8 \qquad (s_1 = .2)$$
$$aa = 1 - s_2 = .4 \qquad (s_2 = .6)$$

Then $\qquad \hat{p} = \dfrac{.6}{.2 + .6} = .75$

The best example of single gene heterosis responsible for balanced polymorphism comes from man. The sickle cell gene (Hb^s) produces an abnormal hemoglobin and in homozygous condition causes sickle cell anemia, a debilitating disease that is usually fatal. This gene has a surprisingly high frequency in some parts of the world. In these areas malaria is endemic, and it has been found that the heterozygotes (Hb^s/Hb^a) for the sickle cell gene are significantly more resistant to subtertian malaria than are the homozygotes (Hb^a/Hb^a) for normal adult hemoglobin. Thus where malaria is prevalent, the heterozygotes are better adapted than the homozygotes, which are apt to die either from anemia on the one hand (Hb^s/Hb^s) or malaria on the other (Hb^a/Hb^a).

Probably the most thoroughly studied case of heterozygote superiority is that of inversion heterozygotes in *Drosophila*. In some species of *Drosophila* (for example, *D. pseudoobscura, D. persimilis, D. miranda, D. robusta,* and *D. willistoni*) two or more inversions may occur with high frequency within a single breeding population. The seasonal shifts in frequency of inversion types have already been mentioned, but even more significant is the fact that the inversion heterozygotes show hybrid vigor or superior fitness as compared to the inversion homozygotes even though their external appearances are similar. The implication is clear that the different inversion types must differ to some extent in their gene contents. Since crossing over is restricted in inversion heterozygotes, the development of these differences is not surprising. This is not to suggest, however, that all chromosomes of, say, the Standard type in a breeding population of *D. pseudoobscura* have the same gene contents, but merely that two Standard chromosomes from the same population will generally be more alike than will a Standard- and an Arrowhead-type chromosome drawn from the same population. Since the block of chromatin within an inversion will be isolated from recombination with other inversions, the gene complex within an inversion will be subject to selection as a unit. These gene complexes can thus be expected to differ from each other in both gene contents and adaptive value. Furthermore, it has been postulated that selection will also operate to favor those combinations of genes in each inversion type that confer maximum heterosis or fitness when in heterozygous combination with another inversion, since inversion heterozygotes are ordinarily more common than inversion homozygotes. Thus, in addition to its adaptive value as a homozygote each inversion type may have an adaptive value as a heterozygote, or will be "coadapted" to the other gene complexes in the population.

One additional observation about these inversion heterozygotes should be noted. In general, the heterozygotes are phenotypically more stable or show less variation under environmental stress than do the corresponding homozygotes. Furthermore, a heterozygous population is better able to adapt to changing environmental conditions without major disruptions than is a relatively homozygous population. These two concepts, in some ways related, have been widely discussed under the terms "developmental homeostasis" and "genetic homeostasis" respectively.

That the different inversions do differ in adaptive value is indicated by their seasonal and altitudinal shifts in frequency. In population studies in California, for example, the Standard type in *D. pseudoobscura* increased in frequency as the weather became warmer, reaching a maximum during the hot summer months. Populations sampled at different altitudes formed a cline with Standard having a low frequency at high altitudes and increasing in frequency with lower elevation. Since altitude also provides a temperature gradient, the Standard gene complex in this region appears to be better adapted to warmer temperatures than the other inversions in these populations. Here, as demonstrated previously, the relative frequencies in this balanced polymorphic system will be determined by the relationship between the selection coefficients of the homozygous types.

Samples taken over the wide geographical range of a species may also show shifts in the frequency and kinds of the different third-chromosome inversions. These differences undoubtedly reflect changing adaptive requirements under different ecological conditions, but they may also reflect historical events, in the sense that different chromosomal mutations may have occurred in different parts of the range. Since selection must operate within the framework of the available variability, some of the geographic variation in inversion types may have arisen in this way.

The amount of inversion heterozygosity has been found to vary greatly, usually being maximal toward the center of the range of a species and decreasing toward the periphery. One theory proposes that chromosomal polymorphism permits the species to exploit a greater variety of ecological niches than would otherwise be open to it. Thus, at the center of the range the species is presumed to be highly successful, exploiting a number of different niches, but at the limits of the range the environment is marginal for the species and a minimal number of niches are habitable.

Another hypothesis is that the primary function of inversion heterozygosity in natural populations is related to its effects on recombination. In the central populations, with a high frequency of inversion heterozygosity, the amount of possible genetic recombination will be considerably restricted. Selection will tend to favor heterozygotes with superior general vigor, and adaptation will be achieved through heterosis. This type of adjustment is only feasible in large populations, for it is made at the expense of the production of homozygotes of low fitness. Any device, such as an inversion, that would tend to reduce the frequency with which relatively unfit homozygotes are formed will have an immediate selective value because it will minimize the cost of maintaining heterosis in the population. When adaptation via heterosis occurs, the population can meet rather drastic environmental changes with relatively minor adjustments in its heterotic genetic system; it is said to be "heterotically buffered." However, such a system imposes a considerable limitation on the possibilities for future evolutionary change.

On the other hand, in marginal populations, small in numbers and relatively isolated, inversion heterozygosity is low and genetic recombination relatively unrestricted. Under these circumstances selection will tend toward the ultimate fixation of those genes conferring superior fitness. It is in these populations, it is argued, that the evolutionary changes occur that lead to genetic divergence and ultimately to the formation of new subspecies and species.

Although a great deal of very fascinating work has been done on chromosomal polymorphism in *Drosophila,* it seems likely that there is still much to be learned. For example, why should inversion heterozygosity be so common in some species of the genus *Drosophila* but rare or absent in other species such as *D. melanogaster* and *D. virilis,* which are widely distributed and highly successful in exploiting a variety of ecological niches? A most interesting observation made some years ago by Dubinin in Russia showed that the frequency of inversion heterozygosity in *D. funebris* was related to the degree of industrialization of the area in which the population lived. Thus, populations in large urban areas showed a high degree of inversion heterozygosity, but the frequency declined in suburban and small-town populations until it was virtually zero in rural districts. This difference may well be related to the number of adaptive niches available in urban as compared to rural areas, but it may also reflect the effect of differences in population size of the flies or of passive transport of flies into the cities. Only further study can resolve these questions.

The material already presented should suffice to illustrate some of the complexities related to polymorphism, but still other aspects of this subject may be mentioned. Many instances of mimicry, for example, also involve polymorphism, sometimes affecting just one sex and not the other. Environmental factors may also induce polymorphic differences; pupa case color in certain species of butterflies is related to the type of background on which chrysalis formation occurs. Green pupae are more common on the green leaves of plants whereas brown pupae are more frequent if the pupae are formed on the brown stems. These differences reflect a delicate adjustment between the genotype and the environment. Still other polymorphisms observed in the field may be due to the ability of the individual organism to change its color to match its background, an ability fairly common in the animal kingdom. Tree frogs among the amphibians, the chameleon among the reptiles, and the cuttlefish, a molluscan invertebrate, are familiar examples of species with great capacity in this respect.

In man, polymorphisms of many kinds may be observed, but their significance is usually unknown. In the past, the blood groups were frequently referred to as adaptively neutral traits, but the discovery of the relation between the sickle cell gene and malarial resistance, and between other blood group genes in the ABO system and the incidence of stomach cancer and duodenal ulcer indicates that this is a hazardous assumption. Other cases present problems of particular interest and importance. Both schizophrenia and diabetes have an incidence in human populations of about 1 percent despite the fact that the reproductive rate of affected persons in the past must have been significantly lower than that of unaffected individuals. Since an underlying genetic basis has been demonstrated for both illnesses, the high frequency of diabetes and schizophrenia suggests the existence of balanced polymorphism, but the possible mechanism remains unknown. The study of polymorphism has been an exceptionally fruitful area of research for students of variation and evolution, and these and many other problems suggest that it will continue to be so for some time to come.

SUMMARY ◄────────────────────────────────

A polymorphic population contains two or more distinct types of individuals. Not only genic but chromosomal polymorphisms have been discovered. Polymorphism may result from the Hardy-Weinberg equilibrium or from the balance between the opposing forces of mutation and selection. Of even greater interest are transient and balanced polymorphism. The most thoroughly studied case of transient polymorphism, industrial melanism, has shown that in industrial regions in Europe, the light, mottled pattern of many moths has been almost completely replaced in a matter of decades by a darker, melanic form, better adapted to the new background. Numerous examples of polymorphism involving dominant mutants are known, and there are various theories of the origin of dominance. Balanced polymorphism may be due to a number of conditions, among them shifting selection pressures and selection favoring the heterozygotes over both homozygotes. The study of balanced polymorphism has loomed large in recent work on the nature and origin of species, and it remains a fertile field for research.

SUGGESTED READING

Cold Spring Harbor Symp. Quant. Biol., Vol. 20, 1955. "Population genetics." Long Island Biological Assoc., New York.

Dobzhansky, Th., 1951. *Genetics and the origin of species,* 3d ed. New York: Columbia University Press.

Sheppard, P. M., 1958. *Natural selection and heredity.* London: Hutchinson.

CHAPTER 27

Genetic Drift

Thus far in our discussions of the genetics of populations we have been making the implicit assumption that the populations were infinitely large. In actuality natural populations are, of course, finite in size and may be quite small. Even when the total population is very large, if it is divided into numerous small, isolated, breeding populations, the dynamics of the changes in gene frequency will be determined by the forces operating in each small population independent of the rest. If there is some migration between the different breeding populations, the evolutionary course of the entire species will be tied together in a very complex manner that depends not only on mutation pressure and the selection pressures within and between populations, but also on the size of the various breeding populations and on the amount of migration between them. We have already considered the effects of mutation and selection. Now we must discuss the effect of population size on an isolated population, before going on in a later chapter to treat migration or gene flow.

The total number of individuals in a species, without reference to the way in which the species may be subdivided into breeding populations, gives little indication of the possible effects of population size on gene frequency changes. Similarly, a simple census of the number of individuals in a single population may not be a true index of the effective breeding size of the population. Some species, for example, undergo drastic periodic seasonal fluctuations in numbers. A census taken in the fall may indicate a size in the hundreds of thousands or even millions for an insect population in the temperate zone. However, if only a fraction of 1 percent of these insects survive the winter, the characteristics of this population will largely be determined by this handful of survivors rather than by the much larger number at the population peak.

We have already seen in the discussion of the Hardy-Weinberg equilibrium that in a large, randomly mating population, in which there is no mutation or selection, gene frequencies will remain constant. However, if the population is small, gene frequencies will tend to fluctuate purely by chance, and the smaller the population, the greater the fluctuations are apt to be. These random changes in gene frequency are said to be due to *genetic drift*. The gene frequencies in a small population will continue to fluctuate until one allele is lost and the other fixed. Subsequently, the population will remain homozygous unless a new mutation appears.

The basis for genetic drift is to be found in the process of *sampling*. In order to understand the relation between population size and drift, we must understand certain elementary principles of sampling. If the gene A is represented by a black marble and its allele a by a white one, then all of the gametes produced by a population can be represented by a large bowl full of marbles, with the black marbles representing the proportion of A genes in the gametes. Obviously not all of the gametes produced will go to form the next generation, for many, especially the sperm, will not take part in fertilization, and many of the fertilized eggs will not survive to maturity. Thus, the gametes that actually give rise to the next generation can be represented by a handful of marbles taken from the bowl. If there are equal numbers of A and a genes in the gametes, the gene frequency of A is 50 percent. However, in a handful of marbles taken at random, it is unlikely that the numbers will be exactly equal. Similarly, because of the random nature of meiosis and fertilization, the numbers of dominant and recessive genes may not be equal. The principles involved in estimating how large the deviations from equality may be are much the same as those used in estimating the expected numbers of heads and tails with a tossed coin. If you tossed a penny four times, you would probably not be surprised if you got three tails and one head. In fact, it can be estimated that such a result would be expected 25 percent of the time when four tosses are made. The probabilities for various combinations of heads and tails on four tosses are calculable from expansion of the binomial $(a + b)^4$, where $a = \frac{1}{2} =$ the probability of heads, and $b = \frac{1}{2} =$ the probability of tails. The complete expansion is:

composition of sample	4 heads	3 heads 1 tail	2 heads 2 tails	1 head 3 tails	4 tails
proportion of heads	1	.75	.50	.25	0
frequency	a^4	$4a^3b$	$6a^2b^2$	$4ab^3$	b^4
probability of sample of above type	$\frac{1}{16}$	$\frac{4}{16}$	$\frac{6}{16}$	$\frac{4}{16}$	$\frac{1}{16}$

Thus, less than half the time ($\frac{6}{16}$) would you expect to get equal numbers of heads and tails, or of black and white marbles, or of dominant and recessive genes in samples of four drawn from a source of supply in which each type has an equal frequency. In terms of gene frequencies, it is clear that there is a sizable chance that the frequency of A will shift either to .75 or .25 or that A may become either fixed or lost from the population.

However, if you tossed a penny 10,000 times, you would be very surprised if you got 7500 tails and only 2500 heads, and rightly so, even though the ratio of heads and tails is the same as for 3 tails and 1 head. Your more or less instinctive reaction can be borne out statistically, for the standard error of a ratio for large samples equals $\sqrt{\dfrac{p \times q}{n}}$ or in this case $\sqrt{\dfrac{(0.50)\,(0.50)}{10,000}}$ = 0.005. Thus with 10,000 tosses, expectations are for 5000 heads, with a standard error of 50. Since the chances are less than 1 in 100,000 that a sample will diverge from its source by as much as four times its standard error, even a ratio of 5200 tails to 4800 heads would be extremely improbable. From this line of reasoning, it should be clear why random fluctuations in gene frequency tend to be larger, the smaller the sample of genes that gives rise to the next generation.

One further point to note is that the sample of genes that goes to form the first generation will then in its turn generate the new supply of gametes from which the genes of the second generation will be drawn. Therefore, if sampling fluctuations have resulted in frequencies of A and a other than 0.5, the sampling situation is likely to be somewhat different in the next generation than it was in the preceding one. If, for example, 1 white and 3 black marbles were drawn at random from a bowl containing equal numbers of black and white, the new bowl of marbles from which the next sample must be drawn would contain, not equal numbers of black and white, but $\frac{3}{4}$ black and only $\frac{1}{4}$ white. Over a number of generations, sampling fluctuations may have a cumulative effect and gene frequencies may diverge considerably from their initial frequencies, hence the name "genetic drift." As a result of random genetic drift a new mutant may occasionally spread through a small population until it becomes homozygous or fixed in the population, but more often random drift will lead to the loss of the new allele before it has even had a chance to spread.

Effective Size of Populations

The effects of genetic drift have been estimated under various conditions, but a special case of rather general interest will suffice to give some indication of the relation between population size and genetic drift. In a population of moderate size with equal numbers of males and females mating at random, the rate of decay of the variability or the rate of decrease in heterozygosis is approximately equal to $1/2N$. Here, N is the effective size of the breeding population rather than the total number of individuals in the population, for many will not survive to maturity and among those that do, not all will leave offspring. Thus, the actual progenitors contributing genetically to the next generation may be considerably fewer in number than the total number of individuals living in the population at any one time. Furthermore, the breeding population may be larger than the so-called effective size of the population. The breeding population will equal the effective population when equal numbers of males and females are mating at random and contributing equally to the next generation. However, if the numbers of males and females are unequal, the effective size will depend to a large extent on the sex which is fewer in number. Thus, for example, in a flock of chickens with a few roosters serving a large number of hens, the effective size of this population will approximate four times the number of roosters rather than the total number of breeding individuals. Similarly, in a population undergoing periodic expansion and contraction in numbers, the effective N will be much closer to the minimum number than to the maximum. As a simple example of the effect of drift, if N were 20, $1/2N$ or 1 out of 40 heterozygous loci on the average would be expected to become homozygous in the next generation. It can be seen that, continued over a number of generations, genetic drift would not only cause fluctuations in gene frequency but also would increase the amount of homozygosity in the population.

Cases to illustrate the effects of genetic drift can be drawn from man. American Indian tribes are known to have formed rather small, isolated, mating populations in recent times and are thought to have formed such units ever since they first migrated to America. Human populations in other parts of the world do not ordinarily consist of such small mating isolates. It is significant therefore that whereas the frequency of the gene producing the A substance of the ABO blood group system ranges in the rest of the world from about 15 percent to 45 percent, in American Indian tribes it ranges from as low as 1 or 2 percent in some tribes to as high as 80 percent in the Bloods and the Blackfeet. A study of a genetic isolate based on religion has also produced some interesting data The Old German Baptist Brethren, or Dunkers, form a community of about 300 persons in Franklin County, Pennsylvania, but the effective size of this population has been estimated to be only about 90. This group was compared for a number of traits both with the population of the German Rhineland, their place of origin, and also with the population in the United States among whom they live and from whom they have drawn a small fraction of their genes by intermarriage. The analysis showed quite clearly that this community had come to differ significantly from the populations both in Germany and the United States in several but not all of the traits studied—exactly the result that might be expected with genetic drift. The evidence, therefore, is highly suggestive that genetic drift does play a considerable role in determining gene frequencies in small isolated human populations.

Genetic Drift and Evolution

Considerable discussion has arisen over the evolutionary significance of genetic drift. The debate has hinged, not so much on whether genetic drift can occur, but rather on whether, even if it does occur, it has any long-range importance in evolution. Given the facts of Mendelian inheritance, there seems little reason to doubt that random genetic drift can take place, and if this is so, it then seems highly probable that in particular instances or under certain circumstances it has played a role in evolution. The fate of most small breeding populations is undoubtedly extinction, due either to the vicissitudes that affect any natural population, or to the populations' inability to adapt to changing conditions because of their low variability, or simply to loss of identity by interbreeding with members of other, larger populations. The question still remains as to the evolutionary role of the occasional small, divergent population that survives. The available data, at best not too abundant, have frequently been analyzed from only one point of view. For example, the "drifters" have sometimes assumed that apparently random gene frequency differences between different breeding populations of the same species are *de facto* evidence for genetic drift, and have made no attempt to determine whether these differences are in any way adaptive. On the other hand, the "selectionists" may consider that by proving that selection is operating in a population they have thereby excluded the possibility of genetic drift, or they may fail to make the essential distinction between effective size and population number. Furthermore, drift seems likely to be of greater significance in some kinds of species than in others. Top carnivores, for instance, which are relatively very few in number and apt to be widely scattered, might well be more likely subjects to investigate for the effects of drift than some of the species studied thus far.

In actual populations, natural selection undoubtedly functions at all population sizes, small as well as large. Therefore, it may be expected that genetic drift in the absence of selection will rarely be found. When selection as well as genetic drift is operative, both will tend to cooperate, and the deleterious genes in small populations will be eliminated more rapidly than in large populations in which selection alone is effective. The reason is that the less frequent allele in a population has a somewhat greater probability of decreasing than of increasing in frequency under genetic drift. Since the constant pressure of selection will keep the deleterious gene at a low frequency, the net effect of selection plus drift is to increase the rate of elimination of deleterious genes. Natural selection is the controlling factor in the evolution of large populations, which usually remain quite heterozygous and hence retain considerable variability, either actual or potential. In small populations, the combined effect of natural selection, genetic drift, and the greater likelihood of inbreeding is to raise the level of homozygosity and thus lower the amount of variability in the population. For this reason, small populations may lose their ability to adapt to changing conditions and become extinct. However, numerous small populations may also come to diverge from each other both as a result of different selection pressures and the chance events stemming from mutation, genetic drift, and inbreeding. Hence each population may be regarded as a separate evolutionary experiment, and even though the fate of most of them is extinction, the possibility for rather rapid evolution in novel directions under these circumstances cannot be ignored.

───►*SUMMARY*

Changes in gene frequencies may occur in small populations as the result of random genetic drift. In essence, genetic drift is a consequence of drawing a small random sample of gametes to form the next generation. This sample, which by chance may differ in gene frequency from the gene frequencies in the parents, then becomes the new gene pool from which the gametes for the next generation are drawn. In this way, numerous unpredictable changes in gene frequency within a population may take place. Although considerable discussion of the evolutionary significance of genetic drift has been generated, there has been little doubt that drift can occur, and thus it remains a factor to be reckoned with in all evolutionary studies.

SUGGESTED READING

Glass, B., 1954. "Genetic changes in human populations, especially those due to gene flow and genetic drift," *Adv. in Genetics,* 6:95-139.

Li, C. C., 1955. *Population genetics.* Chicago: University of Chicago Press.

Wright, S., 1951. "Fisher and Ford on the 'Sewall Wright effect'," *Amer. Scientist,* 39:452-458.

CHAPTER *28*

The Origin of Subspecies

New species can arise in two distinct ways, shown diagrammatically below:

Time ↑   I $\begin{array}{c} d \\ c \\ b \\ a \end{array}$ ↑   II $\begin{array}{c} b \quad c \\ \diagdown\diagup \\ a \end{array}$

In I, only one species exists at any one point in time. Species *a* evolves into *b*, *b* into *c*, and so on; it is a "transformation in time." In II, a single species gives rise to two contemporary species; a splitting or "multiplication in space" has occurred, a process known as *speciation*, in a restricted sense of the word. Whereas the transformation of a single species in time is due to the combined effects of mutation, natural selection, and genetic drift, speciation involves an added problem: the origin, from a single species, of two or more species that no longer interbreed. Once established, they maintain their separate identities and pursue independent evolutionary paths. Our problem now is to consider the ways in which different populations of the same species with essentially the same genetic composition can diverge from each other. To do so, it is necessary to discuss population structure—that is, the way in which the individual members of a species are subdivided into breeding groups.

Population Structure

Some species may be common and widely distributed,

268

forming one large, nearly continuous population over thousands of square miles of a continental land mass. The American robin (*Turdus migratorius*) and the red-winged blackbird (*Agelaius phoeniceus*) are species of this type. However, even though essentially continuous in their distribution, in that there are no gross barriers separating one segment of the species from the rest, nevertheless mating is not random over the entire species range, for obviously one male is not equally likely to mate with all of the females in the species. The chances that a male in Massachusetts will mate with Michigan or Minnesota females are virtually nil; they are isolated by distance.

Other species populations clearly have a discontinuous distribution. A species inhabiting a series of islands is perhaps the most clear-cut example of this type, but a comparable situation is found in species living in a series of isolated lakes or marshes, in clumps of trees surrounded by prairie, on a particular type of soil, or only above a certain elevation in a mountain range. In each case each population is quite clearly delimited from the other populations of the same species by a zone in which no members of that species live.

A variety of other population structures can be visualized, but we shall mention just one more, the linear distribution such as might be found in a species living in or along a river. A similar structure is found in species living along the seashore or at a limited elevation along a long mountain ridge. Here, the distribution is continuous, but again isolation by distance may be a modifying aspect.

The distribution pattern of a species is determined by a number of factors, any one of which may act as a barrier to further expansion of the species' range. The barrier may be some obvious physical feature such as an ocean, a desert, or a mountain range. However, since an impassable barrier for one species may serve as a broad highway for another, even barriers that seem obvious cannot be so termed without reference to the kinds of organisms unable to surmount them. Consider, for example, the different role the ocean has played in the distribution of whales and elephants. Climate, especially as related to temperature and moisture, may set limits on the range of a species, and such limits are quite as rigorous in their way as are the physical barriers. Furthermore, some plants are restricted by their soil, or edaphic, requirements to only limited portions of an otherwise suitable habitat.

The ecological conditions, which are of course in part determined by the physical conditions, may also influence the distribution pattern of a species and serve as a barrier to its expansion. One has but to think of species typical only of the prairie, or of coniferous forest, or of deciduous forest to realize that distribution also depends on the type of habitat available. Destruction of its habitat means the elimination of a species from that area. For this reason, present game and fish management practices are placing increasing emphasis on habitat improvement. These habitat needs may be both general and also quite specific. The distribution, for example, of oak-gall wasps of the genus *Cynips* was shown by Kinsey (who later became better known for other research) to be dependent on the distribution of the oak trees in which they laid their eggs. The yellow-headed and red-winged blackbirds are closely related species, both of which breed in Minnesota in cattail marshes. While the red-wing is found in almost every cattail marsh available, the yellow-head seems to breed only in those marshes where no willows or other shrubs or bushes encroach on the edges of the marsh. It is not surprising, therefore, that it is known as a bird of the prairies.

For genetic divergence to take place within a species, it is essential that the original species population be divided into populations that are physically isolated from each other. If they are not isolated, interbreeding will occur and no divergence will be possible, for the species will be sharing a common gene pool, and continual hybridization will swamp any differences that might arise. The actual distances may be very great or quite small, depending on the species. A few hundred yards of unsuitable habitat may be quite sufficient to separate two snail populations, while several hundred miles' separation may be necessary to achieve the same degree of isolation in birds. The essential factor is not the absolute distance, but the lack of opportunity for mating between members of the different populations because of their separation in space. Some biologists have argued that ecological divergence could occur without physical isolation. However, the initial and crucial steps leading to divergence in ecological requirements would be the most difficult and would be likely to occur only under the most favorable circumstances, if at all.

At this point it may be worthwhile to review some of the terms used to describe the variability of natural populations. A breeding population or Mendelian population is a group of individuals tied together by bonds of mating and parentage and thus sharing a common gene pool. Since these individuals are not of a uniform genotype but are typically variable, the population is *polymorphic*. A species is *polytypic* if composed of genetically distinct breeding populations. Individuals living close enough to one another so that interbreeding between them is possible are said to be *sympatric* (that is, living in the same country). Those living at greater distances are *allopatric*. Thus polymorphic variability should be found in sympatric individuals; if the variations are found only in allopatric populations, they are polytypic.

Races or *subspecies* are biological units below the species level. They are geographically defined aggregates of breeding populations that differ from one another in the frequencies of one or more genetically determined traits. The definition of race or subspecies is rather fuzzy because the concept of race is itself rather fuzzy. For example, it is impossible to say, without being arbitrary, just how different two populations must be to warrant subspecific rank. Furthermore, in some cases the traits of a species seem to change rather gradually across the range of the species and a *cline* is said to exist. These gradual, continuous changes are the result of adaptation to similar gradual changes in such things as annual temperatures or rainfall. The difficulty in defining a race increases in species where clines are found, for even though the terminal populations may be quite different, if no sharp discontinuity exists, it is extremely difficult to delimit racial boundaries. Therefore, the concept is of limited usefulness and should be applied with caution. To dignify all infraspecific variation with subspecific taxonomic names may serve only to compound confusion rather than to clarify it. In certain circumstances the labels may be of sufficient usefulness to justify using them, but the underlying biological situation should be kept clearly in mind.

Isolation and Subspeciation

The brief discussion of population structure above should serve to indicate that a species population usually has a discontinuous distribution. If its range is very large, even a more or less continuously distributed species does not form one large randomly mating population, simply because of the distances involved. Therefore, as a general rule, a species is composed of a number of allopatric breeding populations, each physically separated to some extent from the others and pursuing its own independent evolutionary path. Even though the genetic composition of these populations may initially be very similar, no two environments are likely to be biologically or physically identical, and thus the selection pressures on these populations will almost inevitably be somewhat different. Selection plus the random aspects of mutation and, in small populations, of inbreeding and genetic drift will bring about divergence in the hereditary characteristics of the formerly similar populations. For this reason, it is to be expected that most widely distributed species will show variation among the different breeding populations in different parts of the range. These differences may take the form of clines, or, when the variation is sufficiently well defined, different geographic races or subspecies may be recognized.

A somewhat different mode of origin for genetic diversity between populations, suggested by Mayr, is known as the "founder principle." Although it does not involve any new concepts, the known principles are thought to operate in a somewhat different way from the usual method outlined above. In brief, the suggestion is that if, for example, a small population colonizes a previously uninhabited island, the gene pool introduced into the island may differ somewhat from that of the species as a whole. As a result, the selective value of the genes may be somewhat different from their value in the parental population, because of their new genetic environment as well as the new external environment. Thus, drift and selection pressures are thought to account for the sometimes striking differences between different island populations and between island populations and their continental ancestors.

In order to gain better insight into the nature of the differences between geographically isolated populations, let us consider a few selected cases that have been studied rather carefully. The coast tarweed, *Hemizonia angustifolia,* is a member of the sunflower family and is found in a narrow belt along the sea coast of California. Of the two races, one extends 275 miles along the coast from northern California to south of Monterey Bay; the other, after a gap of 40 miles of unsuitable habitat due to the Santa Lucia Mountains, ranges another 40 miles southward. Although the two races are geographically isolated from each other, they occupy ecologically similar habitats. Nevertheless, because there are small but consistent and significant morphological differences between them, they have sometimes been called distinct species. Plants of the northern race have a low, broad habit, slender open branching, and rather small flower heads. The plants from the southern race have more erect, robust branching, and larger flower heads. The two races cross easily and produce fertile F_1 hybrids. The F_2 showed that the slight differences between the races were due to numerous multiple factors. Of 1152 F_2 plants reared, no two were alike and no plant was exactly like either of the parents. Almost all possible recombinations of the parental traits were found. Whereas 57 percent of the F_2 individuals were as large as the parents, 43 percent were smaller in size, some being as much as 1000 times smaller than other F_2 plants (Fig. 28-1). Thus the genes in these two races have diverged sufficiently so that in some combinations they do not support development to normal size even though the combinations are viable. However, fertility and viability in the hybrids are sufficiently good to warrant calling these two groups geographical subspecies rather than separate species. Since both occupy the coastal plain, Clausen, Keck, and Hiesey, who made this study, consider them to form a single ecotype but two geographic races. To what extent the differences between them may be adaptive and to what extent they are of chance origin has not been determined.

Genetic Differences between Subspecies

A quite different situation has been described in the climatic or altitudinal races of the cinquefoil, *Potentilla glandulosa,* a member of the rose family. This species occurs in central California from the lowlands near the coast up to heights of 11,000 feet in the Sierra Nevada. At least seven climatic races have been identified. The extreme types, the lowland and the alpine races, are strikingly different both morphologically and physiologically. The lowland race grows throughout the year, but the alpine race is winter dormant for nine months. The alpine race is dwarf as are many alpine plants, but it has large flowers; the lowland plants, though large and robust, have small flowers. Transplantation experiments showed that alpine plants remained winter dormant for two or three months, even in the lowland environment, and grew rather poorly.

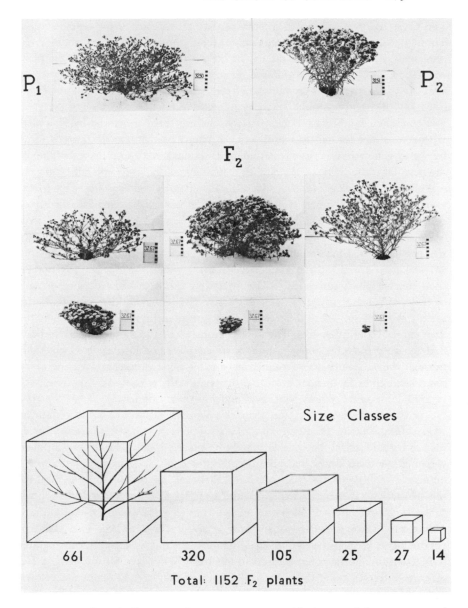

Fig. 28-1. Genetic divergence between two geographical races of the coast tarweed, *Hemizonia angustifolia.* Top, left, the northern race (P₁); right, the southern race (P₂). F₂, top, three vigorous, and bottom, three dwarf segregants. The scale beside each plant is 10 cm high. The cubes represent F₂ size classes, and the numerals below, the number of plants in each class. The cube to the left, 50 cm to a side, is comparable to the parents. The others are 35, 25, 15, 10 and 5 cm respectively.
(Courtesy of Clausen, Keck, and Hiesey.)

The Coast Range plants failed to survive the harsh winter at the alpine station. These transplantation experiments and others showed that even though the phenotype was modified to some extent by the environment in which the plant was raised, the fundamental differences between these races were genotypic and adaptive to the particular environment from which the plants came. The genetic basis for the morphological and physiological differences between these races was confirmed by the results from crosses among them. Since the hybrids were all vigorous and fertile, no reproductive barrier exists among the various races. In the F_2 generation, genetic recombination resulted in a complete reshuffling of the parental traits. Some of the new F_2 combinations showed some rather surprising abilities. For example, some were more vigorous and frost resistant in the alpine habitat than the native alpines. Many that were well adapted to the alpine climate had vegetative characteristics of the parents from the lower elevations. Some thrived at all elevations from sea level to the alpine station, unlike any of the parent races. One recombinant type appeared as though it might be well adapted to the extreme maritime environment, which this species has not yet been able to invade successfully. The races were distinguished from one another by a dozen or more easily recognizable traits. Segregation and recombination in the F_2 showed that these differences were governed by multiple factors rather than single gene differences. The results from all of these experiments indicate that the differences between these races are adaptive and have evolved gradually through the accumulation of numerous small genetic differences. Furthermore, the potentialities for further evolution may be greatly enhanced by the release of variability brought about by hybridization between subspecies.

In the leopard frog, *Rana pipiens,* a somewhat similar but in certain respects quite different situation exists. This species ranges from northern Canada far down into Central America. As might be expected, individuals from different geographical areas show morphological differences, and on these grounds a number of subspecies have been named. However, no general agreement about the subspecies has been reached, for the characters used are not reliable and the continuous distribution of this species makes lines of demarcation difficult to draw. Moore has shown that the leopard frog is able to exist in this wide range of environments because the southern populations of *Rana pipiens* differ in adaptive traits from the northern populations in much the same way that southern species of frogs differ from northern species. Thus, for example, in temperature tolerance and rate of development, the northern frogs were able to tolerate and develop normally at lower temperatures than southern frogs, but could not tolerate the higher temperatures at which southern frogs still developed normally (Fig. 28-2). Data on other traits gave comparable results, suggesting that these populations, too, have become genetically adapted to their environments. However, unlike the crosses between races of *Potentilla glandulosa,* which gave normal, fertile hybrids, crosses between frogs of northern and southern origin

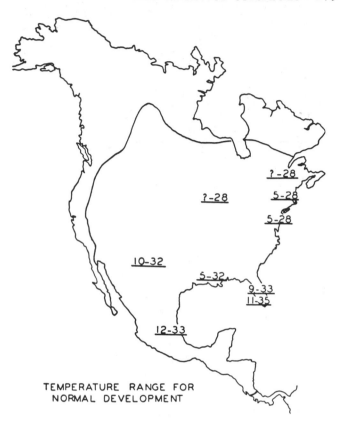

Fig. 28-2. Geographic variation in embryonic temperature tolerance in *Rana pipiens*. Upper and lower limits are given in degrees C. A question mark indicates lack of data. (With permission of Moore.)

gave rise to inviable hybrids. Thus the extreme populations behave as good species toward each other. However, since adjacent populations are fully inter-fertile, no barrier to genetic exchange exists throughout the range of the species, and it is best treated as a single species in which divergent populations have arisen owing to adaptation to local environmental conditions, particularly with respect to temperature.

► *SUMMARY*

A study of the population structure of a species typically reveals that it is composed of a number of more or less isolated breeding populations. Since the habitat is unlikely to be uniformly favorable throughout the species' range, this structure is to be expected. The origin of genetically divergent groups or subspecies within a species virtually requires some degree of isolation between breeding populations, for otherwise, any differences that might arise would be swamped by hybridization. This isolation should not be thought of in terms of any absolute distance between populations, but rather as the lack of opportunity for mating between the members of different groups. Since conditions are seldom, if ever, completely identical, the differing selection pressures, plus the random effects of mutation and genetic drift, tend to bring about genetic divergence between the different populations. The result is the formation of populations especially well adapted to their conditions of existence and differing from other populations of the same species living under somewhat different environmental conditions. Although the possibility of the sympatric differentiation of one population into two distinct breeding populations cannot be completely excluded, it must, in view of the difficulties attendant on such an event, have played only a minor role in the evolutionary process. The establishment of genetic differences between different breeding populations of the same species is the first step toward the origin of species.

SUGGESTED READING

Clausen, J., and W. M. Hiesey, 1958. "Experimental studies on the nature of species. IV, Genetic structure of ecological races," Carnegie Institute, Washington, D. C., Publ. 615.

Mayr, E., 1942. *Systematics and the origin of species.* New York: Columbia University Press.

———, 1959. "Isolation as an evolutionary factor," *Proc. Amer. Philosophical Society, 103*(2):221-230.

Moore, J. A., 1949. "Geographic variation of adaptive characters in *Rana pipiens* Schreber," *Evolution, 3:*1-24.

CHAPTER 29

Hybridization and Evolution

We have just considered the role of isolation in the origin of subspecies, and we must now consider what happens if for some reason isolation breaks down and interbreeding again occurs between formerly isolated and divergent populations. The importance of hybridization to evolution has been overstressed by some, who think there is a hybrid under every bush and often that the bush is a hybrid, too. Others have dismissed it as of no significance. The truth probably lies somewhere between these extremes, with hybridization more important to plant than to animal evolution. In plants there is no psychological isolation, sexual reproduction is more efficient than in animals, and the individuals are longer lived—all factors that contribute to successful hybridization. However, hybrids in animals have been identified in natural populations of fresh-water fishes, toads, and warblers, proof that hybridization does occur in animals as well as in plants.

The breakdown of isolation may come about in a variety of ways. Physical changes in the environment due to fires, floods, earthquakes, volcanic eruptions, or other catastrophes may drastically alter the habitat. Changes in climate, and the resultant changes in precipitation, the retreat of glaciers, land-bridge formation, all may lead to renewed contact between formerly isolated groups. The environment does not remain stable indefinitely, but undergoes both local and regional shifts in character in many ways.

Changes in the biota may also radically alter the environment. The goats introduced on Pitcairn Island have kept the island virtually denuded of large trees. Of all the species, however, man has had the greatest impact on the environment all over the world. His activities—clearing forests, burning over land, planting crops, draining swamps, and building roads, railroads, dams, homes, towns, and cities—have disrupted the environment almost beyond recognition or belief in many instances. With him he has carried weedy species of plants and animals to all parts of the earth. The rabbit with its depredations on the range lands of Australia is a familiar example. The impact of such species as man and the rabbit is direct and obvious, but the interrelationships among organisms are so complex and interwoven that a single change, like a stone in a pond, may set in motion a chain of events in an ever-widening circle. The classical example of the effect of the number of spinsters on the red clover crop will serve to illustrate this point (Fig. 29-1). Clover depends for fertilization on the bumblebee; field mice feed on bumblebee nests; cats prey upon the mice; and it is well known that old maids keep cats for company. Thus, it is obvious that the larger the number of spinsters, the better the clover crop.

The Effects of Migration

The effects of hybridization will differ to some extent, depending on the degree of genetic divergence between the populations involved. Let us consider first the simple case in which the populations differ very little. Imagine a population of mice on an island a short distance off the mainland coast, from which migrants regularly reach the island. Assume that the frequency of the gene A is 0.4 in the mainland population but only 0.2 on the island. The effect of these immigrants on the frequency of A in the island population will depend on their genetic contribution to the island population, which is measured by m, the coefficient of replacement. The value of m is determined by the proportion of gametes contributed to the next generation by the immigrants. The change, due to immigration, in the frequency of A on the island is given by the equation,

$$\Delta p = -m(p - p_m)$$

where
$p = $ frequency of A on the island

$p_m = $ frequency of A among the immigrants

$m = $ coefficient of replacement

If m is equal to 10 percent, then

$$\Delta p = -0.1(0.2 - 0.4) = +0.02$$
$$p_0 + \Delta p = p_1 = 0.20 + 0.02 = 0.22$$

Fig. 29·1. Biological complexity; the effect of spinsters on the red clover crop

When $p = p_m$, an equilibrium will be established. If the above rate of immigration persists, it is clear that an equilibrium will soon be reached and that the island population cannot retain its individuality.

In many respects the effects of *migration* or *gene flow* are similar to those of mutation, for both mutation and migration introduce new genes into a population. By migration, favorable genes or gene combinations can spread throughout a species from the population in which they arose. Thus, migration tends to make local populations more nearly alike in gene frequencies and to prevent any significant local differentiation within a species. If isolation is complete ($m = 0$), each population will pursue an independent course. For values of m other than zero, the consequences of migration will depend on the relationship between the amount of gene flow and the factors such as selection pressure and genetic drift that operate within each breeding population. If, for example, the intensity of selection, as measured in terms of the selection coefficient (s), is greater than the effect of immigration as expressed by the coefficient of replacement, then local gene frequencies will depend largely on selection pressure, with migration having only a minor diluting effect. On the other hand, if m is greater than s, the gene frequencies in the local populations will not differ greatly from the average frequencies in the total population.

Introgressive Hybridization

When hybridization occurs between two subspecies or species, the F_1 is usually quite uniform and intermediate in phenotype to the parents. If formed, the F_2 is quite variable, because of the recombination of numerous gene pairs. However, the rare, naturally occurring hybrids have a much greater chance of back crossing to one of the parent species than of mating with each other, and therefore a simple F_2 would only seldom be expected. Thus, where hybridization is taking place under relatively stable environmental conditions, three distinct groups, hybrids and the two parent species, are generally not found. Instead, the parent species will be somewhat more variable than in other areas where they are not sympatric, and each will show some traits suggestive of the other species. This type of situation is known as *introgressive hybridization.* The nearer a back-cross individual resembles one of the well-adapted parents, the better its chances of survival in a stable environment, and hence the more subtle the introgression of the foreign genes. However, if the hybrids are formed in a highly disrupted, unstable environment, new and different adaptive types may be formed that are better adapted to the new conditions than either of the parents. Thus gene flow may occur, even across partial interspecific barriers. An example of introgression has been found in the Mississippi delta country of Louisiana. *Iris fulva* grew in clay soil and partial shade while *Iris hexagona,* a closely related, but quite different-looking species, grew in full sunlight in the tidal marshes (see Fig. 29-2). The clearing of the woodlands and the draining of the swamps have led to considerable introgression in these two species, in some cases with hybrid populations persisting to fill newly created ecological niches. Numerous other examples have been described in plants, most of them in areas disturbed by man. However, two species of sugar maples, ecologically distinct in southern Michigan, have been found hybridizing in a formerly glaciated part of Quebec. When it is realized that many parts of North America were covered by glaciers as recently as 10,000 to 12,000 years ago and that all the animals and plants now living in these areas must have reinvaded them not so very many generations ago, it is easier to visualize how rapidly conditions may change for a given species and how isolation may arise and then break down.

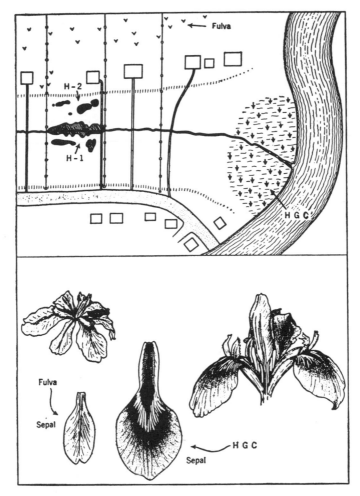

Fig. 29-2. Introgression in iris. Below: Flowers and enlarged sepals of *Iris fulva* (left) and *Iris hexagona* var. *giganticaerulea* (right) to the same scales. Above: Map of the area where these two species are hybridizing. H-1 and H-2 are two somewhat different hybrid colonies. (With permission of Anderson.)

Polyploidy and Evolution

Introgression is possible only if the hybrid is at least partially fertile. However, even if hybrid sterility blocks direct gene flow, genes from two different species may still form viable, fertile polyploids. Most natural polyploids are the result of hybridization between two species, with a subsequent doubling in the number of chromosomes, and hence are allopolyploids. Even many polyploids thought originally to be autopolyploids derived from a single species have frequently, on closer study, been shown to be allopolyploids.

In the broad sense of the word "mutation," polyploidy is a mutational change. It is the only known method by which cataclysmic evolution can occur, giving rise to a new species in a single step, for a new polyploid species is fertile and true breeding yet is reproductively isolated from both parent species. However, it is a specialized and restricted form of evolution, occurring primarily in plants and involving the recombination of existing genes rather than the creation of anything truly new.

Polyploids frequently have different distributions and different ecological preferences from their diploid relatives, and are generally thought to be more tolerant of extreme ecological conditions. For example, in *Biscutella laevigata* of the mustard family Cruciferae, the tetraploids have a continuous distribution over much of Europe including the Alps, the Carpathians, and the mountains of Italy and the northern Balkans. The diploids have a discontinuous distribution and are confined to the valleys of the Rhine, Elbe, Oder, and upper Danube. See Fig. 29-3. The diploids are confined to regions that were not covered by the ice sheets during the glacial period and hence were open to habitation for a long time. The tetraploids exist now in the areas formerly covered by the ice sheet and must have invaded these areas from elsewhere while the diploids were apparently unable to do so. The wider distribution of polyploids may be due to a wider range of adaptability, which permits them to invade and colonize areas newly open to plants.

In several cases it has been possible to resynthesize naturally occurring polyploids and thus prove not only their hybrid origin but also their exact parentage. For instance, the mint *Galeopsis tetrahit* with $2n = 32$ has been resynthesized from *G. pubescens* and *G. speciosa,* each with $2n = 16$. The synthetic polyploid is similar in morphology, cytology, and genetics to the natural species.

In animals, polyploidy is rare and must, therefore, have played only a minor role in animal evolution. The few known animal polyploids occur almost exclusively in hermaphroditic or parthenogenetic species. Its rarity is very probably due to the separation of the sexes in animals, for polyploidy almost inevitably upsets the chromosomal sex-determining mechanism. The normal diploid female in most animal species has two sets of autosomes plus two X chromosomes; the male has two sets of autosomes plus an X and a Y chromosome. In triploid or tetraploid individuals there may be an imbalance between the X and the Y chromosomes (XXY, XYY, XXXY, etc.) or between the sex chromosomes and the autosomes, so that in most cases they are intersexes or sterile or otherwise abnormal. Under these circumstances, maintenance of a stable polyploid condition is very improbable. Since polyploid tissues have been observed

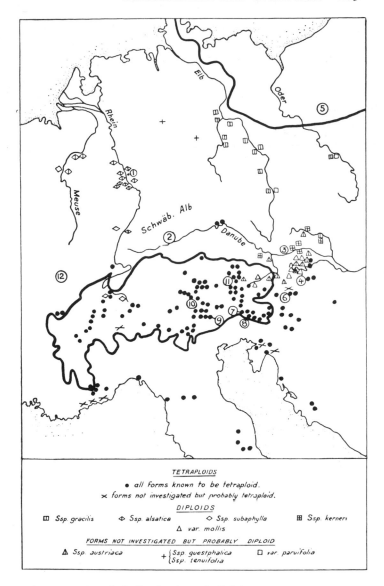

Fig. 29-3. Detailed distribution of diploid and tetraploid forms of the cruciferous plant *Biscutella laevigata* in Central Europe. (Adapted by Manton from Machatschki-Laurich.) The thick black lines represent the boundaries of the ice sheets.

in diploid species, polyploidy is at least possible in animal cells; in fact, polyploid animals have occasionally been reported. Even in man a triploid has been found, and Klinefelter's syndrome, characterized by faulty development of the seminiferous tubules, has been shown to be an XXY intersex condition. Hence, the abnormal sexual development in animal polyploids appears to constitute a major barrier to their success.

Since animal evolution has proceeded normally in many lines in which no polyploids are found, polyploidy cannot be an essential part of the evolutionary mechanism. On the other hand, at least one third of all species of higher plants are polyploid, an indication that polyploidy has obviously played a major role in plant evolution. Nevertheless, it has been suggested that major evolutionary advances have been confined to the diploid lines even in plants, and that polyploids may lead to evolutionary dead ends because of their greater phenotypic stability.

Evolutionary changes involving major adaptive shifts typically occur at exceptionally rapid rates under changing environmental conditions. Mutation rates are thought to be generally too low to provide at any one time the variability necessary to permit such rapid rates of evolution. However, the primary effect of hybridization between members of different populations is to increase greatly the available genetic variability through genetic recombination. Therefore, hybridization has been hypothesized as being especially favorable to rapid rates of evolution. If this is the case, then hybridization has a peculiarly significant role in the evolutionary process. Furthermore, the familiar phylogenetic diagram in the form of a branching tree is incomplete, for the pattern should be reticulate as well as branching.

SUMMARY ◄────────────────────────────────────

Hybridization between members of different breeding populations may result from a breakdown in isolation between the groups. The consequences of hybridization depend upon a number of circumstances. If the populations are genetically rather similar, hybridization may be treated as migration or gene flow from one population to the other, which will tend to reduce and eventually eliminate the genetic differences between them. Thus, extensive gene flow tends to prevent local differentiation of populations within a species. Hybridization between species or relatively well-defined subspecies may lead to introgressive hybridization, the introduction of some genes from one population into the other. An increase in genetic variability may thus occur without a complete swamping of the identity of the parental populations by hybridization. In plants, hybridization followed by chromosome doubling has frequently resulted in the cataclysmic origin of new polyploid species, reproductively isolated from their parents.

SUGGESTED READING

Anderson, E., 1949. *Introgressive hybridization.* New York: Wiley.

Stebbins, G. L., 1950. *Variation and evolution in plants.* New York: Columbia University Press.

———, 1959. "The role of hybridization in evolution," *Proc. Amer. Philosophical Society, 103*(2):231-251.

CHAPTER 30

Isolating Mechanisms

In the two previous chapters we discussed the causes of genetic divergence between allopatric populations and the effects of hybridization on such populations if they again become sympatric. However, during periods of isolation, populations may diverge to the point where they do not interbreed even when they become sympatric again. This reproductive isolation is due to the development of various isolating mechanisms, which serve to prevent or reduce the amount of interbreeding. Geographical or spatial isolation effectively prevents gene exchange only so long as it exists, but isolating mechanisms are under genetic control and will maintain reproductive isolation even between populations that again come in contact with one another. Virtually all of the evidence suggests that the initial stages in the development of isolating mechanisms must occur during a period of spatial isolation. Therefore, the changes leading to reproductive isolation must be incidental to the genetic divergence that occurs during a period of isolation. Crossing between members of closely related groups may be prevented in a variety of different ways, of which we shall consider several for purposes of illustration.

Types of Isolating Mechanisms

Ecological isolating mechanisms are quite common. In the deermouse, *Peromyscus maniculatus,* two races inhabit immediately contiguous areas in Michigan but nevertheless retain their identities. One race is confined to the sandy lakeshore beaches while the other inhabits the forest that starts just a short distance back from the shore. Their habitat preferences are evidently so well defined that interbreeding is negligible. The white crappie and the black crappie (fresh-water fish) inhabit the same streams in Indiana, but despite similar food and other habits, they seldom interbreed, for the white crappie is active by day and the black at night. Edaphic, or soil, conditions isolate the spiderwort, *Tradescantia canaliculata,* which grows in full sunlight at the tops of cliffs, from *T. subaspera,* which grows in the shade at the bottom. Given the opportunity, these two species hybridize readily.

Seasonal isolation may be a very effective barrier to gene exchange. In cockleburs, for example, the flowering times of two species have become so different that in the same area one species flowers only after the other has formed its seed capsules, and the chances of crossing are nonexistent. The American toad (*Bufo americanus*) and Fowler's toad (*B. fowleri*) have quite similar distributions and form fully fertile and viable hybrids in laboratory crosses. However, the two species remain distinct because *B. americanus* breeds early in the season whereas *B. fowleri* breeds late. The occasional hybrids between the species are found in situations where the habitat has been disturbed, indicating a difference in ecological requirements of the species as well.

The most complex behavior patterns in animals are generally in some way associated with reproduction. In essence, courtship consists of a series of stimuli and responses between male and female, with each response serving as a new stimulus. It apparently functions primarily to arouse readiness for mating and to synchronize mating behavior rather than to influence the choice of mates. However, if a male starts to court a female of an entirely different species, the courtship is usually broken off rather quickly because their behavior patterns do not mesh. In this sense, courtship does restrict the choice of mates. This type of isolating mechanism is usually referred to as *sexual isolation* and is based on "psychological" or ethological differences. The lack of mutual attraction has been traced to differences in scents, behavior patterns, sexual recognition signs, and similar traits. Ethological isolation generally precedes the development of sterility barriers and thus is one of the first isolating mechanisms to appear. American ducks such as the mallard and the black duck cross readily in captivity and produce fully fertile offspring, but hybrids in nature are very rare. The eastern meadowlark (*Sturnella magna*) and the western meadowlark (*S. neglecta*) are much alike in appearance and have broadly overlapping ranges but nevertheless seldom interbreed in the zone of overlap. In both cases sexual isolation must play a major role in their reproductive isolation even though other factors undoubtedly contribute also. Although not a factor in plant evolution, the evolution of behavior patterns is of great interest to zoologists, and comparative ethology has been a rapidly growing field of study.

Another group of phenomena may be called *physiological isolating mechanisms.* For example, the sperm of *Drosophila virilis* males show a lower viability in the reproductive tract of alien females (*D. americana*) than in their own females. After copulation in some species of *Drosophila,* the vagina swells greatly owing to the secretion of fluid into the cavity. This *insemination reaction* is accentuated to such an extent in interspecific crosses that fertilization and egg laying may both be blocked for days. In plants, the growth rate of the pollen tube may be slower than normal on a foreign style or in some cases the pollen tube may even burst. Physiological barriers of this sort serve to limit or prevent the union of the gametes so that fertilization does not occur.

Even if fertilization between gametes from different populations takes place, *hybrid inviability* may intervene to prevent the development of a viable hybrid organism. The zygote may cease development at almost any stage, early or late, or may develop into a grossly deformed monster. Such a situation even exists within a single species, *Rana pipiens,* in which hybrids from crosses between leopard frogs from northern and southern United States are deformed and inviable. The inviability of the hybrids results from a disharmony within the embryo, preventing normal development. In plants, another type of disharmony, between the hybrid embryo and the seed coat, a maternal tissue, sometimes blocks normal growth. This effect can be circumvented by removing the embryo from the seed and culturing it *in vitro.* Embryo culture has been used to rear several plant hybrids that had never before been successfully grown.

Interspecific crosses occasionally result in progeny that are all of the same sex. Hybrid inviability is thus confined to just one of the sexes. Haldane perceived that when one sex is absent or rare or sterile in such F_1 hybrids, then that sex is the heterogametic sex. This generalization is sometimes known as Haldane's rule. Accordingly, the male hybrids are defective in most species crosses except in birds, moths, and butterflies, the groups in which the females have ZW sex chromosomes and hence are the heterogametic sex.

In many cases, normal, vigorous hybrids are formed, but are sterile. The further exchange of genes is in this way completely blocked. The mule is the classical example of *hybrid sterility.* Any one of a number of conditions may cause hybrids to be sterile. In general, either the sex organs fail to develop sufficiently for meiosis to take place, or else abnormalities in the meiotic process itself (for example, in synapsis or spindle formation) prevent the formation of normal gametes.

Even when vigorous, fertile F_1 hybrids are produced, *hybrid breakdown* in the F_2 or back-cross generations may contribute to reproductive isolation. In such instances the subsequent generations may manifest reduced vigor or fertility or both.

All of the isolating mechanisms mentioned above are in some way genetically controlled and will restrict the exchange of genes between different groups of animals or plants. Once reproductive isolation of this sort is firmly established, the evolutionary paths of these groups will have passed the point of no return. No longer will they combine to form a common breeding population. Generally, several isolating mechanisms exist between different species; thus, even though no one mechanism is completely effective, their combined effects cause total reproductive isolation. A major problem is to account for their mode of origin, for the achievement of reproductive isolation is the crucial step in speciation.

The Origin of Isolating Mechanisms

Two major theories have been proposed to explain the origin of isolating mechanisms. Muller suggested that reproductive isolation is an incidental by-product of the genetic divergence that occurs during the origin of subspecies and species in allopatric populations. In other words, as the evolving populations adapt to their different environments, a reshuffling and restructuring of the genes, the chromosomes, and the entire genotype occurs. As a result, if the populations again become sympatric, incompatibilities causing reproductive isolation will already exist. Dobzhansky's theory is that reproductive isolation arises as a result of natural selection. He, too, recognized the genotypes as integrated systems of genes that, when drawn from different populations, may be incompatible. Hybrids often are poorly adapted or partially sterile and hence they will tend to be eliminated by natural selection. Since selection eliminates not only the hybrids but at the same time the genes of the parents that hybridized, selection is acting against hybridization itself. Those individuals that hybridize and those genes favoring hybridization will gradually be eliminated from the population. Natural selection thus acts to reduce the wastage of gametes on the less-fit hybrids. These theories, of course, are not mutually exclusive but complementary. Although some relevant evidence is available, additional research is needed to evaluate the relative importance of these two mechanisms and to clarify still further the basis for the reproductive isolation between closely related populations.

► *SUMMARY*

Isolating mechanisms, which are mechanisms for maintaining reproductive isolation between sympatric populations, are under genetic control. They may be ecological, seasonal, ethological, or physiological barriers to fertilization; or, if fertilization occurs, hybrid inviability, hybrid sterility, or hybrid breakdown in the F_2 may intervene to restrict the successful exchange of genes between different populations. Isolating mechanisms have been thought to arise as an incidental by-product of the genetic divergence occurring during speciation, but it has also been postulated that natural selection against poorly adapted hybrids—in the final analysis, selection against hybridization itself—will tend to build up barriers to crossing.

SUGGESTED READING

Dobzhansky, Th., 1951. *Genetics and the origin of species,* 3d ed. New York: Columbia University Press.

Mayr, E., 1942. *Systematics and the origin of species,* New York: Columbia University Press.

Stebbins, G. L., 1950. *Variation and evolution in plants.* New York: Columbia University Press.

CHAPTER 31

The Origin of Species

Up to this point we have used the word "species" without defining the term. This vagueness has been purposeful. Now, however, as we begin our discussion of the origin of species, a definition is clearly in order. One reason for having avoided the question until now is that so many definitions exist. For example, a serological species definition runs like this:

A species of helminths may be tentatively defined as a group of organisms, the lipid-free antigen of which, when diluted 1:4,000 or more, yields a positive precipitin test within one hour with a rabbit antiserum produced by injecting 40 mg of dry weight, lipid-free antigenic material and withdrawn 10 to 12 days after the last of 4 intravenous injections every third day.

This definition certainly has precision, though just what it signifies is a little less obvious.

Another type of definition: "A species is what a competent taxonomist considers to be a species." The problem is now simplified. Rather than classifying organisms, we now classify taxonomists into two categories: A. Competent; B. Incompetent.

A definition rather surprising in that it came from a geneticist is, "Distinct species must be separable on the basis of ordinary preserved material. This is in order to make it possible for a museum man to apply a name to his material." This statement is an extreme form of a whole group of definitions that use morphological criteria to distinguish between species. Furthermore, it suggests that the primary purpose of taxonomy is to facilitate the handling of museum specimens.

The Species as a Biological Unit

Another group of definitions has come to be known as biological species definitions in contrast to the morphological definitions. Mayr has said, "Species are groups of actually or potentially interbreeding natural populations that are reproductively isolated from other such groups." Dobzhansky wrote, "Species are formed when a once actually or potentially interbreeding array of Mendelian populations becomes segregated in two or more reproductively isolated arrays," or, more briefly, "A species is the most inclusive Mendelian population." These definitions treat the species as a dynamic unit, a stage in the process of evolution, and not as a fixed static entity. The emphasis lies on the achievement of reproductive isolation, with the critical point in the origin of species the fixation of discontinuity between different populations. At the point when genetic discontinuity has been reached so that two populations thenceforward pursue independent evolutionary paths, species status is attained; up to that point they must be regarded as races or subspecies. The morphological species definitions are subjective, for they depend on the judgment of the taxonomist as to the degree of morphological similarity or difference worthy of species status. The biological definitions are more objective, for the behavior of the organisms themselves is the factor that determines their relationship. The significant question is whether they do or do not interbreed. The question is *not* whether they *can* interbreed but whether they actually *do*. Under experimental conditions, many "good" species can be induced to cross-and may produce viable, fertile offspring; but if, under natural conditions, little or no gene flow occurs between them, their evolutionary paths remain separate and distinct. Most North American ducks, for example, are completely interfertile, but hybrids are extremely rare, and so they remain distinct species.

The primary objective of a species definition is to describe as well as possible the natural biological relationships of the populations involved. The species is a natural biological unit tied together by bonds of mating and sharing a common gene pool. For this reason, it has objective reality. All of the other taxonomic categories—subspecies, genera, families, orders, etc.—are the subjective creations of taxonomists, for the criterion of reproductive isolation is inapplicable. Among the various taxonomic categories the species is unique.

Although the biological definition comes closest to describing the biological realities, its application may lead to difficulties. For one, the definition is essentially nondimensional, not applicable to species living in different places or at different times, for it cannot be determined whether populations isolated from each other either in space or in time will actually interbreed. To the museum taxonomist working with dead specimens, and especially to the paleontologist, who has no choice but to work with nonliving materials, this definition is of no value. However, again we must return to the objectives of a species definition.

Undoubtedly, if it were possible, paleontologists would prefer to use a biological criterion; it would probably considerably simplify the nomenclature in some groups. And modern taxonomy is rapidly moving beyond the point of relying solely on morphological traits in dead specimens, but is utilizing information on all aspects of the biology of a group in arriving at valid taxonomic groupings. A further implication of the biological definition is that two morphologically similar groups may be distinct species while two groups widely divergent in morphology may belong to the same species. The reasons for this situation are relatively simple. The morphology of an organism is essentially a reflection of its physiology, and physiological changes leading to reproductive isolation may well precede any major morphological changes. On the other hand, adaptive shifts leading to morphological changes may not affect the basic reproductive pattern sufficiently to lead to reproductive isolation. These possibilities are not merely theoretical; certain reproductively isolated species of *Drosophila* show virtually no major morphological differences. *Drosophila pseudoobscura* and *D. persimilis,* for instance, were formerly known as races A and B of *D. pseudoobscura.* In contrast, European and American sycamores of the genus *Platanus* are quite different in appearance and have been assigned specific rank (*P. orientalis* and *P. occidentalis*); yet their interfertility when grown together indicates that species distinction may be unwarranted. One final difficulty with the biological species definition is that it is limited to sexually reproducing species. In groups reproducing asexually, evolutionary change can occur only by sequential mutations in a given line, with selection between lines. Since each line of descent is isolated from the others, each is pursuing an independent evolutionary path, but this hardly justifies assigning specific rank to each. Sexual reproduction is practically universal among the more complex or highly evolved animals and plants, very probably because evolution can proceed more rapidly in sexually reproducing species. Genes and gene combinations favored by selection can be combined and recombined in a manner impossible with asexual reproduction, and hence adaptation and evolution are more flexible and more rapid. However, in spite of the difficulties inherent in the biological species definition, the morphological species and the biological species generally agree, and the exceptional cases are most instructive.

Modes of Evolution

The ways in which species originate are two or possibly three. Speciation, or the multiplication of species, leads to an increase in the number of contemporary species. All the basic problems of evolution are wrapped up in the process of speciation, the way in which one species can split into two, and to this question we have devoted most of our attention. In brief, two or more populations of a species, upon becoming physically isolated, may diverge as the result of different mutation pressures, selection pressures, random genetic drift, or the net effect of all three. If gene flow is still possible through hybridization, migration pressures will be exerted, with the more favorable genes or gene combinations being disseminated throughout the species. In this fashion a complex evolutionary pattern may develop, involving interpopulation selection. However, if the isolated populations diverge to the point of reproductive isolation, they will have achieved the status of distinct species. The process of speciation is diagramed in Fig. 31-1.

The transformation of a species in time is a second mode of evolution. Simpson recognizes two types of transformation, which he has called "phyletic" evolution and "quantum" evolution. Phyletic evolution involves a sustained, directional shift in the average characters of a population; it is, in other words,

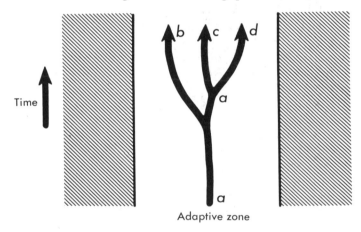

Adaptive zone

Fig. 31-1. Speciation: an increase in the number of species, achieved when the different populations become reproductively isolated. (After Simpson.)

a line of succession rather than an increase in the total number of existing species. Phyletic evolution may be due to adaptation to a shifting environment or to increasing specialization or improved adaptation in a constant environment, and may be thought of as leading eventually to the origin of new genera and families. Diagrammatically, phyletic evolution is shown in Fig. 31-2. Most paleontology is devoted to the study of phyletic evolutionary changes.

Quantum evolution, also known as mega- and macroevolution, is the term applied to the rapid shift of a population to a new equilibrium distinctly unlike the ancestral condition, thus leading to the origin of higher taxonomic categories such as new orders and classes. The origin of the higher taxonomic categories has presented a problem because new orders and classes generally appear suddenly in the fossil record, without evidence of intermediate fossil types. If evolution is a gradual process, as both Darwin and modern theory hold, then it might be expected that fossils connecting different orders would be found as evidence of the gradual evolutionary transition from one group to another. Their absence has led some students of evolution to postulate that a different mechanism is responsible for the origin of higher groups, and that mutation, selection, gene flow, and genetic drift are responsible only for microevolutionary changes. Macroevolution has, for instance, been attributed to extremely rare macromutations or systemic mutations, which have such drastic effects that they give rise to "hopeful monsters." If, perchance, a "monster" is adapted to a new and different way of life, then the new adaptive type survives, and because it is so different, it clearly belongs in a new taxonomic group. For example, the Diptera, or two-winged flies, are clearly derived from the four-winged insects, with the

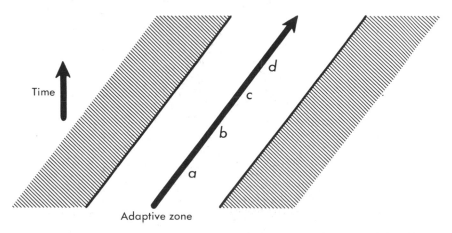

Fig. 31-2. Phyletic evolution: transformation in time leading to origin of new genera and families. (After Simpson.)

gyroscopic halteres homologous to the second pair of wings. Since a mutation, *tetraptera,* is known that converts a dipteran into a four-winged insect, thus at one step excluding it from its own order, it is quite conceivable that at some time in the past the reverse occurred and the Diptera were derived from some four-winged insect order by a single systemic mutation giving rise at one step to a two-winged insect and hence to a new order. However, such an origin for higher taxonomic groups seems very improbable. Aside from the fact that no systemic mutations have ever been demonstrated, among the arguments against this explanation two seem particularly telling. It is extremely unlikely that a single chance mutation would cause all of the many changes in the physiology and morphology of the organism that would be necessary to produce a type sufficiently well adapted to a new mode of existence to be considered a new order. The differences between orders are numerous and varied and have clearly involved the reorganization of the entire genotype rather than a single mutation, no matter how drastic its effects. Furthermore, if systemic mutations are so precious and so rare, and give rise to new orders at one bound, then in sexually reproducing species this lone individual of the new order becomes a voice in the wilderness seeking its mate, which does not exist, and hence the order that originated at one step becomes extinct in one step. If they are frequent enough to occur contemporaneously, they should have been observed by now. On the other hand, if the mutant mates with members of the parent species, it has not even achieved reproductive isolation and can hardly be regarded as anything but a rather drastic mutation, certainly not a new order.

The Origin of Higher Taxonomic Groups

If quantum evolution cannot be explained by systemic mutation or other even less satisfactory theories, how can it be explained within the existing theoretical framework and why are large gaps so common in the fossil record between the orders and other higher taxonomic categories? In order to discuss this question it seems advisable to discuss preadaptation, a word often subject to misinterpretation. We shall use it, not in the sense that the organisms foresee the course of their own evolution and make the necessary adaptive shifts before they are actually needed, but rather in the sense that in the process of becoming adapted to existing conditions, the organisms are modified in such a way that they are also adapted, *by chance,* to some other set of conditions under which they have never existed. The first step in the evolution of an internal parasite, for example, would be the development of the ability to survive within the body of its host. Of necessity, this type of change would have to be preadaptive. The lungfish are adapted to survive in warm, stagnant waters with a low oxygen content because the lungs enable them to obtain oxygen from air. However, lungs were preadaptive for terrestrial life. Hence, it appears that preadaptation can arise as an incidental by-product of adaptation.

It is, therefore, entirely conceivable that numerous preadaptations may exist at any particular time. If a new evolutionary opportunity or ecological niche opens up to a preadapted population, it may occupy the new niche relatively rapidly though still by the gradual neo-Darwinian process involving mutation, natural selection, and possibly genetic drift and gene flow. The shift has been visualized in terms of a shift from one adaptive zone to another or from one adaptive peak to another, as shown in Fig. 31-3.

Next let us consider the conditions under which evolutionary changes will occur most rapidly. These conditions exist when a species is subdivided into many relatively small, partially isolated populations. Each constitutes essentially a separate adaptive experiment, for divergence is not only possible but probable as each population adapts to its own immediate environment. Any particularly successful group can spread rapidly either by migration and gene flow into adjacent populations (since isolation is incomplete) or by winning out in inter-population competition. Striking new adaptive types appear most likely to emerge when a species range covers a diversified environment or when the environment itself is unstable, for then a variety of selection pressures is exerted.

Therefore, the origin of a higher taxonomic group such as an order may occur in a single, rather small, preadapted population of a species to which a new ecological niche becomes available. The entire transition may occur in a relatively short time, geologically speaking, and involve relatively few individuals compared to the numbers of the old and new orders that lived before, after, and even during the transition. Viewed in this light, it is not at all surprising that so

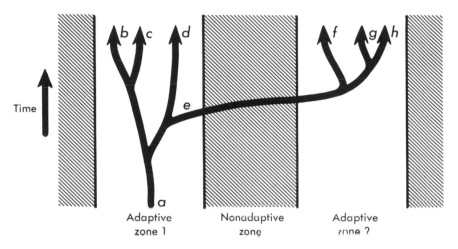

Fig. 31-3. Quantum evolution: transformation in time leading to the origin of major higher categories such as orders. Note that speciation, phyletic evolution, and quantum evolution may go on simultaneously and that at all times the basic evolutionary unit is a breeding population. (After Simpson.)

few transitional fossil types have been found. It becomes simply a matter of statistics and not a unique or mysterious process. It should be noted that the species is the evolutionary unit even when it is giving rise to higher taxonomic levels. Evolution at all levels and rates is due to changes in gene frequencies within breeding populations. Phyletic and quantum evolution are useful descriptive terms, but they do not imply a different mechanism of evolution. All three processes may be concurrent, and the changes may be rapid or slow, requiring millions of years, but the species remains the basic unit of evolution under all circumstances.

The fossil record of the horse family or Equidae is probably as well known as that of any other group. Early horses were small browsing animals, feeding on the tender foliage of trees and shrubs. They evolved and diversified within the browsing adaptive zone. One group gave rise suddenly to the grazing horses, which fed on harsh grasses, but despite the wealth of fossil Equidae material, no intermediates are known. The preadaptive change in this case appears to be the development of the larger and higher crowned teeth required to grind up the necessary amount of vegetation to support the larger body that had evolved in some of the browsing horses. These teeth were preadaptive for grazing, and if the horse now supplemented its diet with grass, a new ecological niche was opened up. Since the prairie habitat was apparently not occupied by significant competitive herbivores, selection pressures would then be very strongly in favor of the transition, for competition would be keen for the browsing animals and slight at this point for grazing animals. The ultimate result—adaptation by the Equidae to two kinds of food—permitted an increase in the total number of existing horses.

One point, however, should be made in relation to the models of quantum evolution. The species must remain well adapted during any and all transitions. If it did not, it would become extinct. For example, major changes in the form and function of the foot have not required that the members of a species hobble around during the transition period, which could well have been a million years or more. Thus, the nonadaptive zones or the nonadaptive valleys are misleading. One species' peak may be another species' valley; or, for a given species, the peak itself moves as the species evolves.

Although much still remains to be learned, the broad outlines of the course of evolution and of the mechanism of evolution are now fairly well understood. More research on the effect one species has on its own evolution or on that of other species is needed. Darwin's theory of sexual selection, now more or less in limbo, was an attempt to study the effect of a species on its own evolution (see Fig. 31-4). The cooperative as well as the competitive aspects of natural selection are decidedly in need of further study, for cooperative efforts may confer a reproductive advantage to a particular population in competition with other populations. Evolution then may reflect the effects of both cooperation and competition.

A breeding population is an array of genes, temporarily embodied in individuals, but endlessly combined and recombined by the process of sexual reproduction. New genes may be added to the existing array by mutation or by gene flow, while random genetic drift may lead to chance fluctuations in the existing gene pool. Each individual, each new combination of genes, is a unique

Fig. 31-4. Darwin's finches: speciation, following the initial invasion of the Galápagos Islands by finches from South America, has given rise to fourteen closely related but divergent species. (With permission of Lack.)

adaptive experiment to be tested by natural selection. Similarly, each breeding population is a unique adaptive experiment to be tested by natural selection in competition with other populations. Although our discussion, by focusing primarily on events at a single gene locus, has oversimplified a very complex mechanism, it has indicated the general nature of the process of evolution.

SUMMARY ◄───────────────────────────

Although many species definitions have been proposed, most of them can be categorized as either "morphological" or "biological." The morphological species definitions use the degree of morphological similarity as the criterion for distinguishing between species. The biological species definitions emphasize reproductive isolation as the essential criterion without regard to morphological traits. The biological definitions are more objective, in that the judgment is based on the behavior of the organisms in nature rather than on the subjective opinion of a taxonomist. The fundamental question is not whether the members of the two populations can interbreed but whether, in fact, they do. If they do not, they are pursuing independent evolutionary paths and must therefore be regarded as separate species. The nature of this definition makes it applicable primarily to sympatric sexually reproducing organisms. Three types of evolutionary change have been recognized—speciation, phyletic evolution, and quantum evolution—but all the fundamental questions about evolution are related to the process of speciation. Even the origin of higher taxonomic groups appears to have been the result of relatively gradual changes in the hereditary traits of an interbreeding group of organisms.

SUGGESTED READING

Amadon, D., 1950. "The Hawaiian honeycreepers," *Bull. Amer. Museum of Natural History,* Vol. 95.

Clausen, J., 1951. *Stages in the evolution of plant species.* Ithaca, N. Y.: Cornell University Press.

Darwin, C., 1872. *The origin of species.* New York: Mentor Books (1958).

Dobzhansky, Th., 1951. *Genetics and the origin of species,* 3d ed. New York: Columbia University Press.

Lack, D., 1947. *Darwin's finches.* New York: Cambridge University Press.

Mayr, E., ed., 1957. *The species problem.* AAAS Symp. 50.

CHAPTER 32

Evolution of Genetic Systems

Thus far we have discussed evolution almost exclusively in terms of sexually reproducing, diploid species. This type of genetic system is undoubtedly the most familiar reproductive mechanism because it is predominant among the higher animals and plants. However, it is by no means the only scheme possible, and many other systems are known. In view of these possibilities, the question may well be posed as to why sexuality and diploidy should have come to assume their predominant position. If evolution and natural selection have affected the hereditary characteristics of organisms in such ways that they become phenotypically better adapted to survive and reproduce in their physical and biological environments, there is no reason to suppose that the hereditary mechanism itself is not similarly subject to modification and improvement under the influence of evolutionary forces. The fossil record gives some clues to the course of evolution in morphological traits, but no similar clues are available for the evolution of genetic systems, and conclusions in this area are based primarily on inferences derived from our knowledge of living species. Although our surmises as to their mode or sequence of origin must be regarded as rather speculative, the fact that a great diversity of different genetic systems exists cannot be disputed.

Genetic Recombination

Except for several viruses in which RNA is utilized, the control and transmission of hereditary traits, from viruses up to man, reside in a single type of compound, DNA. In viruses, bacteria, and the blue-green algae, the DNA does not appear to be organized into well-defined structures, comparable in organization and behavior to the chromosomes of higher plants and animals. For a long time it was assumed that these rather simple, primitive organisms reproduced only asexually, and that sexual reproduction, leading to genetic recombination, had evolved from asexually reproducing species. However, the recent discovery of various kinds of genetic recombination in bacteria and viruses has reopened the question of which is the more primitive condition, sexuality or asexuality.

The processes observed in these simple organisms are in several respects different from sexual reproduction in higher plants and animals. It should be noted and emphasized that sexual reproduction has very little to do with sex in the Freudian sense. Though separate sexes, male and female, are sometimes involved, the essence of sexual reproduction is genetic recombination. Corn and earthworms, for example, do not have individuals of different sex, yet they reproduce sexually. If those processes resulting in genetic recombination are termed sexual, then the unusual forms of recombination in viruses and bacteria fall within the realm of sexuality.

Transformation, the artificial recombination in *Pneumococcus* induced when DNA from one strain is added to a culture of a different strain, has already been mentioned in an earlier chapter. In *Escherichia coli,* the colon bacillus, strains have been found that regularly undergo genetic recombination during cellular contact. In this case, however, only part of a single "chromosome" or linkage group from one type of strain (F+ or Hfr) enters an F- cell to form a partial heterozygote. The size of the transferred fragment is related to the time allowed for cellular contact. Still another type of genetic recombination in bacteria, known as transduction, is mediated by bacterial viruses or bacteriophages. In transduction, DNA from one strain of bacteria is transferred to a different strain by means of the phage. Thus three rather different recombination mechanisms are known in bacteria: transformation, transduction, and cellular fusion. They differ in amount of DNA transferred (least in transformation, greatest with fusion) and they also differ from recombination in higher organisms in that less than a complete genetic complement may be involved.

A whole new field of genetics has been opened up by the discovery that genetic recombination occurs in bacteriophages. Since a phage particle consists of a DNA core covered by a protein sheath, it is of great interest that even at this simple level of organization genetic recombination is possible. Since the phages multiply only in association with a bacterial host, recombination occurs only when a single bacterium harbors more than one type of virus particle. As yet sexual processes have not been reported in blue-green algae or in many types of bacteria. However, it would not be surprising if future studies reveal recombination mechanisms in additional groups of microorganisms.

The evolution of the somewhat more complex unicellular algae and protozoans was accompanied by a more complex and precise organization of the genetic material itself. The genes were organized into chromosomes within a nucleus, and mitosis provided for the exact distribution of a complete set of hereditary material to each daughter cell following asexual cell division. Similarly, meiosis insured the exact segregation and union of complete chromosome sets during sexual reproduction. These three advances, the origin of chromosomes, mitosis, and meiosis, represent major steps in the evolution of the genetic material.

Asexual versus Sexual Reproduction

In spite of the fact that genetic recombination is known from even the simplest and most primitive of organisms, it is nevertheless true that asexual reproduction is very common among organisms at many levels of organization and complexity. This observation raises questions about the adaptive advantages and disadvantages of both asexual and sexual modes of reproduction. On the assumption that asexuality is the more primitive condition, then sexual reproduction has arisen independently a number of times. On the contrary assumption, that sexuality is more primitive, then asexual reproduction has evolved repeatedly. In either case, the indications are that the genetic system has adaptive value and has been modified during the course of evolution. Arguments and theories favoring both assumptions have been advanced in recent years, with perhaps a preponderance favoring sexuality as the more primitive state in view of the recent discovery of genetic recombination in viruses and bacteria. It is appropriate, therefore, to consider now the adaptive significance of asexual reproduction.

Any asexual method of reproduction provides a means whereby rapid self-duplication of a particular genotype is possible. If this genotype is well adapted to a given stable environment, asexual reproduction is then a more efficient means of rapidly colonizing this environment and maintaining a well-adapted population there than is sexual reproduction. With genetic recombination a variety of new genotypes is produced, many of which may be poorly adapted to the existing stable environment. Asexual reproduction will also be advantageous where the numbers of individuals are so small that the probability of encountering suitable mating partners is low. However, an asexually reproducing population is poorly equipped to adapt to rapidly changing environmental conditions. Its sole means of adapting to changed conditions is through the chance occurrence of rare favorable mutations. In species such as bacteria with large numbers and high rates of multiplication, this method of adaptation may be sufficient as a buffer against extinction, but in other species it is not.

Sexual reproduction, on the other hand, through the shuffling and sorting of genes into new and different combinations with each generation, provides a constant source of new phenotypes for testing against the environment. Although at any one time and place there will be a smaller proportion of well-adapted individuals than would be produced by a well-adapted asexual population, a sexually reproducing population is better able to adjust to changing environmental conditions and to exploit new and different ecological niches. It is not surprising, therefore, that among the so-called higher or more complex organisms, sexual reproduction seems to be the mechanism through which this complexity has evolved.

If sexual recombination is truly the more primitive mode of reproduction, then asexual reproduction is a condition derived from it. The asexual status of many bacteria, protozoans, and other groups of microorganisms can then be interpreted as an adaptive phenomenon in these organisms. Many of them exist in relatively stable environments in which rapid asexual multiplication is advantageous. Others, living under unstable conditions, are nonetheless capable of such rapid multiplication and can adapt so readily via single mutations that asexual reproduction would still have an adaptive advantage over any benefits from genetic recombination.

Haploidy versus Diploidy

Although there may still be some doubt as to the primitive status of sexual phenomena, it seems reasonably clear that haploidy is the primitive state from which diploidy has been evolved in a number of different unrelated groups. At the level of organization above the viruses, bacteria, and blue-green algae—namely, the flagellates and the green algae—the genetic material is organized into chromosomes that undergo mitosis and meiosis. The most primitive flagellates and green algae are haploid; the only diploid cell is the zygote, and this cell undergoes two meiotic divisions that immediately restore the haploid condition. In the evolution of both higher plants and animals, there has been a definite trend toward prolongation of the diploid phase. In other words, the interval between fertilization and meiosis has increased, with a number of mitotic divisions of the diploid nucleus intervening before meiosis. This observation raises at once the question of the adaptive advantages of diploidy.

The Metazoa and some groups of Protozoa are completely diploid except for the gametes; that is, meiosis is deferred until just prior to gamete formation. In plants, a similar situation exists in the diatoms, yeasts, certain green algae, and some of the brown algae. Among the algae, the haploid life cycle has frequently given rise to an alternation of haploid and diploid generations that are morphologically very much alike. In this case the zygote divides mitotically to form the plant body, but the deferred meiosis, when it occurs, produces haploid spores rather than gametes. The spores then germinate and develop into a haploid organism similar in form to the diploid. It appears that from this type of life cycle, known as an isomorphic one, two different types of heteromorphic life cycles have been derived. The predominant diploid type is found in the vascular plants and some of the more complex brown algae. A predominantly haploid life cycle is found in a few algal groups and in the mosses and liverworts. The early theory that the evolution of a predominant diploid generation made possible the invasion of the land by plants now appears to be incorrect. For one thing, the complex marine brown algae also have a predominant diploid phase, whereas many terrestrial fungi have retained the haploid condition. Furthermore, the bryophytes, supposedly representative of a stage intermediate between the haploid algae and the predominantly diploid vascular plants, are apparently more recent in origin than the oldest vascular plants and represent an evolutionary dead end rather than a transitional form. Therefore, it appears that the adaptive advantages of diploidy must be sought elsewhere than in its relationship to the invasion of the land.

In a haploid organism, the genotype, whatever it may be, is immediately expressed. All of the genotypes in a population are exposed to selection at all times, and little variability can be retained since all mutants unfavorable at the moment will be eliminated. A diploid, however, may carry a considerable amount of unexpressed variability in the form of recessive genes in the heterozygous condition. A portion of this variability will be released and exposed to selection each generation owing to genetic recombination. In this way a population retains its ability to adapt to changing environmental conditions while at the same time remaining well adapted to the prevailing conditions. The flexibility should not be regarded as simply dependent upon the appearance of new homozygous recessive mutant types, however, for diploidy also opens up the possibility for interallelic, epistatic, and heterotic effects which may be of considerable importance. In general diploidy is associated with the more complex organisms that have a long, precisely integrated sequence of development. In haploids, evolution is primarily dependent upon the appearance of suitable favorable mutations. Diploidy, through gene recombination and interaction, permits the formation of new and different integrated systems of genes without serious loss of fitness. The effects of most single gene mutations on a complex developmental sequence are deleterious, and in organisms with low reproductive rates and a long developmental period, favorable individual mutations would customarily be too rare to give adequate adaptive flexibility. Thus, diploidy would appear to be an adaptive means of conserving and releasing variability in higher organisms. In the mosses and liverworts the predominant haploid gametophyte may have evolved in relation to their pioneering tendency, for a well-adapted initial invader can quickly produce a colony of similarly well-adapted descendants.

The Separation of the Sexes

We have already seen that genetic recombination has been observed in even the simplest of organisms. The evolution of organisms of greater complexity has been accompanied by the evolution of more complex systems for ensuring sexual reproduction. In the Protozoa, two types of sexual process are known. In conjugation, a temporary contact between two protozoans—for example, paramecia—permits nuclear exchange. In syngamy, an actual fusion of sex cells or gametes takes place to form a zygote. In some cases the fusing gametes, known as isogametes, are identical in size and form to, and little different from, the parent cells. In other species, the sex cells, called anisogametes, are similar in form but quite different in size, while in still others differentiation of the gametes into sperm and egg cells has occurred. All of these types of reproduction have been observed in one flagellate group, the Phytomonadina, and suggest how the differentiation of sex cells could have taken place.

In the colonial flagellate, *Volvox,* a single colony is capable of producing both sperm and egg cells. The production of two kinds of gametes, sperm and egg, by a single individual is known as hermaphroditism. Hermaphrodites are found throughout the plant kingdom, though some plants such as willows or the ginkgo have separate sexes. Hermaphroditism is widespread among animals though not so common as in plants; in such important groups as nematodes, insects, and vertebrates it is rare or absent. Because it is so common, particularly among the lower animals and plants, it appears that hermaphroditism, among multicellular animals and plants at least, is the ancestral condition from which the separation of the sexes has been derived. Furthermore, the separation of the sexes has even been obtained experimentally in hermaphroditic species—for example, in corn—through the suppression of functional male flowers in one type of plant and functional female flowers in another. (Species with separate sexes are frequently referred to in the literature as bisexual, an unfortunate and confusing choice of terms since bisexual is synonymous with hermaphroditic.)

Sex Determination

In hermaphrodites, such as corn or an earthworm, male and female sex cells are produced by an individual with a single genotype. In this case sexual differentiation cannot be determined genetically, but rather by subtle differences in the internal environment comparable to those leading to the differentiation of other organs of the body.

In species with separate sexes, a variety of methods of sex determination have evolved. Here, too, environmental sex determination occurs. The best-known example comes from the marine echiurid worm, *Bonellia.* If the free-swimming larva, when it settles to the sea bottom to undergo further development, happens to land on the proboscis of a female, it will enter the body of the female where it differentiates into a minute male, living a parasitic existence in the nephridium near the uterus. If the larva lands on the sea bottom, it differentiates into a free-living female some 500 times as large as the male. The environmental nature of sex determination in this species can be demonstrated by

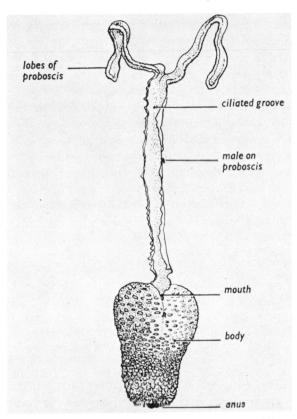

lobes of
proboscis

ciliated groove

male on
proboscis

mouth

body

anus

Fig. 32-1. The echiurid marine worm *Bonellia,* showing the vast size difference between the sexes despite environmental sex determination. (With permission of Begg.)

rearing larvae in sea water containing female proboscis extract. All of the larvae then become males. See Fig. 32-1.

In the majority of species with separate sexes, sex determination has been brought under genetic control. A number of different types of genetic sex determination have been identified. The most familiar type involves a heterogametic male. In this situation the male carries two different kinds of sex chromosomes, the X and Y, and produces two kinds of sperm, bearing either an X plus the autosomes, or a Y plus the autosomes. The XX females produce only one type of egg, having a single X and a set of autosomes. A variation is found in some species in which the females are XX and the males XO, having one less chromosome than the females.

In the heterogametic female type of sex determination, it is the female that has two different kinds of sex chromosomes, conventionally called Z and W. Consequently, the female produces two kinds of eggs. Here, too, a ZO modification has been demonstrated in some species. Heterogametic females are found in moths and butterflies, in birds, and in some fishes. Heterogametic males are found in most other groups with separate sexes.

The work of Bridges on sex determination in *Drosophila melanogaster* led to the development of the balance theory of sex determination. As a result of his findings he concluded that the presence of two X chromosomes was not alone sufficient to determine femaleness nor were an X and a Y sufficient for maleness. Rather, sex was influenced by the autosomes as well as the sex chromosomes and the significant feature was the ratio of X chromosomes to haploid sets of autosomes. The basis for his conclusion was a study of the sexual characteristics of flies with abnormal numbers of sex chromosomes and autosomes. Some of the types he obtained were as follows:

chromosome complement (X = X chromosomes; A = sets of autosomes)	ratio X/A	Phenotype
3X : 2A	1.5	superfemale
3X : 3A	1.0	normal triploid female
2X : 2A	1.0	normal diploid female
2X : 3A	0.67	intersex
1X : 2A	0.50	normal male
1X : 3A	0.33	supermale

Of particular interest is the intersex shown above. It has two X chromosomes, but is not a normal female since the balance between sex chromosomes and autosomes has been upset. All of the types observed were consistent with the rule that an X/A ratio of 1.0 or above resulted in a female (normal or super) and a ratio of 0.5 or below in a male (normal or super). Ratios between 0.5 and 1.0 produced intersexes, showing varying admixtures of male and female traits. The subsidiary role of the Y chromosome in *Drosophila* is shown by the fact that an XXY individual with two sets of autosomes is a fertile female.

In the bryophytes (the mosses and liverworts) a somewhat different type of chromosomal sex determination has been observed—the heterozygous sporophyte. In this case the diploid sporophyte is neither male nor female but carries an X and a Y chromosome as well as the autosomes. The spores produced by the sporophyte are of two kinds: X-bearing spores develop into female gametophytes; Y bearing, into male gametophytes.

Even more significant is the type of sex determination exemplified by *Melandrium album,* a member of the pink family. In this species, some plants bear only male flowers and others only female flowers. The females have two X chromosomes plus two sets of autosomes; the males, an X and a Y chromosome in addition to the autosomes. However, sex determination in polyploids of *Melandrium* has shown the mechanism to be different from that in *Drosophila.* In *Melandrium,* the Y chromosome is male determining. As long as the Y is absent, any ratio of X to A in diploids, triploids, or tetraploids will produce fertile female plants and no intersexes. A single Y is sufficient to produce male plants even in triploids and tetraploids. Thus, for example, the following types are all male plants:

diploid	2A—X—Y
triploid	3A—X—2Y
	3A—2X—Y
tetraploid	4A—2X—2Y
	4A—3X—Y

None are intersexes, though occasionally a male plant will bear an hermaphroditic flower. Thus, quite a different use is made of the XY mechanism in *Melandrium* and in *Drosophila.* In *Melandrium,* the X chromosome seems to bear genes for femaleness, the Y carries genes for maleness, and the autosomes are without apparent influence on sexuality. In *Drosophila,* the factors for femaleness seem to be borne on the X chromosomes, those for maleness on the autosomes, and the Y, aside from an effect on fertility, seems to have little influence. The work on *Melandrium* has recently assumed new interest with the discovery that sex determination in mice and men, and probably in other mammals, is similar to that in *Melandrium* and not like that in *Drosophila.* This conclusion is based on the discovery that sterile human females with a condition known as Turner's syndrome are XO diploids. A fruit fly of this constitution would be phenotypically male. Furthermore, sterile human males with Klinefelter's syndrome are XXY and diploid for the autosomes. As mentioned above, in *Drosophila* such individuals are phenotypic females and not males. Thus in man the Y chromosome is male determining.

In the Hymenoptera (the ants, wasps, and bees), still another type of sex determination exists. Here the female is diploid; the male, haploid. The sex of an individual depends upon whether the egg is fertilized. Fertilized eggs develop into females; unfertilized eggs develop parthenogenetically into haploid males. Hence, whereas in most groups the sex ratio is fixed, in the Hymenoptera it may vary considerably. In the social insects especially, a great preponderance of females may be produced. A haploid male receives a single haploid set of chromosomes from his mother and passes it intact to all of his daughters; he has no father, and he fathers no sons of his own. The first meiotic division is abortive; the second produces two identical functional sperm. In fact, all of his sperm cells are genetically the same, for there can be, of course, no synapsis or crossing over.

Sexual Differentiation

In the honey bee there are two kinds of females, the workers and the queens. The workers ordinarily do not reproduce, but the queen mates and lays the eggs for the entire colony. Genetically, the queens and workers are the same. The differences in morphology and fertility between them have been traced to the kind of food they receive as larvae. Larvae destined to become queens are fed royal jelly, a food far richer in pantothenic acid, a vitamin, than the food given to worker larvae. The honey bee provides an insight into the relationship between sex determination and sexual differentiation. Even though both workers and queens are genetically determined females, the workers are sterile and only the queens become functional females. The sexual differentiation of the two groups is modified by environmental factors. Hence, although in species with chromosomal sex determination the sex of the individual is determined at the time of fertilization, subsequent events may modify or even inhibit normal sexual differentiation.

A variety of influences may affect sexual differentiation to the extent that sexual anomalies result. The *Drosophila* intersexes resulting from chromosomal imbalance have already been mentioned. They show a curious blending of male and female traits, the gonads and the secondary sexual characteristics being intermediate in form. Another quite different type of intersex is the gynandromorph. In these peculiar individuals, one part of the body is male and the other is female. The most striking cases have been found in insects because the insects evidently do not have an endocrine system responsible for the circulation of sex hormones throughout the body. A clear-cut line of demarcation exists between male and female sectors. Thus, each cell is autonomous with respect to its sexual differentiation. The differences arise when developmental accidents lead to differences in the sex chromosome complement in different body regions. In *Drosophila,* occasional individuals are male on one side and female on the other (Fig. 32-2). These individuals began as genetic females, but the loss of an X chromosome from one of the nuclei at the two-cell stage resulted in the gynandromorph.

One of the more surprising phenomena in sexual differentiation is sex reversal. Frogs and toads are particularly subject to this type of transformation. For example, it was found that a temperature of 32° C during development would cause genetically female frogs to develop into fertile males. It then became possible to mate two genetic females, one a normal XX female, the other also XX but male. Since only X-bearing gametes are possible, only female off-

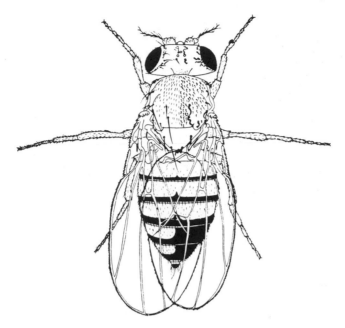

Fig. 32-2. A gynandromorph in *Drosophila,* the left half female, the right half male. On the male side, note the sex comb on the right foreleg, the dark tip to the abdomen and the mutant trait, singed bristles, all of which are absent from the female half. (With permission of Stern.)

spring should result under normal developmental conditions; and indeed, among a large progeny, no males were found.

A rare situation in chickens offers an even more spectacular type of sex reversal. In these cases a normal hen gradually assumed the appearance and behavior of a rooster and actually fathered chicks. Only one ovary in a normal hen is functional, and when this ovary was destroyed, the primary sex cords in the other vestigial gonad differentiated into a testis. The male sex hormone from the testis then induced the changes in the secondary sexual traits (Fig. 32-3).

Another example of the role of the sex hormones in sexual differentiation in vertebrates comes from cattle. When twin calves of opposite sex are born, the female is almost always sterile and is called a "freemartin." The sex organs are usually modified, and in extreme cases the ovaries have been transformed into structures resembling testes. In twin cattle, fusion (anastomosis) of the placental blood vessels occurs and so to some extent their bloods are mixed. Since the hormone system causing male differentiation comes into play somewhat earlier than the female system, the female twin is affected by the male's hormones before her own hormonal system becomes effective. The female is transformed into an hormonal intersex but does not become a functional male.

Fig. 32-3. Sex reversal. A female fowl whose ovary was removed when thirteen days old resembles at maturity a typical cock. (Courtesy of Snyder and David.)

Still another type of intersex has been discovered in the gypsy moth, *Lymantria dispar.* Crosses between males and females from the same locality produce normal male and female offspring. However, crosses between individuals from different races sometimes result in intersexes as well as normal progeny. In these moths the female is heterogametic and the male-determining factors seem to reside on the Z chromosomes. The female-determining factors appear to be carried by the W chromosome, the autosomes, and perhaps in the cytoplasm. In different races the effectiveness of these factors in determining sex varies, so that some races are "weak" and others "strong." For example, if a "weak" European female is crossed to a "strong" Japanese male, the sons are normal but the daughters intersexual. The single "strong" Japanese Z chromosome is sufficient to overcome the effects of the female-determining factors so that the ZW individuals differentiate into intersexes rather than females. The F_2 from this cross again produces normal sons, but the daughters are half normal and half intersexual. The reciprocal cross, "strong" Japanese female with "weak" European male, gives a normal F_1, but in the F_2 the daughters are normal, while half the sons are intersexes and half normal. Here again as in *Drosophila* a balance between factors of opposite effect is essential to normal sexual differentiation. However, in *Drosophila* the intersexes resulted from chromosomal imbalance. In *Lymantria* all of the individuals are diploid, and the intersexes result from a genic imbalance. Therefore, it must be concluded that the factors regulating normal sexual differentiation have been mutually adjusted in the different races of the gypsy moth by many generations of natural selection.

This brief review of sex determination and sexual differentiation is intended to show that an individual is not irrevocably one sex or the other. Every cell appears to have the potential to become either male or female in its characteristics. The sex that actually develops depends upon the type of reaction system that is set up in the cell. If one system is brought into play, a male develops; the other produces a female. The factor determining which system will prevail may be environmental, as in *Bonellia,* or it may be genetic, as in the familiar chromosome mechanism of sex determination. If the sex-determining machinery itself is thrown out of kilter—for example, because of chromosomal imbalance—abnormal sexual development will ensue. However, even if the sex-determining mechanism operates normally, this may not be sufficient to insure normal sexual differentiation, for unusual environmental influences such as hormones, temperature, nutrition, etc., may modify differentiation to the extent that intersexes or sexually aberrant individuals result.

The Control of Recombination

From an evolutionary standpoint the separation of the sexes into male and female individuals may be regarded as a means of insuring cross fertilization and genetic recombination. A comparative examination of the genetic systems in numerous groups of plants and animals reveals a wide range in the amount of recombination. The available evidence suggests that recombination itself is under the control of natural selection, and that the differences between groups in the amount of recombination are adaptive.

Numerous mechanisms are known to increase recombination. Meiosis provides for a regular segregation and reassortment of the chromosomes, and a high chromosome number and a high frequency of chiasma formation will also increase the amount of recombination taking place. The separation of the sexes, of course, makes cross fertilization mandatory, but even in hermaphrodites, devices that reduce or prevent selfing are common. Differences in time of maturation of the gametes, or flower structures that make self-pollination unlikely are cases in point. Species with reciprocal cross fertilization often have the male and female reproductive tracts completely separated. Systems of self-sterility alleles also prevent self-fertilization in many species. More or less permanent hybridity, which appears in many cases to take advantage of heterotic effects, is maintained by systems of balanced lethals, inversion or translocation heterozygotes, or by allopolyploidy.

On the other hand, several factors are known that tend to reduce or suppress recombination. The organization of the genetic material into linkage groups in the chromosomes prevents free recombination among genes. The smaller the number of chromosomes, the greater the restriction on recombination.

Furthermore, reduction in chiasmata frequency will still further limit genic recombination. Interference in regions adjacent to a chiasma limits the number of crossovers and hence the amount of recombination possible within a linkage group in any one generation. Thus, integrated gene complexes will not be completely disrupted by crossing over. In *Drosophila,* not only are the chromosome numbers low, but crossing over is completely suppressed in the males so that recombination between homologous chromosomes is possible only in the females. Structural hybridity for inversions or translocations may effectively prevent recombination within the affected chromosome pairs. However, the cross-over frequency is often increased in other chromosome pairs in the presence of a structurally heterozygous pair. In this way recombination within the chromosome complement can be brought under quite specific control by natural selection.

Self-fertilization will also, of course, reduce the frequency with which new gene combinations are formed. The effect of selfing is to increase the frequency of homozygotes in the species population. The recessive mutations as well as the dominants are soon brought to expression and exposed to natural selection. The elimination of the less well-adapted types results in a loss of variability, which is replenished only by mutation and not by recombination. A self-fertilizing species then sacrifices evolutionary plasticity in favor of immediate fitness, and forms a complex of relatively homozygous individuals no longer capable of gene exchange. In hermaphroditic species, a range of conditions may be found from virtually complete self-fertilization to obligatory outcrossing. The cross sterility observed in numerous instances is one way in which inbreeding is enforced. The range of possibilities for breeding systems in hermaphrodites suggests that their modes of reproduction have been adaptively modified. In general, it appears that the various devices leading to selfing are of more recent origin and represent a method for restricting recombination.

The suppression of recombination is even more effective in species reproducing asexually. Asexual methods of reproduction have arisen independently in various ways and in many different groups of sexually reproducing plants and animals. Apomixis is the term used to describe a variety of kinds of asexual process in which the outward appearance of sexual reproduction is retained but no fertilization occurs. Parthenogenesis refers specifically to the development of unfertilized eggs. Asexual reproduction in animals frequently occurs by means of parthenogenesis, though budding or fission is characteristic of certain groups. (Though often classified as sexual, parthenogenesis in effect more nearly resembles asexual reproduction.) In plants, many additional types of asexual reproduction are known: adventitious buds, bulblets, and stolons, in addition to the apomictic formation of seeds not only by parthenogenesis but also from various types of somatic cells. Many species combine the advantages of sexual and asexual reproduction. In the aphids, for instance, cyclical parthenogenesis permits a very rapid build-up in numbers during the favorable warm summer months. Since every individual is a female and reproduction is not delayed until after mating, the reproductive potential of such a population is almost inevitably greater than that of a population containing both males and females. In the fall, a sexual generation intervenes, and from the fertilized eggs emerge the females that start the parthenogenetic phase once again the following spring.

The various types of asexual reproduction are similar to self-fertilization, in that groups of individuals of identical genotype are formed that no longer are capable of gene exchange with members of other groups. They are dependent upon mutation for further evolution. However, unlike species where selfing is the rule and homozygosity is the norm, asexual methods of reproduction ordinarily preserve the heterozygosity intact from one generation to the next. The descendants of a single individual will all have the same genotype and form a clone, but this particular genotype may be highly heterozygous. In fact, one advantage of asexual reproduction is its preservation of heterotic or otherwise favorable gene combinations, or of favorable chromosome combinations, aneuploid or polyploid, which are meiotically unstable.

Generally, the changes in the genetic systems that result in the restriction or elimination of recombination have taken place in species where immediate fitness and a high reproductive rate are at a premium. There are three major mechanisms that limit recombination: a reduction in chromosome number and chiasma formation, a shift toward self-fertilization, and the development of asexual methods of reproduction. These devices, which lead to similar results, are apt to be mutually exclusive. If one type of mechanism prevails within a group—for example, self-fertilization—it is unlikely that the others will be found to any significant degree within the same group. Furthermore, the retreat from the cross fertilizing, diploid condition, though it confers immediate adaptive advantage and fitness, does so at the expense of long-range adaptability. The loss of the flexibility made possible by genetic recombination seems destined to lead ultimately to the extinction of those groups that travel too far down this path, for they will be unable to cope with or adapt to changing environmental conditions.

Sexual Selection

In 1871 Darwin published a work entitled *The descent of man and selection in relation to sex.* In this book he set forth his opinions on the origin and evolution of man, a subject he had deliberately dismissed with just a sentence in *The origin of species,* in the hope that he would thereby not add to the prejudices against his views. Darwin's writings on human evolution are still cited rather regularly. However, the greater part of this book was actually devoted to sexual selection, and his theories in this area have generally been either rejected or ignored. It seems clear that he regarded the theory of sexual selection as almost equal in importance to the theory of natural selection. As he put it, "Sexual selection depends on the success of certain individuals over others of the same sex, in relation to the propagation of the species; whilst natural selection depends on the success of both sexes, at all ages, in relation to the general conditions of life." One reason the theory of sexual selection has received so little attention is that it is now realized that sexual selection is merely one aspect of natural selection. Today natural selection is defined in terms of reproductive fitness. Those genes conferring fitness, whether they contribute to survival or to mating success, in the final analysis tend to increase in frequency in subsequent generations in much the same way. Thus, sexual selection is comparable in its effects to differential viability, longevity, or fecundity, and can quite properly be grouped with them as one of the elements in natural selection.

A second reason for the rejection of sexual selection is that Darwin postulated that it came about in two ways, through male competition or through female choice. These two intrasexual selective mechanisms have been subject to strong criticism ever since they were first proposed: female choice, primarily because it is anthropomorphic; male competition, because in many species there is little evidence that the male successful in competition with other males necessarily leaves more progeny.

Nevertheless, the phenomena that led Darwin to formulate the theory of sexual selection still remain, but little progress has been made toward a more adequate theory or a better understanding of the facts. The trend in the evolution of the higher animals has been toward sexually reproducing species with the sexes separate. In most such species, sexual dimorphism prevails, which in some cases is quite striking. Darwin's proposal was an attempt to account for the origin of sexual dimorphism. As such, it is undoubtedly inadequate. However, the significant aspect of his theory is its emphasis on the fact that the appearance and behavior of individuals can influence the course of evolution through their effects, via the nervous system, upon other organisms. Thus, the behavior and appearance of an individual not only affects its own chances of survival, but also influences the activity, behavior, survival, and reproduction of other individuals. The evolution of the nervous system thereby added a new dimension to evolution. Darwin's theory was inadequate, not so much because it was wrong, but because it was incomplete. In polygamous species especially, male competition may have played a significant role in the evolution of males larger and better equipped for combat than the females (for example, in deer and seals). To some extent, female "choice" may also be significant, in the sense at least that the male with the more effective courtship pattern will have greater success in gaining the acceptance of the female as a sexual partner. However, these possibilities are but two among many that could lead to sexual dimorphism. The allesthetic traits, as they have been called, which become effective via the nervous systems of other organisms, serve a variety of functions in addition to sexual selection.

Even with respect to reproduction these traits have functions other than influencing female choice or success in male competition. For example, various stimuli serve to bring the sexes together. Male moths are attracted to the females over considerable distances by their scent, which is species specific. The calls of male frogs and toads in their breeding ponds and of male birds on their nesting territories are comparable in advertising their presence and attracting the females. Furthermore, the elaborate courtship patterns involving a complex sequence of stimuli and responses between male and female serve for attraction, sexual recognition, synchronization of mating behavior, and arousal to the peak necessary for the successful completion of coition. Even ovulation has been shown in many species to be dependent upon not just hormonal stimuli but on the interplay between hormonal stimuli and the nervous stimuli set off by courtship and mating. Those traits in males and females that are epigamic—that is, contribute to the successful union of the gametes—will have adaptive value and will tend to be favored by selection.

One of the fundamental problems in the origin of secondary sexual dimorphism is genetic and developmental. The differences between males and females are known to be due in mammals to the influence of the endocrine system during development. In insects, cellular autonomy exists with respect to sexual differentiation. Furthermore, it is known that the genotypes of males and females are, to a very large extent, the same, for the autosomes are identical in both sexes. The genetic differences may be merely haploidy versus diploidy, one X versus two X chromosomes, presence or absence of a Y; or, some seemingly trivial environmental difference may determine which path sexual development will follow. The problem, very simply, is to explain the origin of the very considerable differences between the sexes when the genetic differences between males and females are so slight. Sexual differentiation is rather well understood, for example, at the level of hormonal control. The initiation and regulation of sexual development under the control of pituitary and gonadal hormones has been extensively studied experimentally. However, at the level of gene action, no comparable knowledge is available. The nature of the genetic control that brings one developmental system into play rather than the other is not at all well understood and poses a particularly difficult problem since to a large extent the same genetic material is responsible in each case. This area of developmental genetics seems to hold problems of considerable interest from the standpoint of genetics, embryology, and evolution.

In addition to their epigamic functions, the allesthetic traits may promote conspicuousness or, quite the reverse, be cryptic in function. Most epigamic traits, whether behavioral or morphological, are conspicuous, and these same traits may sometimes serve other functions. In threatening another male invading his territory, for example, a brightly colored male may use the same colors in the threat display as he uses in the courtship display before the female. Conspicuous traits have evolved not only in relation to threat but also for use as warning signals. The various aspects of group behavior, too complex to be detailed here, but including care of the young, colony and flock formation, cooperation of various sorts, and the social behavior of insects, are built upon intricate and carefully integrated systems of interactions among individuals, and are mediated by the nervous system. These behavorial systems have emerged as a product of evolution. The relatively inflexible behavior patterns that we call instincts are clearly under hereditary control. The capacity to learn, also an evolutionary product, makes possible more flexible behavior patterns that can be modified as the result of experience.

Cryptic behavior and form have also resulted from the operation of evolutionary forces. The ability to select a favorable habitat or resting place, cryptic behavior such as shadow elimination, and mimicry and cryptic coloration —all have evolved as the result of natual selection favoring those individuals best able to avoid perception by their enemies. In the light of these few examples, to which so many more could be added, there can be little doubt that Darwin, in his theory of sexual selection, was on the track of a significant phase of evolution, the psychological or ethological aspect. The course of evolution in animals has been greatly influenced by the interactions that occur among individuals and are mediated by the sense organs and the nervous system. A killdeer, when its nest is threatened by an intruder, dramatically feigns injury. Anyone who has ever been deceived and led astray by such a display can hardly fail to be impressed by the subtlety and power of the forces of evolution.

SUMMARY ◄───────────────────────────────

A major thesis of this chapter is that not only organisms but their underlying genetic systems have undergone evolutionary change and that the genetic system itself may have adaptive value. With few exceptions the hereditary material in living things is deoxyribonucleic acid (DNA). A variety of methods of genetic recombination have been discovered, from the novel types described in viruses and bacteria to the orderly system in higher plants and animals. This orderliness became possible with the organization of the genes into chromosomes that undergo regular mitotic and meiotic cell divisions. Asexual reproduction is especially well suited to the rapid self-duplication of a particular genotype, and thus is favorable to the maintenance of a well-adapted genotype in a stable environment or to rapid colonization. A sexually reproducing population, on the other hand, is better able to adjust to changing environmental conditions and to exploit new and different ecological niches. Haploidy is the more primitive condition, whereas the predominance of the diploid generation is associated with the evolution of organisms of considerable complexity. The evolution of sex has led to the evolution of numerous methods for controlling sex determination and sexual differentiation. Sexual anomalies may result when either of these processes is disrupted. In sexually reproducing species, the amount of genetic recombination is regulated in a variety of ways, which range from self-sterility or enforced outcrossing to self-fertilization. The release of genetic variability appears to be under rather precise control. Darwin's theory of sexual selection, though inadequate in many respects, seems to merit further study, for it focuses attention on the fact that the appearance and behavior of an individual not only affects its own chances of survival but also influences the activity and behavior, survival and reproduction of other individuals as well.

SUGGESTED READING

Darlington, C. D., 1958. *The evolution of genetic systems.* New York: Basic Books.
Stebbins, G. L., 1960. "The comparative evolution of genetic systems," *Evolution after Darwin,* Vol. 1, *The evolution of life.* Chicago: University of Chicago Press.

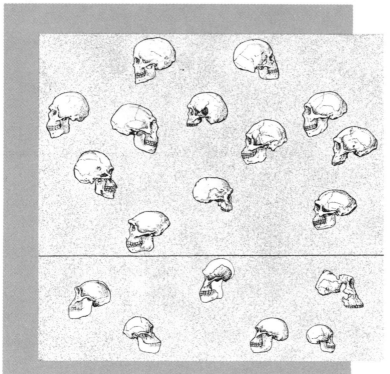

PART *IV*

Evolution
and Man

CHAPTER 33

Human Evolution

The Mammalia are a class of vertebrates or back-boned animals characterized by mammary glands, hair, and body temperature regulation. The subclass Eutheria, or placental mammals, bear living young that undergo a period of development within the uterus of the female. The Primates are placental mammals with elongated limbs and enlarged hands and feet, each with five digits. The digits have nails rather than claws or hoofs, and the thumb and the great toe are usually opposable to the other digits. Primates are generally arboreal and are found primarily in tropical and subtropical regions. Their orbits are directed forward so that they have binocular vision. Except for the highly developed brain and nervous system, the Primates are a relatively generalized group. Any objective analysis of human traits will lead inevitably to the conclusion that man is a vertebrate, a placental mammal, and a primate. He differs from other primates primarily in his enlarged brain and erect posture. He is cosmopolitan rather than tropical, terrestrial rather than arboreal, and the great toe is not opposable. His mastery of the arts of making fire and clothing first permitted him to extend his range beyond the tropics, and without these he would once again be a tropical species. The unusual size of the great toe and shape of the foot are clear indications of his ancestors' descent from trees in the not too remote past. The Primates have been classified as shown in Table 33-1.

The Prosimians

The most primitive, generalized mammals such as shrews and moles belong to the order Insectivora, from which all other

TABLE 33-1

The Primates

Suborder	Superfamily	Family	Common name	Distribution	Remarks
Prosimii lower Primates	Tupaioidea		Tree shrews	Oriental	6 genera. Moderate number of species
	Lemuroidea		Lemurs	Madagascar	19 species
	Daubento-nioidea		Aye-Aye	Madagascar	1 species
	Lorisformes		Loris, galagos, bush babies, pottos	Africa and Oriental	10 species
	Tarsiiformes		Tarsiers	East Indies	3 species
Anthropoidea higher Primates	Ceboidea	Cebidae	New World monkeys	New World tropics	12 genera, 140 species
		Calli-thricidae	Marmosets		2 genera several species
	Cercopi-thecoidea	Cercopi-thecidae	Old World monkeys	Old World tropics except Australia	16 genera, 200 species
	Hominoidea	Pongidae	Apes	Old World tropics except Australia	10 species
		Hominidae	Man	Cosmopolitan	1 species, *Homo sapiens*

orders of mammals are thought to have descended. For many years the tree shrews were included among the insectivores. More recently, however, they have been grouped with the primates, for even though conforming to the basic mammalian plan, they show in their slightly enlarged brains and eyes the beginnings of primate traits. Superficially, the tree shrews resemble squirrels, for they are small, bushy-tailed animals that are active by day. They possess claws rather than nails, but their simple incisor teeth are quite different from those of the squirrels, which are typical of the chisellike gnawing incisors of the rodents. Their digits, their eyes, and their brain separate them from the insectivores and place them with Primates. Thus the Primates, the order to which man belongs, are linked directly through the tree shrews to the oldest group of mammals. Certainly in this instance, there is no reason to speak of a "missing link."

The true lemurs and the aberrant aye-aye are found now only on the island of Madagascar, but formerly they ranged over much of the Old World and North America. About the size of a mouse or a cat, the lemurs are usually both arboreal and nocturnal. Although they display primate characteristics, they are rather foxlike in appearance due to their elongated, moist muzzles and rather large, mobile ears. Their brains, compared to those of monkeys or men, are relatively simple, for the cerebral cortex is small and smooth, lacking the folds that greatly increase the surface area in the higher primates.

The Lorisiformes include species with such appealing names as bush baby and potto, and are in general rather like the lemurs. The lorises of Asia are slow-moving climbers with relatively large eyes and a shorter snout than most of the true lemurs. The galagos or bush babies native to Africa are small and active, with their hind legs specially adapted for jumping.

The tiny tarsiers, the size of small kittens, though formerly found in much of the Old World and North America, today live only in the East Indies. They have an unusual combination of primitive characters that link them to the lemurs, and advanced traits that suggest relationship to the monkeys. The tarsiers have a short face with relatively enormous eyes facing to the front, undoubtedly an adaptation to their nocturnal, arboreal habits. Their limbs and feet are specially modified for both grasping and jumping, so that they flit through the trees with surprising ease. The tarsier's large brain, well-developed senses of vision and hearing, and the structure of nose and lips all suggest relationship to the monkeys, but his fossil relatives show him to be more closely related to the lemurs.

It is of particular interest that within the rather heterogeneous suborder Prosimii, the animals range in kind from the tree shrews, which are not far removed from the most primitive placental mammals, the insectivores, to the tarsiers, which foreshadow the monkeys and the other Anthropoidea (see Fig. 33-1).

The Higher Primates

The higher primates, including the monkeys, apes, and man, belong to the suborder Anthropoidea. Though called "higher," there is not much that is strikingly different about them as compared to the lower primates. The differences, however, are of considerable significance. In particular, their eyes show several changes that permit superb vision. The yellow spot, or macula lutea, in the retina directly opposite the pupil is a region of especially acute sight. Furthermore, the color vision of the Anthropoidea is superior to that of any of the other mammals. The placement of the eyes, in sockets facing directly forward, permits both eyes to cover the same field of vision. This arrangement differs greatly from that of a deer, for example, where each eye has a separate field of vision with relatively little overlap. The higher primates are thus able to see not only clearly and in color but also in three dimensions. The effect of binocular vision is similar to that of an old-fashioned stereopticon, for each eye views an object from a slightly different direction, and the object seems to stand out in three dimensions so that very accurate estimates of distance are possible. In contrast to the nocturnal prosimians, the higher primates are active by day. They are also typically larger than the lower primates. Incidentally, even though man is often pictured as a weak, defenseless creature, in reality even without

Fig. 33-1. Representative prosimians. (*a*) Tree shrew (*Tupaia minor*); (*b*) Mindanao tarsier (*Tarsius carbonarius*); (*c*) Galago (*Galago crassicaudatus*); (*d*) Aye-aye (*Daubentonia madagascariensis*); (*e, left*) Mouse lemur (*Microcebus murinis*). (With permission of Zoological Society of London [*a, d,* and *e*], Walker [*b*] and Chicago Zoological Park [*c*].)

modern weapons he is a rather formidable animal, as are the orangutan, chimpanzee, and gorilla. In addition to improved vision, the most striking difference between higher and lower primates lies in the larger brain of the former, with the cerebral cortex assuming ever-greater importance. The cerebrum, where the higher mental functions are localized, covers more and more of the brain until in man it virtually overlies the rest of the brain.

The Anthropoidea have been divided into two major groups, the platyrrhines of the Americas, including the New World monkeys and marmosets, and the Old World catarrhines, including men, apes, and the monkeys of the Old World tropics. The platyrrhines are flat nosed, with the nostrils widely spaced. In the catarrhines the nostrils are close together and point downward.

In addition to their noses, perhaps the most striking trait of the New World monkeys is their prehensile tail by which most of them can hang or swing from branches or use as a fifth hand. The little marmosets scarcely look like monkeys, for they have claws rather than nails (except on the big toe) and their thumbs are not opposable. Furthermore, some of them have manes, and their fur typically has a banded pattern.

The monkeys of the Old World lack prehensile tails and some species such as the baboons have become terrestrial, living in rocky, open country. As a group, the Cercopithecidae are more generalized in body form than the New World monkeys, and are not so completely adapted to arboreal life. Their hands look rather human, for the thumbs have good opposability. The Old and New World monkeys differ not only in their distribution and the traits just mentioned but also in such fundamental anatomical traits as dentition and structure of the skull. See Fig. 33-2.

The two remaining groups of catarrhines, because of their similarities, have been placed in a single superfamily, the Hominoidea. These two groups are the anthropoid apes of the family Pongidae and the family to which man himself belongs, the Hominidae. The living anthropoids are the gibbons, the orangutans, the chimpanzees, and the gorillas. Man and the apes show many more similarities than man and the monkeys. Not only are they large in size and lacking a tail, but in many fundamental morphological and physiological traits they are much alike. In the details of their brain and skull, dentition, and skeleton they show rather close affinities. Many of these resemblances result from the adoption of an erect posture with the associated changes in such traits as the shape of the chest, the position of the abdominal organs, and the shape of the pelvis. Furthermore, in such matters as reproductive physiology, blood group chemistry, and even susceptibility to parasites, they show evidence of rather close genetic ties. The main differences between man and the apes are associated with their modes of locomotion, for the apes are essentially brachiators, swinging upright through the trees by their hands, while man walks erect on the ground. The gibbons, superb aerialists, live in the tropical forests of Southeast Asia. The orangutan also lives in this region but is now confined to the islands of Borneo and Sumatra. Orangs, like the gibbons, are completely arboreal, but since they are much larger than gibbons, they are comparatively slow moving and deliberate in their actions. The

Fig. 33-2. Representative monkeys. New World: (*a*) Humboldt's woolly monkey (*Lagothrix lagotricha*); (*b*) Lion-headed or golden marmoset (*Leontocebus rosalia*). Old World: (*c*) Pig-tailed macaque (*Macaca nemestrina*). (With permission of Walker [*a, b*] and National Zoological Park, Smithsonian Institution [*c*].)

Fig. 33-3. The anthropoid apes. (*a*) Gibbon (*Hylobates*); (*b*) Orangutan (*Pongo*); (*c*) Gorilla (*Gorilla*); (*d*) Chimpanzee (*Pan*).

other two anthropoids, the gorilla and the chimpanzee, inhabit the tropical forests of west central Africa. However, they are not as strictly arboreal as the Asiatic apes, for they spend a considerable part of their time on the ground. Nevertheless, their body structure is still essentially that of a brachiator though not so completely specialized for this mode of life as the gibbon or orangutan. See Fig. 33-3.

Man is not only a Primate, he is an Old World catarrhine and even more specifically, his anatomy shows him to be a hominoid, a member of the same superfamily as the great apes. The hominid traits, which set him apart from the apes, are his feet and legs, which enable him to walk erect on the ground, with his hands free for tasks other than locomotion (see Fig. 33-4). Man's skull

Fig. 33-4. The upstart.

and brain also set him apart from the apes, but these are apparently differences in emphasis rather than in basic structure, and moreover they arose after the differences in leg structure had evolved. Aside from his obviously larger brain, man's head differs from the apes' in that the face is reduced in size and has shrunk back under the forehead. This recession of the face appears related to the better balance of the skull on the spine achieved by man as compared to the apes. Associated with this change has been a reduction in the size of the teeth and jaws and the emergence of the distinctive human nose and chin (see Fig. 33-5).

Fossil Primates

The actual fossil record of the Primates is fragmentary and in many ways unsatisfactory. However, it does suffice to show that the Primates are one of the oldest orders of mammals, having a fossil record extending well back into the Mesozoic. By the Paleocene at the beginning of the Tertiary a number of prosimians, such as lemurs, lorises, and tarsiers, were present in relative abundance over most of the world. After flourishing during the Paleocene and Eocene, the prosimians vanished completely from the Oligocene in North America and Europe and were reduced in numbers in Asia and Africa. The reasons for their decline are not known, but the prosimian hard times coincided not only

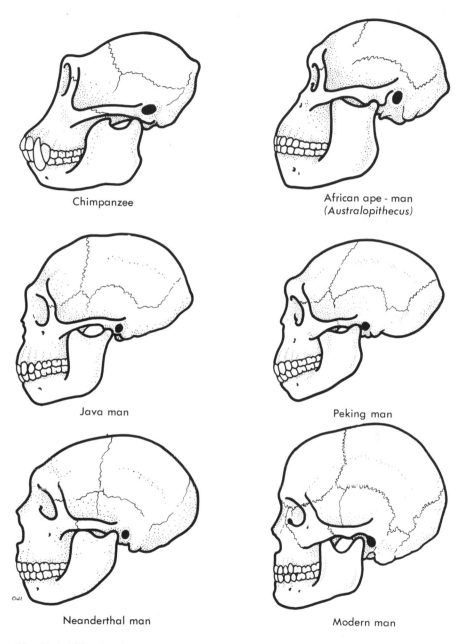

Fig. 33-5. Five hominid skulls shown with that of an anthropoid ape for comparison.

with the rise of such mammalian groups as the carnivores and rodents but also with the appearance of the higher primates, fossils of which first appear in the early Oligocene. It seems a fairly safe assumption that competition from these highly successful groups played a significant role in the decline of the lower primates. On the island of Madagascar, which the lemurs reached but the higher primates did not, the lemurs continued to survive and evolve, long after they became extinct elsewhere in the world.

Fossils that suggest the hominoid line leading to the apes and man also appear at about this time, some fifty million years ago. More is known of the fossil precursors of the gibbons than of the other hominoids. Propliopithecus from the Oligocene of Egypt some 35 million years ago, Limnopithecus from East Africa, in the Miocene some 10 million years later, and Pliopithecus from the late Miocene and early Pliocene in Europe lead quite clearly up to the modern gibbon, Hylobates. The gibbons thus were separated quite early from the other lines of hominoids. Furthermore, they were not as specialized for brachiation as the modern gibbons, but had more generalized limbs for climbing.

Only in the Miocene do the forerunners of the other apes begin to appear in the fossil genera Dryopithecus and Sivapithecus, found rather abundantly in Europe, Asia, and Africa. The remains consist almost exclusively of jaws and teeth, so that little is known about whether they were brachiating animals. However, the teeth and jaws seem clearly to be of a type that today are found in modified form in the great apes (gorilla, chimpanzee, and orangutan) and in man. Fossils of an even earlier type of ape known as Proconsul have been found in relative abundance in lower Miocene deposits in East Africa. Although Proconsul has been thought to be a forerunner of the modern chimpanzee, in reality he shows differences from all other hominoids, the gibbons, the great apes, and man, as well as from the fossil Dryopithecus group, and he probably represents a separate evolutionary line. A significant point brought out by the fossil record of the apes is that the living populations of apes are essentially relict populations; the fossil apes were evidently much more widespread and abundant than are the living groups.

The Fossil Record of Man

The existing races of man are descended from other somewhat different populations that lived in the past. The evidence for human evolution comes from the fossil record. If man has evolved, then it is necessary to try to define the stage in his evolution when he first became human. This stage can be defined as having been reached when man's ancestors became intelligent enough to make tools. His ancestors between the ape and human levels can then be termed prehuman. Though arbitrary, this definition is essentially objective. The fossil record of man or preman is largely confined to the Pleistocene, and our knowledge, therefore, covers primarily the last million years of human evolution. Prior to that time there is a gap of several million years in the actual fossil record.

The fossil evidence indicates that the prehumans must have come from a generalized anthropoid ape, which lived on the ground but had arboreal ancestors. The major evolutionary change leading to man was the shift to bipedal locomotion. This change led to changes in the bones and muscles of the pelvis, legs, and feet, including the realignment of the big toe, and in the angle of attachment of the skull to the spine. The net effect enables man to keep his body erect, not by muscular action as the apes do, but on a bony supporting column. The erect posture freed the hands from use for locomotion. The ancestral hominids were probably omnivores who shifted toward carnivorous ways and developed systematic hunting habits, for the earliest known men were hunters using weapons to kill game. It is probable that sticks and stones were used first, and that this, in turn, led to weapon making. The fossils indicate that much of the increase in brain size came later during the Pleistocene after the shift to bipedal locomotion.

Man and his tools appear first in the major warmer parts of the Old World—that is, in Africa and southern Eurasia—and presumably prehuman evolution occurred somewhere in this area. No living or fossil apes or prehumans are found either in America or in the Australian region, a fact that would also seem to rule out northern Eurasia as the place of man's origin, for expansion to North America via the Bering land bridge would then have been a simple matter, as it was for many other species. The prehumans presumably evolved in open country where running on two legs was an advantage to incipient hunters. Such a setting points to Africa, where there was much open country and much game to run after. Whatever the place, they then dispersed, as other dominant successful groups of animals have done, in a complex fashion over the warmer parts of the Old World during the Pliocene. The first known tools of worked stone, from Olduvai Gorge in Tanganyika, are estimated to have been made 1,750,000 years ago, or only 70,000 generations ago.

During the previous 70 million years or so in the Tertiary the climate of the earth was rather warm and stable. With the beginning of the Pleistocene about a million years ago, the earth's climate became changeable and a period of cooling was followed by four major ice ages, with intervening warmer periods. Four times, tremendous continental glaciers pushed their way down into the more temperate regions, covering major portions of Europe, North America, and parts of Asia. The glacial stages were followed by warmer interglacial stages during which the weather became even warmer than at present. Thus the Pleistocene was a time of fluctuating, unsettled climatic conditions. The stages have been most carefully studied in Europe and North America, and their names and approximate durations are shown in Table 33-2 together with relevant information about fossil man.

TABLE 33-2. *Fossil Men*

Glacial and interglacial stages (estimated years ago)	Cultural period	Fossil hominids
Postglacial	Iron Bronze Neolithic Mesolithic	
10,000	—————————	
IV Wisconsin or Würm Glacial	Upper Paleolithic	Cro-Magnon
	—————————	
80,000		Florisbad Combe-Capelle
	Middle Paleolithic	Neanderthal Solo Rhodesian Mount Carmel
Third Interglacial		Neanderthal Fontéchevade
150,000	—————————	
III Illinoian or Riss Glacial		Kanjera Rabat-Casablanca
225,000		
Second or "Great" Interglacial	Lower Paleolithic	Steinheim Swanscombe
350,000		Peking
II Kansan or Mindel Glacial		Java
425,000		Ternifine
First Interglacial		Heidelberg Telanthropus Paranthropus Java Meganthropus Australopithecus
500,000 I Nebraskan or Günz Glacial		Kanam (?)
625,000 Possible earlier glacials		Australopithecus
1,750,000		Zinjanthropus Unnamed Olduvai hominid

The tendency to assign each newly discovered fossil member of the Hominidae to a separate genus has led to a confusing welter of names. Rather than bringing out the similarities and differences among these fossils, the system has obscured their relationships. Use of the same taxonomic criteria for hominids as for other groups would considerably reduce the number of genera and species.

Although the fossil record of man is largely confined to the last million years (the Pleistocene), a recent restudy of a fossil known as Oreopithecus from the lower Pliocene in Italy some ten million years ago may carry our knowledge further back in time. When found a century ago, he was assigned to the Old World monkeys or Cercopithecidae and was more or less ignored. However, further finds and restudy in the light of modern knowledge have shown that Oreopithecus clearly is neither a monkey nor a Proconsul nor a Dryopithecus. If he must be assigned to one of the three hominoid groups (gibbons, great apes, hominids), he comes closer to being a hominid than anything else. This is not to say that he is necessarily a direct ancestor of man, but rather that he probably belonged some ten million years ago to the same group of related species that included the ancestors of man.

The most primitive kind of fossils that are clearly those of Hominidae come from deposits in South Africa. Dr. Raymond Dart, the anatomist who made the original discovery, called his find Australopithecus and pointed out its human characteristics. This conclusion was at first widely doubted and challenged by many of the recognized authorities. However, further discoveries by Broom, Robinson, Leakey, and others have shown almost beyond question that Australopithecus was indeed an early hominid and not simply an anthropoid ape with some slightly human traits. These additional fossils, as is customary, have been given separate generic names (for example, Paranthropus, Plesianthropus, Telanthropus, and Zinjanthropus), but all are enough alike (except perhaps Telanthropus) to be put in the same subfamily, the Australopithecinae. Further material and additional study may in time lead to taxonomic revision toward greater simplicity. However, the fossils fall into two main groups, typified by Australopithecus and Paranthropus. The Australopithecus type was rather small, probably weighing no more than 50 or 60 pounds; Paranthropus was considerably larger and heavier. The most significant features of these australopithecine "ape-men" were their rather small brains, with a cranial capacity of about 600 cc—not much greater than that of a gorilla or a chimpanzee—associated with pelvic and leg bones very similar to those of modern man. Thus, it seems that erect bipedal locomotion on the ground—in other words, walking erect—evolved first in the human line and that the increase in size and capability of the human brain evolved later. This conclusion is contrary to what was long believed to be the case, that man was an intelligent ape who climbed down from the trees to take up his abode on the ground. Furthermore, the "ape-men" had relatively massive jaws, but the details of the jaws and of the dentition were fundamentally human and not apelike at all, and the skull, despite the small size of the brain, was of the human pattern. Finally, evidence has been accumulating, climaxed by the recent discovery by the Leakeys of a new fossil hominid that they called Zinjanthropus and another hominid as yet unnamed, that the Australopithecinae were already capable of using and even fabricating simple stone and possibly bone tools some 1,750,000 years ago. This discovery has again required a considerable revision in our thinking about the course of human evolution. If we are to define as "human" those hominids who could make tools, then the terms "man-apes" and even "ape-men" seem to be inappropriate for the Australopithecinae. Knowledge of this group has greatly increased our information about the course of evolution in the Hominidae and makes even more urgent the need to find additional early hominid remains.

A more advanced stage of human evolution is represented by the fossils first found by Dubois and known as the Java man. They illustrate very nicely the taxonomic problems in paleoanthropology. Dubois christened his find *Pithecanthropus erectus* and placed him in a new family, Pithecanthropidae, between the Pongidae and the Hominidae. The quite similar Peking man was originally placed in a new genus and species, *Sinanthropus pekinensis.* However, the similarities have led some authorities to regard them as two species in the same genus, *Pithecanthropus erectus* and *P. pekinensis,* and Mayr has argued that by the usual taxonomic criteria they are merely different races of the same species and that this species is sufficiently like modern man to be placed in the same genus, Homo. Thus Java man would become *Homo erectus erectus* and Peking man *H. e. pekinensis.* These differences over nomenclature may seem to be trivial, but the implications of each system are quite different. It now appears certain that the two finds belong to the Hominidae rather than to a separate family and that they belong together in the same genus. Since their cranial capacities were quite different, they differed more than the living human races, and thus the best course may be to take the middle ground and consider them as separate species within the same genus, Pithecanthropus. The Java and Peking men, living perhaps half a million years ago, were hunters with stone tools who lived in caves and used fire. They had thick skulls with heavy brow ridges, a prognathous profile with large teeth but no chin, and a cranial capacity of approximately 750 to 900 cc in Java man and 900 to 1200 cc in Peking man. The rest of their skeleton did not differ from that of modern man. One habit of these early humans is clearly recorded. They picked each others' brains and tossed the skulls aside in their caves, there to be discovered thousands of years later as evidence of their cannibalism.

Another stage in the evolution of man represented by abundant fossils is known as Neanderthal man, after the valley in Germany where the first carefully studied fossils of this type were discovered in 1856. Numerous fossils of Neanderthal men (and here we are clearly dealing with members of the genus Homo) were found in North Africa, in western Asia, and over most of Europe except Britain and the northern regions. They persisted for about a hundred thousand years, first appearing in the Third or Last Interglacial, and being found in even greater numbers in the first part of the Fourth or Wisconsin

Glaciation. Then, quite suddenly (a matter of centuries, actually) they disappeared, being replaced throughout their range by men like ourselves. The average size of their brains (about 1450 cc) was somewhat larger than the average for the brain of living men (about 1350 cc). The skull was thick walled and low and bulged at the sides, with the rear drawn out into a projecting occipital region, which was marked by a ridge for the attachment of massive neck muscles. The retreating forehead sloped back from heavy brow ridges, and the face and teeth were relatively large. The lower jaw was heavy, but lacked the protruding chin of modern man. The rest of the skeleton indicates that Neanderthal men were only about five feet tall but of an exceptionally powerful, muscu-

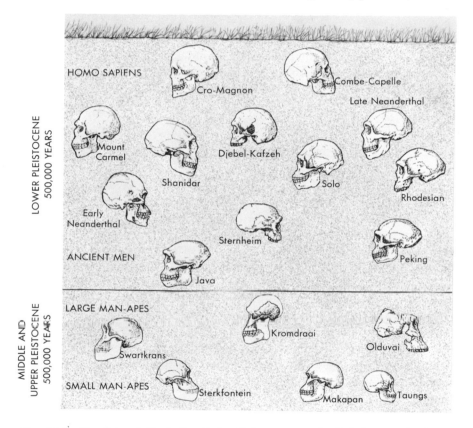

Fig. 33-6. Fossil hominid skulls of the Pleistocene epoch. Relative age is shown by position; the names indicate the initial place of discovery. The general trends in hominid evolution can be observed from the Australopithecinae at the bottom through Pithecanthropus (Java, Peking, and Solo men) and Neanderthal (including Shanidar) to *Homo sapiens* (Cro-Magnon and Combe-Capelle) at the top. The Mount Carmel skull shows traits of both Neanderthal and modern man. (Redrawn after Washburn.)

lar build. Because of these rather well-defined differences from living men, the Neanderthals have been placed in a separate species of the genus Homo, *H. neanderthalensis,* though they have also been called a race of *Homo sapiens.*

Men of our own species, *Homo sapiens,* do not appear in the fossil record until about 35,000 B.C. These tall and well-built men, of the so-called Cro-Magnon type, had a distinct bony chin on the front of the jaw, a high-domed, thin-walled skull, and greatly reduced brow ridges, and are indistinguishable from modern men. These are the people who, in a relatively short time, completely replaced the Neanderthal type. However, just where this modern type of man came from and who his immediate predecessors were are far from clear. At the present time only a single genus of the family Hominidae and a single species within that genus, *Homo sapiens,* exists on the earth. All mankind belongs to this one species. Human fossils of types clearly belonging to the genus Homo have been found as far back as the late Middle Pleistocene, but the record is quite fragmentary and incomplete, and the relations of these fragments to one another and to modern man are obscure. See Fig. 33-6.

The Origin of Modern Man

The theories of the origin of the living races of man range from a simple straight-line evolution from Australopithecus → Pithecanthropus → Neanderthal → Modern man, to a polyphyletic scheme in which each living human race is derived from a different series of fossil ancestors. Although it is a fairly safe assumption that neither of these theories is correct, the available evidence is insufficient to establish man's lineage. Many of the known fossil hominids are listed in Table 33-2 where it can be seen that fossils of rather different types (for example, Paranthropus and Pithecanthropus, and later, Pithecanthropus and Homo, represented by the Steinheim and Swanscombe skulls) were contemporary. Such information suggests that in the Hominidae as in other groups, evolution gave rise to several diverging lines, many of which became extinct while others eventually gave rise to new species. Though only one species, *Homo sapiens,* now exists, it has already diverged to some extent in the formation of the various human racial groups. The details of the skull and facial skeleton of Cro-Magnon man show that he was a member of the Caucasoid racial group. However, it does not necessarily follow that the other races are derived from the white race. Indeed it is unlikely that any existing race was ancestral to the others. Rather, it is probable that all of the living races have diverged somewhat from the ancestral population of *Homo sapiens* from which they all are descended. What is suggested is that, even though the exact time of origin of *Homo sapiens* is not yet known, the Caucasoid Cro-Magnon men show that divergence toward modern races had already occurred and that modern man must have originated at some time prior to 35,000 B.C.

The relationship between Neanderthal and modern men has constituted somewhat of a puzzle. Similarly, while it is reasonably certain that the modern *Homo sapiens* type of human replaced Neanderthal man throughout his range in a rather brief interval, the cause of his extinction remains unknown. Direct combat leading to extermination of the Neanderthals may be the answer, but it is not the only one possible, for more subtle forms of competition—for game or caves, for example—could have had the same ultimate effect. It has even been suggested that where the two groups met, they interbred, and that the Neanderthals were absorbed rather than eliminated. For the most part, the evidence does not support this idea. However, on the eastern shore of the Mediterranean in caves on the slopes of Mount Carmel in Palestine have been found skeletons that show a strange mixture of Neanderthal and *sapiens* traits. One interpretation of this material is that it is the result of hybridization between the two groups. Although it is true that the Near East has long been the crossroads of the world for mankind, and from that standpoint this interpretation seems reasonable, nevertheless other explanations have also been advanced; for example, that these people represent the last stage in a transition from Neanderthal to *sapiens*. However, other evidence makes this hypothesis difficult to uphold. For one thing, skulls quite different from Neanderthal and tending toward *sapiens* are already known from the late Middle Pleistocene (Steinheim and Swanscombe), and definitely *sapiens*-like skulls (Fontéchevade and Kanjera) are found in the early Upper Pleistocene, well before the time of the Mount Carmel material and even before the time of the Neanderthals themselves. Furthermore, the early Neanderthal men from the Third Interglacial were not as extreme in their distinguishing features as those from the Fourth Glacial. What this evidence suggests is that, rather than being the direct ancestors of modern man, the Neanderthalians were a divergent group, which perhaps became especially well adapted to survive the rigorous climate of the last ice age, but were eventually overrun and supplanted by a new and even more successful human type. That this explanation may be correct is suggested by the fact that the new people apparently brought with them a new and more advanced culture. The Mousterian tools associated with Neanderthal man were replaced by the more refined Aurignacian stone tools of the Upper Paleolithic men. The Neanderthalians had developed a distinctive culture of their own. There is evidence of religious concepts in their ceremonial burial of the dead and in their worship of cave bears, the fearsome enemies with whom they fought for the caves essential to their survival during the last ice age. They were skilled hunters, able to take game as large as the mammoth and the woolly rhinoceros. However, the culture of their Cro-Magnon successors was considerably more advanced, marked not only by new and improved stone tools and weapons, but by evidence of great hunting skill and the notably graceful art in their caves.

At present we have a glimpse here and there of stages in human evolution during the past million years sufficient to show that evolution in the Hominidae has progressed quite rapidly during this time. The major adaptive shift that led to the separation of the hominids from the apes was the change in the lower limbs and pelvis, which permitted walking erect. This shift was essentially complete in the Australopithecinae, and the evolution of a progressively larger brain was a subsequent development. Fossil hominids of diverse kinds are widely scattered over the Old World, signs of a successful, expanding group, but the place of origin of the Hominidae is as yet unknown. Although indications at present point to Africa, this may be simply because the record is more complete from that area. Although Pithecanthropus (Java and Peking men) may be regarded as a stage intermediate between the Australopithecinae and modern man, they may or may not be in the direct line of descent. Of the other fossil men available, many are poorly known, either because only a few fragments have been found or because the material has not been adequately dated. Although the relationship between Neanderthal man and modern man, as represented by the Cro-Magnon type that so dramatically superseded the Neanderthalians, is still in doubt, the best guess is that both were derived from one of the earlier types of Homo now known only from a few scattered skeletal remains.

Therefore, the fossil record of man, incomplete and fragmentary though it is, is sufficient to show that in the past somewhat different human types did exist from which modern man has descended; it is not complete enough to show exactly what the course of evolution leading to *Homo sapiens* has been. New human fossils are being found at an accelerating pace, however, and there is reason to hope that in time some of the basic questions about man's origins can be answered more fully than at present. The picture may appear to become more confusing before it is clarified, for it seems unlikely, since isolation exists between different human populations, that evolution leading to man would follow a simple, straight-line pattern any more than it would in any other group.

We cannot leave our discussion of man's fossil record without some mention of one of the most successful hoaxes in history, the Piltdown man, dignified by the scientific name, *Eoanthropus dawsoni*. Fragments were reported from a gravel pit at Piltdown in Sussex, England, between 1908 and 1915. When reconstructed, they took the form of a brain case much like that of modern man, though thicker, and a lower jaw like that of a large ape. This find fulfilled the then-current concept of what the "missing link" between man and the apes would be like. Accepted as authentic, studied and puzzled over by experts, the Piltdown man went unexposed for over forty years. The subsequent finds of fossil hominids, especially the australopithecines, made an ever-greater anomaly of Eoanthropus, for they all agreed in having hominid jaws and dentition associated with a skull rather like an ape's instead of the reverse. Eventually with the aid of modern techniques, the Piltdown man was shown beyond question to be a clever fraud concocted from a human skull and the carefully doctored jaw and teeth of an orangutan. Even the tools and animal fossil bones found at the same site turned out to have been planted. Surely this was one of the most successful practical jokes in history, but modern methods of dating and analysis, if not the lesson learned here, make it very improbable that anthropologists will ever again be fooled in this way.

Man, a Polytypic Species

Although it has been argued that there are several living human species, it is clear that if the same taxonomic criteria are applied to man as have been applied to other species, there is but one human species living at the present time. This species, *Homo sapiens,* is polymorphic, for every human population manifests considerable variability, a fact easily confirmed by a quick glance at your friends and neighbors. It is also polytypic, for many geographic subspecies have been distinguished and named. They are not separate species, however, because the different races can and do interbreed. Probably the only racial cross that has not occurred is between Eskimos and African Bushmen. Furthermore, it is not possible to draw sharp, distinct lines of demarcation between human racial groups since one race usually blends into another in the zone of contact. The different human races differ from each other in the incidence of certain of their genes, and this is the basic distinction between races. While all living men must share fundamentally similar genotypes that cause them to develop into members of *Homo sapiens,* different human populations have diverged from one another to some extent. Human populations, past and present, are subject to the effects of mutation, natural selection, random genetic drift, and gene flow just as are other species.

Far too little is known about adaptive values in man, and man's present high mobility tends to obscure still further his adaptations to local conditions, but the indications are that the different human races are adapted to their immediate environments. The relation between degree of skin pigmentation and amount of exposure to the sun is a familiar example, but perhaps a somewhat shaky one since the skin has functions other than to serve as a filter for the ultraviolet light needed to form vitamin D in the body. Body form shows an even closer relation to climate than does skin color. The surface-to-volume ratio is maximized for more efficient heat dissipation in the lanky desert Arabs and Nilotic Negroes living under the searing tropical sun, but is minimized in the roly-poly Eskimos. The nasal cavities of Eskimos and north Europeans have also been shown to be better suited for warming and moistening cold, dry air than those of peoples living under milder climates. In fact, the entire Mongoloid face is thought to be adapted for life in a cold climate, for the nose is reduced and the entire face is flattened out and padded with fat, and the eyes are protected by the so-called Mongoloid fold. The steatopygia or fat on the buttocks of African

Bushwomen is another trait often cited as adaptive, for they store fat there in remarkable quantities. Although it has been suggested that steatopygia is functionally analagous to a camel's hump—an energy reserve that does not limit heat dissipation—this explanation fails to explain why the trait is absent in the male. It may be related to food storage for sustaining pregnancy, but sexual selection may also play a role, for the trait is said to be much admired by the men.

The sickle cell gene discussed earlier is one of the best-understood cases of adaptation in man. In regions where malaria is prevalent, the heterozygote for this gene is better adapted to survive than either homozygote; for one individual (Hb^s/Hb^s) is done in by his harmful genes, whereas the other (Hb^a/Hb^a) is apt to be carried off by malaria. Hence a balanced polymorphism due to heterosis exists, and in some regions over 40 percent of the population may carry the sickle cell gene, a high frequency out of all proportion to what might be expected of a gene with such drastic effects in the homozygous condition. Though this gene is most common in Negro Africa where its highest frequencies coincide roughly with the highest incidence of malaria, it is not restricted to this region or to this race, for it has also been found in malarial regions of India, Greece, Italy, Turkey, and Arabia. The most reasonable explanation for the distribution of the sickle cell gene is that it arose by mutation, probably among the Negroes in Africa, and has been introduced into other regions and races by gene flow through occasional matings between the Mediterranean peoples and Negro carriers. Once established, its frequency increased owing to its selective advantage in malarial areas. It is not, however, found in all regions of the world where malaria exists, presumably because it never got there either by mutation or by migration. However, other genes similar in function but distinct from the sickling gene have been discovered. As a final footnote to this story, the primary effect of the sickle cell gene, so far-reaching in its ultimate effects, has been shown to be merely the substitution in normal adult hemoglobin of a single amino acid, valine, for another, glutamic acid, in one of the peptides making up the hemoglobin protein molecule.

Many questions remain to be answered. What adaptive value, if any, is there in the different eye colors in man or in the different color and shape of human hair? Why do some races have much more body hair than others? What factors are responsible for the development of the pygmy tribes? The list could be considerably extended, but the answers in nearly all cases are unknown or at best merely informed guesses. In principle, we know that the differences must have arisen through the combination of directive and chance elements that govern the course of evolution within breeding populations (mutation, selection, genetic drift, and migration); in detail, however, our knowledge of the origin and function of the traits that distinguish one human race from another is quite sketchy. Many traits seem unlikely to confer any adaptive value, but even this assumption cannot be taken for granted. The different blood groups of the ABO system were long cited as traits in man governed by neutral genes, but it now appears, for example, that stomach cancer is somewhat more likely to develop in people of type A, and people of type O are somewhat more susceptible to duodenal ulcers, and thus this example must be discarded.

The Races of Man

There is not and probably cannot be any general agreement on the number of distinct human races. More than thirty have been distinguished. However, at least six rather distinct racial groups can be recognized as follows (see also Fig. 33-7):

Race	*Distribution before 1492*
1. Negroid	Widely scattered. Tropical Africa and Old World tropics— India, Andaman Islands, Philippines, Queensland, New Guinea, islands east to Fiji and southeast to New Caledonia
2. Caucasoid	North of tropics in North Africa, Europe, and Western Asia, southeast into tropics in India
3. Mongoloid	North and East Asia, south into Sunda Islands, North and South America
4. Bushmen	South Africa
5. Australoid	Australia
6. Polynesian	Remote Central Pacific islands from New Zealand to Hawaii

In terms of numbers and widespread distribution, the Negroid, Caucasoid, and Mongoloid groups are the three major human races at the present time. Negroids are usually dark skinned with black woolly hair, broad, flat noses, and thick lips. Caucasoids generally have rather light skin, long, narrow noses, and relatively straight hair. The hair of Mongoloids is straight and black, an eye fold is common, and the face is flattened with high cheekbones. As soon as these descriptions have been given, they must immediately be qualified because there is a great deal of variation within each group. All the races vary considerably in skin color, for example. The Caucasoid or so-called "white" race varies all the way from the blond, blue-eyed Scandinavian to the dark-eyed, dark-skinned Hindu of India. The Mongoloid group includes not only the "yellow" skinned Asians and Eskimos but the American "redskin." In size, Negroids vary from the tall Watussi (Batutsi) tribe whose members approach seven feet, to the Pygmies whose males average under five feet in height. Furthermore, the contacts between Negroids and Caucasoids in northern Africa and between Mongoloids and both Negroids and Caucasoids in the Orient have effectively blurred any distinctions between the races. In fact, the concept of "pure races," the idea that *Homo sapiens* in prehistoric times consisted of a group of separate, distinct racial groups whose differences are gradually being eroded away by the coming of civilization is so improbable as to be relegated to the realm of myths. Although local populations in the past undoubtedly were somewhat more isolated than at present, variability within populations and gene flow between populations, then as now, would have prevented the development of a "pure race."

Fig. 33-7. Representatives of major human races. (*a*) Mongoloid: Alaskan Eskimo woman; (*b*) Negroid: South African Bantu woman; (*c*) Bushmen: Hottentot woman with steatopygia; (*d*) Australoid: Girl from Northern Australia; (*e*) Polynesian: Maori woman; (*f*) Caucasoid: United States. (Courtesy of Peabody Museum, Harvard University.)

The Nazi concept of a pure Nordic race as the original Europeans and the builders of modern civilization simply does not stand up in the light of our knowledge of modern genetics and anthropology. Human populations have never been static entities. They have adapted to changing physical and biological conditions. The net result of natural selection, hybridization, mutation, and genetic drift has been an ever-shifting pattern in human breeding populations. Some have disappeared, either completely or by absorption into others by inter-marriage, while distinctive new populations have appeared. In the past, isolation by distance appears to have been the significant factor that permitted the differentiation of *Homo sapiens* into recognizably different racial groups. At present, isolation is breaking down, and new and different human types are arising as the result of hybridization. The mestizos of Latin America, a mixture of European, Indian, and some Negro ancestry, and the inhabitants of Pitcairn Island, descended from Europeans and Polynesians, represent examples of this sort.

The remaining three races of man mentioned above, the Polynesians, the Australoids, and the African Bushmen and their Hottentot relatives, are in a sense peripheral human groups. The Bushmen are found only in southern Africa, the Australoids in the Australian region, and the Polynesians on the islands in the far reaches of the Pacific. This distribution pattern calls to mind the distribution of relict populations in our discussion of biogeography. Although the analogy may hold with respect to the Bushmen and the Australoids, who appear to have occupied their present territory for some time, the Polynesians seem to have reached their island realm only quite recently. The Polynesians, despite the arguments based on the Kon-Tiki voyage, appear very definitely to have originated in Asia and not in South America.

Cultural Evolution

In addition to his own fossil remains, early man left behind him another type of record, a record of his culture. These cultures are known as the Paleolithic (or Old Stone Age), Mesolithic, Neolithic, and the Bronze and Iron Ages. These broad stages are used to indicate the cultural status achieved by a people and do not necessarily indicate absolute divisions of time, for some peoples are just now emerging from the Neolithic, a stage through which others passed several thousand years ago. The nature of past human cultures is inferred from the form of their tools and weapons and other implements (see Fig. 33-8). The Stone Age ranged in time from the Pliocene up until a few thousand years ago. The Neolithic, which marked the invention of agriculture, began only about ten thousand years ago; man, therefore, has been a hunter and gatherer of wild plant food for all but about 1 percent of his known existence. Even a high level of skill in hunting was reached only about thirty-five or forty thousand years ago in the Upper Paleolithic. Hence early cultures changed only very slowly and

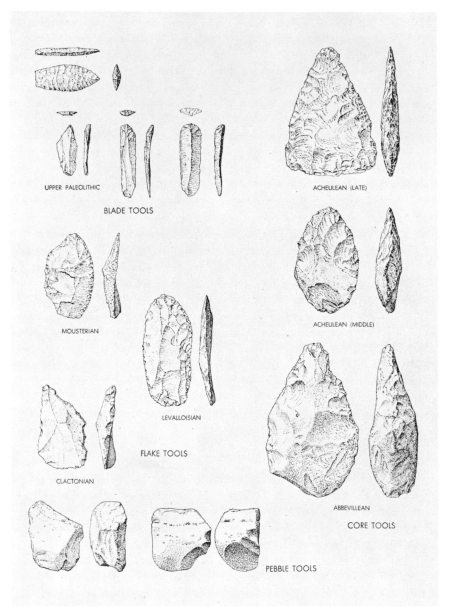

UPPER PALEOLITHIC

BLADE TOOLS

ACHEULEAN (LATE)

MOUSTERIAN

ACHEULEAN (MIDDLE)

LEVALLOISIAN

FLAKE TOOLS

CLACTONIAN

ABBEVILLEAN

CORE TOOLS

PEBBLE TOOLS

Fig. 33-8. The tool traditions of Europe form the basis for classifying Paleolithic cultures. The tools are arranged according to age, with the oldest at the bottom. Two views of each tool are given except for the blade tools, which are shown in three views. Tool traditions have been named for the site of discovery. (With permission of Washburn.)

persisted for long periods, but the pace of cultural changes has been ever increasing.

The stone implements were made by chipping and flaking pieces from a flint core to fashion the desired tool or weapon, and in some cultures the flakes were also used for a variety of smaller implements. Since the tools were fashioned with different techniques and varying degrees of skill and complexity, it has been possible to recognize a number of different tool traditions, and these have usually been named after the place where they were first discovered. Since tool making underwent gradual change and improvement, the evolution concept has been applied to the succession of tool traditions. Although perhaps useful for descriptive purposes, such application holds certain pitfalls, for the evolution of tools is not biological evolution and does not necessarily parallel the biological evolution that must have been going on in man at the same time. Furthermore, two quite different types of men could learn to fashion the same type of tool. Hence, a new type of inheritance, cultural inheritance, appears. Cultural patterns and traditions could not only be passed from one generation to its successors, but could be imitated and widely and rapidly disseminated without the necessity for any sort of biological continuity. Thus the attempts to link a particular tool tradition with a particular kind of fossil man are really valid only when there is positive evidence of association.

The earliest recognizable tools were associated with the Villafranchian fauna. The recent discovery of Zinjanthropus in association with stone tools of the pre-hand-axe Oldowan type shows that even the australopithecines had a true stone culture. The Abbevillian and Chellean hand-axe cultures were succeeded by the advanced Acheulean type of hand axe. The Clactonian flake industry, contemporaneous with these early hand-axe based cultures, was followed by the Mousterian-Levalloisian type of stone implements, which were more elaborate and carefully made than anything that preceded them. The Mousterian stone tools seem to have been fashioned by Neanderthal men, for Neanderthal skeletal remains have often been found with Mousterian weapons and tools. The rapid replacement of *H. neanderthalensis* by *H. sapiens* in Europe coincided with the appearance of Aurignacian implements, followed in a relatively short period by the Solutrean and Magdalenian types. It seems safe to assume that this new kind of man had developed new capabilities in fashioning his tools and weapons, for they were of a refinement and variety not previously seen. In addition to stone he used materials such as bone, horn, and ivory to fashion ornaments as well as weapons and tools. The Paleolithic, then, endured for by far the greater part of man's existence and was marked by gradual but accelerating advances in his ability to fashion stones and other materials to his own uses. The conclusion is difficult to avoid that the advances were so slow at first because the earlier species of men were of a lower order of intelligence than the men who followed them.

With the passing of the last ice age about 10,000 years ago a new phase of culture, the Mesolithic, appeared. These people both hunted and fished, for not only did they make bows and arrows, but they fashioned nets and canoes and lived on fish and shellfish as well as on game.

The Neolithic is marked by the appearance of ground and polished stone tools, and by pottery and weaving, but the real significance of the New Stone Age lay in the invention of agriculture. It was the domestication of plants and animals that permitted man to give up his essentially nomadic existence and to settle down in relatively permanent communities. Agriculture can support greater numbers of people than a hunting and gathering culture. Only with this advance did modern civilization become possible. The oldest known ground stone tools, cultivated plants, and domesticated animals (except for the dog) come from southwestern Asia and are less than ten thousand years old. This period seems even shorter when it is realized that agriculture was invented less than 400 generations ago. Agriculture apparently arose independently in at least three separate places. In southwestern Asia it was based on wheat, in southeastern Asia on rice, and in the Americas on maize. The stone implements of the Neolithic were soon augmented by implements made of new materials, and the Bronze Age, which spread from the Near East, was soon followed by the Iron Age. These early civilizations bring us up to the beginnings of recorded history.

With the development of civilization and culture, man has become a biologically dominant species that has expanded its range to the farthest corners of the earth and greatly increased in numbers. He is now cosmopolitan, the dominant mammalian species in all parts of the world, who has no reason to fear any competing species or predators, so complete is his domination by means of his weapons. Furthermore, he has gained mastery over most of his parasites and has remodeled his environment, using other species for his purposes. All of these developments became possible with the evolution of the human brain, the source of man's adaptive advantage over all other species. Human evolution has reached a new plateau, for superimposed on the biological evolution that still continues in man is cultural evolution. This new facet in evolution, the transmission of knowledge through culture, has opened up new vistas. Not only has he controlled the evolution of other species as he has modified domesticated plants and animals better to serve his needs, but he now has sufficient knowledge to control the course of his own evolution. Human cultural and biological evolution are going to continue in any event. The fundamental question is whether man has the wisdom to guide his own future.

SUGGESTED READING

Boule, M., and H. V. Vallois, 1957. *Fossil men*. London: Thames and Hudson.
Boyd, W. C., 1950. *Genetics and the races of man*. Boston: Little, Brown.

Clark, W. E. L., 1955. *The fossil evidence for human evolution.* Chicago: University of Chicago Press.

———, 1957. *History of the primates.* Chicago: University of Chicago Press, Phoenix Books.

———, 1959. "The crucial evidence for human evolution," *Proc. Amer. Philosophical Society, 103*(2):159-172.

———, 1959. *The antecedents of man.* Edinburgh: Edinburgh University Press.

Coon, C. S., 1954. *The story of man.* New York: Knopf.

Dart, R. A., and D. Craig, 1959. *Adventures with the missing link.* New York: Harper.

Demerec, M., ed., 1950. "Origin and evolution of man," *Cold Spring Harbor Symp. Quant. Biol.,* 15. New York: Long Island Biological Assoc.

Evolution and anthropology: a centennial appraisal, 1959. Washington, D. C.: Anthropol. Society.

Howells, W., 1959. *Mankind in the making.* Garden City, N. Y.: Doubleday.

Kluckhohn, C., 1949. *Mirror for man.* New York: McGraw-Hill. (Also Premier Reprint, 1957.)

Tax, S., ed., 1960. *Evolution after Darwin,* Vol. 2, *The evolution of man.* Chicago: University of Chicago Press.

"The human species," *Scientific American, 203*(3) Sept. 1960.

Weiner, J. S., 1955. *The Piltdown forgery.* New York: Oxford University Press.

CHAPTER 34

Radiation, Genetics, and Man

One has only to look at his friends and relations to get some idea of the variation that exists in a natural population. Some of this variation, of course, is of environmental origin. The genetic portion is due either to the recombination and interaction of existing genes or to new mutations. Since existing genes at some time in the past also arose through mutation, mutation looms large as a source of variation. Mutations have been defined as self-duplicating changes in the hereditary material. In a broad sense, they include submicroscopic point mutations and the microscopically detectable rearrangements following chromosome breakage. The "spontaneous" mutations may be due to the natural or background radiation coming from radioactive minerals and cosmic rays. Background radiation alone is insufficient to account for all "spontaneous" mutations, but a variety of chemical mutagens has been discovered, and these plus the effects of temperature and the mutation rate genes mentioned previously undoubtedly play a role in the induction of naturally occurring mutations.

The Frequency of Harmful Genes

The great majority of "spontaneous" point mutations are deleterious. It has been estimated that at a maximum only 1 in 1000 is beneficial under existing conditions. The reasons for this fact are fairly simple. Existing genes are the product of prior evolution and, since they have survived the winnowing action of natural selection, they give rise to well-adapted organisms. Hence, any change in an existing gene is far more likely to impair its function than to improve it. Most genes appear to be concerned with the presence and specificity of enzymes, and mutations, in disrupting the metabolic pattern, are generally harmful. For every lethal mutation, it is estimated that four detrimental mutations, reducing viability at least 10 percent, occur. Since this estimate is based on radiation-induced mutations in *Drosophila* (Fig. 34-1), the proportion of detrimentals among spontaneous mutants may actually be higher than four to one.

Most new mutations are recessive. In other words, the normal gene is effective in a single dose in masking or covering up the effects of the deleterious or lethal mutant. Less than 1 in 100 mutants is fully dominant. Therefore,

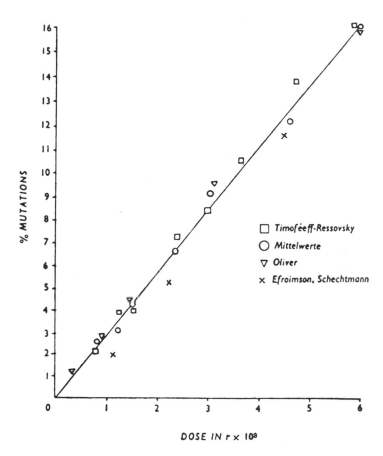

□ *Timoféeff-Ressovsky*

○ *Mittelwerte*

▽ *Oliver*

× *Efroimson, Schechtmann*

DOSE IN r × 10³

Fig. 34-1. Linear relation between radiation dose and mutation rate for sex-linked lethals in *Drosophila.* (With permission of Begg.)

contrary to a widespread belief, mutation does not lead at once to a host of monsters in the next generation. The rare dominants are rapidly eliminated by natural selection, dominant lethals disappearing in the first generation. The recessives are added to the gene pool of the population. They will produce maximum damage only when present in double dose, which may not occur for many generations. However, the recessive mutants are generally not completely recessive, for two doses of the normal gene ordinarily are better than a single dose plus the mutant and hence harmful mutations can cause damage even when heterozygous. This damage may be very difficult to detect since it is on the order of a 2 to 4 percent reduction in fecundity, fertility, viability, or longevity, with no obvious visible defects. Thus, a gene mildly deleterious in single dose may eventually do as much harm as a grossly harmful one, for it persists longer and has a chance to cause impairment to more individuals. Eventually it will lead to the extinction or "genetic death" of the line of descent carrying it, and this will usually happen before it becomes homozygous.

At the present time 4 to 5 percent of the children born alive in the United States are in some way defective. This startling statistic may at first glance seem unreasonably high, but it includes not only congenital malformations but mental deficiency and epilepsy, and defects of vision or hearing and of the gastrointestinal, genitourinary, neuromuscular, hematological, and endocrine systems. When it is realized that estimates of the frequency of mental deficiency alone range as high as 5 percent in this country, the above estimate seems fairly conservative. About half of these children, or 2 percent of the total live births, are suffering from disorders that have a simple genetic origin and will appear prior to sexual maturity. Thus, of the next 100 million children born in the United States, two million can be expected to have some sort of hereditary defect. These defects are the result of deleterious "spontaneous" mutants induced in the past by natural causes and now present in the gene pool of our population.

Many of these inherited conditions are severe enough to cause the death of the child or else to limit or prevent his reproduction. These defective genes, then, are constantly being eliminated from the population by natural selection. Why, if these genes have been selected against for centuries, are they still so frequent? The answer is that they are being generated by recurrent spontaneous mutations. An equilibrium between their rate of origin by mutation and their rate of elimination by selection has been approximated.

In this connection it may be pointed out that the practice of medicine has changed radically in the past 100 years. One hundred years ago the major killers of human beings were infectious diseases. Today, where modern medicine is practiced, the physician is turning his attention away from combating microorganisms. (The microorganisms have by no means surrendered; the origin of resistant strains has tempered the initial optimism that greeted the various antibiotics and chemotherapeutic agents.) The major causes of death at the present time do not involve infectious organisms, but they do involve, to varying degrees, harmful genes, the new objects of medical assault. To the extent that the physician succeeds in combating the effects of deleterious genes by suitable environmental manipulations (for example, insulin for diabetes), the results are dysgenic, for the proportion of these genes in the population will increase in subsequent generations. The physicians of the next generation, therefore, will have a greater proportion of such cases to treat. It is estimated that the average person carries the equivalent of about 4 genes, any one of which, in the homozygous condition, would cause his death. In other words, he may carry 4 lethals, or 8 deleterious genes with a 50 percent probability of causing death, or 100 genes with only a 4 percent chance. Actually, there is undoubtedly a mixture of these types descended from past mutations that still persist in the population. Unless some way is found to prevent their increase in frequency, this load of hidden mutations will inevitably become heavier as the medical control of genetic defects improves.

The average spontaneous mutation rate for a given gene locus has been estimated to be from 1 to 2 new mutations per 100,000 genes per generation. This statement means that in 100,000 sperm cells, 1 or 2 can be expected to carry a newly arisen spontaneous mutation for a particular gene. However, the total rate, a measure of the mutations at all gene loci on all chromosomes, is considerably higher. The total number of genes is not known in any species. Indirect estimates lead to a value of at least 10,000 gene loci in *Drosophila,* and this figure is probably a conservative estimate for man. The total mutation rate therefore equals $\frac{1}{100,000} \times 10,000 = \frac{1}{10}$. Hence, 1 in 10 gametes or about 2 in 10 diploid individuals can be expected to carry a newly arisen mutation. At equilibrium, this frequency represents the risk of genetic death since the rate of elimination of the mutants equals their rate of origin. This risk is shared by all of us since everyone carries several to many detrimental mutations. It indicates the loss of fitness of the average individual as compared to a hypothetical person with no detrimental mutants at all. It should be pointed out that the above estimates are based primarily on data from *Drosophila* and mice, with the mutation rates in mice somewhat higher than those of the fruit flies. Man's mutation rate, because of his greater generation length, is apt to be higher than that of mice. More and better data for man are needed, but the fundamental conclusions are unlikely to change.

Genetic Effects of Radiation

The original discovery of the mutagenic effects of x-rays by Muller in 1927 was of great interest to geneticists, but only with the coming of the atomic age have the biological effects of ionizing radiations become of general concern.

The biological effects are of two major kinds: somatic or direct effects on exposed individuals, causing either death or immediate or delayed pathological effects; and genetic effects in the germ cells of exposed individuals, which are then transmitted to subsequent generations. Ionizing radiations such as x-rays and gamma rays (similar to x-rays but emanating from radioactive substances such as radium) have been shown to induce chromosome breakage as well as gene or point mutations. In their passage, these radiations break existing chemical bonds and lead to the formation of positively and negatively charged ions. Presumably the biological effects are the result of the subsequent reactions in which these ions are involved.

Induced mutations are in general similar to spontaneous mutations, though chromosome breakage is relatively more frequent among the induced mutations. The vast majority of induced mutations are recessive and deleterious under existing conditions. There is no threshold dose of radiation below which no mutations are induced. Any increase in ionizing radiation above the background can therefore be expected to cause a corresponding increase in the number of mutations. The mutation rate has been shown to be directly proportional to the dosage of radiation. A doubling of the dosage will result in a doubling in the number of induced mutations. For chromosomal rearrangements such as inversions or reciprocal translocations, however, the number of rearrangements

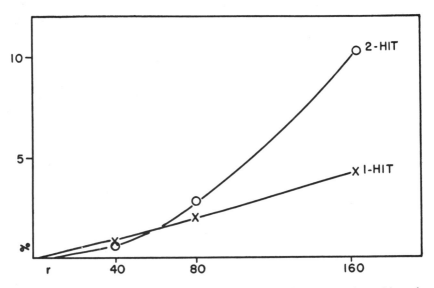

Fig. 34-2. Relation between x-ray dosage and the frequency of one-hit and two-hit chromatid rearrangements. One-hit rearrangements increase in direct proportion to the dosage but two-hit rearrangements tend to increase as the square of the dosage at relatively high intensities. (With permission of Sax.)

increases more nearly as the square of the dosage. This difference is attributed to the fact that two independent breaks are required for the rearrangements, whereas mutations are single-hit events. See Fig. 34-2.

Although an intensity effect has recently been reported in mice, the number of gene mutations induced is usually independent of the intensity with which the radiation is delivered. One hundred roentgens in 5 minutes causes the same number of point mutations as 100r in 5 months or 5 years. A roentgen of x- or gamma radiation is the amount that will, when applied to air at standard conditions (0° C, 760 mm mercury), produce 2.1×10^9 ion pairs per cubic centimeter (1 electrostatic unit of charge). In water or tissue, the number of ion pairs produced by 1r is estimated to be about 800 times greater. Much easier to remember is the fact that 1r causes approximately 2 ionizations per cubic micron of tissue. The effect of the radiation, then, is cumulative, for a mutation, once it occurs, does not heal, but is self-duplicating and persists until it causes a genetic death.

Somatic Effects of Radiation

A severe exposure to radiation may be lethal. The acute lethal dose for 50 percent of the exposed individuals (the so-called L.D. 50) has been estimated in man to be in the range of from 400 to 600r. Lesser doses produce a variety of somatic effects, and the parts of the body where cell division is rapidly occurring appear to be particularly sensitive. Early symptoms, for example, among the survivors of the explosions at Hiroshima and Nagasaki were disturbances of the gastrointestinal tract and in the blood-forming tissues. Temporary or in some instances permanent sterility may be induced. Later effects of acute exposure or of low-level chronic exposure include skin cancer and leukemia, which may not develop until long after the exposure. Finally, in addition to these rather specific ailments, there are nonspecific effects such as a lower immunity to disease, damage to the connective tissue, and signs of premature aging. In mice, the most sensitive index of somatic damage is the shortening of the life span.

All of the biological effects of radiation mentioned thus far have been observed in man except for one, the induction of gene mutations. Skin cancer, leukemia, etc., are known consequences of exposure to radiation that have been made more or less familiar by newspaper reports. Shortening of the life span is indicated by data on radiologists (Table 34-1). Even the breakage of human chromosomes has been demonstrated in human cells in tissue culture by Bender. In view of these effects in man, there is no reason to suppose that he has some sort of mysterious immunity to the mutagenic effects of radiation. Why, then, has it not yet been demonstrated?

TABLE 34-1

Effects of Radiation on Life Span*

Group	Average age at death
U.S. population over 25	65.6
Physicians (not exposed)	65.7
Physicians (some exposure—urologists, dermatologists, etc.)	63.3
Radiologists	60.5

* National Academy of Sciences, 1956. "The biological effects of atomic radiation," Summary reports. Washington, D. C.

Radiation Effects in Man

The largest study of the genetic effects of radiation was made under the auspices of the United States Atomic Energy Commission on the children of the survivors of the explosions at Hiroshima and Nagasaki. Among these children, as compared to the controls, there were no statistically significant increases in the number of stillbirths or abnormalities but a possible slight effect on the sex ratio was reported. The Genetics Conference that set up the project expected these results from the outset, but the opportunity for such a study was unique and it seemed wise to seize it.

Let us consider the reasons for the lack of significant differences between exposed and control populations. The unexposed controls showed more than 1 percent visible, though slight, malformations at birth, a part of the 4 to 5 percent defective mentioned previously. Furthermore, less than 1 in 100 induced mutants are dominant and will be immediately expressed in the next generation. Therefore, it has been estimated that out of 1000 children whose parents both received 100r (that is, the most heavily irradiated survivors), it can be expected that 30 percent will carry a newly induced mutation. However, only about 1 percent of these mutations will be dominant and expressed in the children. Simple arithmetic ($1000 \times 0.3 \times 0.01 = 3$) shows that only 3 among the 1000 childen can be expected to be malformed at birth due to the irradiation. Since 1 percent or 10 in 1000 can be expected to be malformed at birth due to causes other than the radiation, a statistical comparison is required between 10 in 1000 and 13 in 1000. Obviously, such a small difference will be subject to random fluctuations unless very large numbers are available for study. Special genetic techniques that are, fortunately, not available to the human geneticist would be needed to reveal the much more numerous induced recessives. However, lack of the techniques is no reason to suppose that mutations have not occurred and been added to the existing load of mutations. Other studies of the children of radiologists and of children whose parents have received therapeutic pelvic irradiation of 1000r or more (skin dose) have indicated a genetic effect.

These data were assembled by questionnaire and are possibly subject to bias since the returns were not complete. One conclusion that can be drawn, perhaps, from the genetic studies is that man cannot be much more susceptible to radiation than are mice.

A useful way to look at the problem is in terms of the doubling dose, that amount of radiation which will induce as many mutations as now occur spontaneously. The doubling dose was independently estimated by two groups in the United States and Great Britain with surprisingly good agreement as $50r$ and 30 to $80r$. In other words, if the population of the United States were subjected to an additional $50r$ per generation, the number of children born with genetic defects would gradually rise from 2 percent to 4 percent as the new equilibrium is reached. Taking all factors into account, the National Academy of Sciences has recommended that the total accumulated dose of ionizing radiation from humanly controllable sources to the reproductive cells from conception to age 30 should not be more than $10r$. This recommended dose is by no means harmless but is considered reasonable. However, for 100 million children an increase of $10r$ is estimated to give rise to 50,000 new inherited defects in the first generation and ultimately at the new equilibrium to 500,000 per generation. Clearly, any increase at all must be regarded as harmful. Recent estimates for the average exposure to radiation of the gonads of the population of the United States are as follows:

Source of radiation	
background	3.1r per 30 years
medical uses of radiation	4.6r per 30 years
fallout from atomic explosions	0.1r per 30 years

There apparently is a threshold for most somatic effects of radiation, for with two possible exceptions, doses several times as large as the recommended $10r$ limit are necessary to cause detectable somatic damage. One possible exception is the shortening of the life span. Even though doses of up to $100r$ spread over a period of years have not been shown to shorten human life, it is still possible that there is no threshold. If, for example, large numbers of people exposed to a gradually accumulated dose had their life expectancy lowered very slightly, the individual effect might seem trivial, but the total effect would be very great.

The other possible exception is the effect of strontium-90. This radioactive element, rather similar chemically to calcium, tends to accumulate in bone. The major hazard from Sr^{90} is the internal radiation of the red bone marrow, which may lead to the development of leukemia. The maximum permissible concentration (MPC) of Sr^{90} in man has been set at 1 microcurie per 1000 grams of calcium. (A microcurie produces an amount of radiation equivalent to that emanating from a millionth of a gram of radium. The body of the average human adult contains about 1000 grams of calcium.) Just 0.1 of the MPC would give a dose rate of 0.1 to 0.2r per year to the red bone marrow. For the present population of the United States, the expected number of additional cases of leukemia at this dosage level would be 500 to 1000 per year. Since there are currently about 10,500 deaths from leukemia in the United States each year, one-tenth the MPC of Sr^{90} would be expected to increase the present incidence of leukemia about 5 or 10 percent. However, the present levels of Sr^{90} in bone are about 1/1000 rather than 1/10 of the MPC, and therefore Sr^{90} cannot now be regarded as a major hazard to the human population; the level of Sr^{90} in bone must be watched, however, for if it rises, the hazard will increase. Furthermore, it seems unlikely that the existing levels of exposure are causing any major shortening in the human life span. However, there is no question that much additional research is needed to back up the available estimates and to clarify still further the somatic effects of radiation.

The major hazard at the present time is the genetic effect of radiation, and the major source of man-made radiation for the population of the United States is the medical use of radiation. The amount received currently from fall-out is only 1 or 2 percent as great as the amount received in the course of the various medical uses of ionizing radiation. While some scientists have greatly emphasized the dangers inherent in nuclear weapons testing, others equally reputable have suggested that the dangers are trivial or nonexistent or may even be beneficial. Under these circumstances the public cannot be blamed for being somewhat confused about the hazards involved. A true concern for human welfare would seem to dictate that the problem of radiation hazard must be faced as a whole, and that the solution must encompass not only nuclear tests but the medical and industrial uses of radiation as well. The evidence now available indicates quite clearly that the net effect of any increase in the exposure of the human population to radiation will be harmful. However, it is also clear that more research is desirable and necessary to delineate more specifically just how great are the hazards to man.

The varied uses of radiation raise questions to which there are no simple answers. For the physician, each use of radiation requires that he weigh the immediate benefits to his patient against the possible genetic damage to future generations. And this, of course, raises the question of just what are our obligations to future generations. Is it possible that the doctors of another day will be able to mend damaged genes as they now mend broken legs? If it is possible, how much radiation can the human species safely absorb until that day comes? The weapons tests similarly require an evaluation of the benefits and hazards of testing versus not testing. Unfortunately, the decisions on testing are based in the final analysis on political rather than on scientific or humanitarian considerations.

SUGGESTED READING

Effect of radiation on human heredity, 1957. Geneva: World Health Organization.

"Ionizing radiation," *Scientific American, 201*(3) Sept. 1959.

Medical Research Council, 1956. "The hazards to man of nuclear and allied radiations," Cmd. 9780. London: H. M. Stationery Office. 2d Report, 1960. Cmnd. 1225.

Muller, H. J., 1950. "Radiation damage to the genetic material," *Amer. Scientist, 38:*33-59; 399-425.

————, 1950. "Our load of mutations," *Amer. Jour. Human Genetics, 2:*111-176.

National Academy of Sciences, 1956. "The biological effects of atomic radiation," summary reports. Washington, D.C. 2d Report, 1960.

Wallace, B. and Th. Dobzhansky. 1959. *Radiation, genes, and man.* New York: Holt, Rinehart and Winston.

CHAPTER 35

Man as a Dominant Species

The human population is subject to the effects of natural selection, mutation, gene flow, and random genetic drift just as are the populations of other species. In the future as in the past, the qualitative characteristics of the human population during the course of its evolution will be determined by the net effect of the action of these factors. However, in addition to changing qualitatively, the human population may also change quantitatively. The most noteworthy aspect of human biology in the last few centuries has been the tremendous increase in the size of the human population, an increase of such overriding significance that any consideration of human affairs that fails to include it is seriously deficient.

The population problem is an involved, controversial, and paradoxical subject, so beset by emotion and prejudice that discussing it objectively is far more difficult than discussing factors that regulate the numbers of grasshoppers or deer or field mice. There are two schools of thought about the hazards of man's increasing numbers. One group will state flatly that Malthus has long since been proven wrong, that man can produce all the food and goods necessary for any possible increase in his numbers, and that his ingenuity and resourcefulness (or science and technology) will insure that production will more than keep pace with population growth. Any present difficulties in getting sufficient food and other necessities are attributed to a failure in the system of distribution rather than to overpopulation. One cannot help but wonder at times whether these people have ever read the words of Malthus whom they so readily dismiss. Opposed to this group is another group, who will point out that right now three-fifths of the world's people are living at a bare subsistence level, and that since we can not even take care of our present population in a satisfactory way, there is no reason to suppose that we can do so in the future if the present rate of increase continues. The question is whether the earth's resources are sufficient to support the present population and the potential future population at a standard of living above the bare subsistence level. The future of mankind may well hinge more on the answer to this question than on any other single factor.

In order to make an objective appraisal of the pros and cons of this question, certain relevant facts must be reviewed. All living organisms, including man, are ultimately dependent for their very existence on the photosynthetic processes of green plants by which the sun's energy is utilized to form organic materials (that is, food) from simple inorganic compounds. This fact is inescapable at the present time, and it appears unlikely that other means of synthesizing food in significant quantities will be devised in the near future. The maximum size of the human population, then, ultimately depends on the amount of food that can be grown to support it. The areas available on the earth in which food might be grown consist of the following:

A. Land	1. Fertile regions	33,000,000 square miles
	2. Steppes	19,000,000 square miles
	3. Deserts	5,000,000 square miles
B. Water		140,000,000 square miles

This is all there is; there isn't any more. (The implications of the space age can safely be ignored in the present discussion, for the problems of transportation and distribution have not yet been successfully solved here on earth and will be infinitely greater in any interplanetary situation.) Crops can only be raised in the fertile regions. The vegetation of the steppes is made available to man through its use as pasture; the vegetation of the seas is the pasture, in a sense, of the fishes. The amount of fertile land can be increased through irrigation. The yield can be improved through improved agricultural methods and the use of improved varieties of plants and animals. These changes have been and are continuing to be made in many parts of the earth with spectacular success in many instances in increasing the productivity of the land.

Man has existed for at least several hundred thousand years. Although exact figures are not available, the best estimates indicate that until 1650 human population growth was relatively slow and erratic. By that time the human population was estimated to be about 500 million. In less than 200 years, by 1825, world population had doubled, and for the first time more than a billion people inhabited the earth. In another 100 years the population had again doubled to 2 billion. In the few decades since 1925 this growth has continued, until the present world´population is estimated to be over 2.8 billion people. Thus from a species of limited range and numbers, man has seemed almost literally to explode over the face of the earth. He is now a cosmopolitan species, yet it seems likely that 50,000 years ago North and South America were completely uninhabited by man, and that in the inhabited areas the population density was low, typical of a hunting or nomad population. See Fig. 35-1.

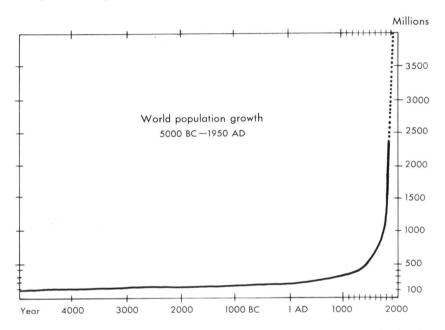

Fig. 35-1. World population growth, 5000 B.C. to 1950 A.D. Not only the size of the human population but the annual rate of growth has increased markedly since 1800. (With permission of Sax.)

Not only has the human population increased, but it has increased at an accelerating rate. The annual rate of increase has grown from an estimated 0.4 percent between 1650 and 1850 to 0.8 percent between 1850 and 1950, and is currently estimated to be about 1.7 percent per year. The numerical increase is thought to be nearly 45 million a year or about 123,000 per day. Projection of these figures into the future has led to estimates of 6 billion people by the year 2000 and nearly 13 billion by 2050. The facts are, then, that we have on the earth a limited amount of space and fertile land on which to support a human population rapidly growing at an accelerating pace. Obviously this growth cannot and will not continue indefinitely and these figures may never be reached. However, the way in which this trend is slowed or reversed will have a tremendous impact on the future welfare and happiness of mankind.

Elementary Demography

Under favorable conditions, the human population could easily double every 25 years. The fact that it has not done so is an indication that man's existence has been rather precarious, with disease, pestilence, famine, natural catastrophes, and war all having exacted a heavy toll in the past. The size of any population is determined by the relationship between the death rate and the birth rate, and even though birth rates were high in the past, death rates were also high so that growth of the human population was slow and irregular. The most common way to express birth rates or death rates is in terms of the number of births or deaths per 1000 population, the so-called crude birth and death rates. Since both birth rates and death rates vary with age, the crude rates will also depend on the age structure of the population and may not be directly comparable in two populations having different age distributions.

The rapid population growth in the Western world during the last few centuries has been due to the scientific revolutions in the fields of public health, agriculture, and industry. The initial effect of these revolutions was a reduction in the death rate, and this can be attributed primarily to the revolution in medicine and public health. Many diseases have been eliminated or brought under control so that infant mortality has been reduced from about 200 to about 30 per thousand infants and the average crude death rate has fallen from about 40 to about 12 or less per thousand. As a consequence, life expectancy at birth has risen from between 25 and 30 to between 60 and 70 years.

The revolution in agriculture has resulted from mechanization and from scientific advances in plant and animal breeding as well as in the methods of cultivation and fertilization; yield per acre and also yield per agricultural worker have risen dramatically among the Western nations. In the United States in 1700, for example, it took 4 farm families to produce enough food for 5 families. Today one farm family produces enough food for 6 families, or for 10 families living at the standards of 1700. Therefore, since the efforts of 5 out of 6 families can now be diverted from the production of food into the production of other goods and services, the standard of living has risen rapidly.

The industrial revolution, which went more or less hand in hand with the agricultural revolution, increased the food supply through the mechanization of farming and through the improved transportation system, by which food could be shipped from areas of high production to areas of consumption where it was exchanged for manufactured products. Emigration from crowded regions in Europe to empty lands in America and elsewhere overseas became possible, and helped to relieve the pressure of an expanding population.

Still another transition has taken place in most of the Western nations, perhaps as revolutionary as any thus far mentioned. This revolution, more recent in onset than the others, has resulted in declining birth rates. As a result of the time lag between the fall in the death rates and the fall in the birth rates, the so-called demographic transition from a high birth rate-high death rate agricultural society to a low birth rate-low death rate industrial society has always historically been accompanied by a rapid increase in population size (see Fig. 35-2). When the death rate is lower than the birth rate, the difference between the two can be regarded as a measure of the net increase; when the birth rate falls below the death rate, the population will, if this relation persists, decline in numbers.

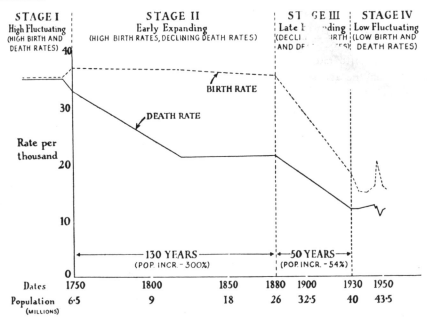

Fig. 35-2. The demographic transition in England and Wales from a society with high birth and death rates to one with low rates of births and deaths. (With permission of P.E.P. Report. World Population and Resources.)

During the demographic transition, various stages can be recognized. Initially there is an agricultural society, with high birth rates, high death rates, a slow and irregular increase in numbers, and a relatively low standard of living. In the next stage the death rate starts to fall quite rapidly while the birth rate continues high. The decline in the death rate comes first because the measures needed to control the death rate are relatively simple and easy to put into effect. Thus the initial impact of modern scientific knowledge on a backward society has been on the death rate. The sensitivity of the death rate to changed conditions can be illustrated by the spectacular drop in Japan from a death rate of 32 per 1000 in 1945 to 12 per 1000 in 1948. In Ceylon an antimalarial campaign using DDT brought the death rate from 20.2 in 1946 down to 14.2 in 1947 and to 9.8 by 1956. In 1946 there were 12,578 deaths from malaria; in 1947, 4557; and in 1956, 144. Life expectancy at birth rose from 45.8 years to over 60 years. Obviously when death rates decline in this fashion and a decline in birth rates does i immediately follow, the population increase is rapid.

During the next phase, the birth rate also starts to decline rather rapidly while the death rate continues to fall. The causes of declining birth rates have never been clearly defined, but, and here is the paradox, birth rates have started to fall in the past only after standards of living have improved. Thus, birth rates are highest in just those areas where people are least able to support large families. During this period when both birth and death rates are declining, population continues to increase but at a decelerating pace.

The final stage, reached when the demographic transition is completed, is marked   th and death rates and near equilibrium conditions. Usually the birth remains somewhat higher than the death rate so that the population continues to grow at a slow rate. In countries that have made the transition, standards of living are high, life expectancy is long, and birth rates are very sensitive to economic forces.

Burma may be cited as an example of an underdeveloped nation with high birth rates (47.5, 1951-53), high death rates (35.7, 1951-53), and a rather slow rate of growth (though declining death rates may lead to more rapid growth). The island of Mauritius appears to have reached the second stage, since the birth rate (1949-53) was 46.5 while the death rate was only 14.9, the result being a sizable natural increase. Puerto Rico has recently reached the third phase of the demographic transition, for her birth rate had fallen (1953) from between 40 and 50 to 34.8 and the death rate to 8.1. The United Kingdom has essentially completed the change, for in 1953 the birth rate was 15.9 and the death rate was 11.4, and the rate of natural increase was quite low.

In Western Europe the change from a high birth rate-high death rate society to a low birth rate-low death rate society brought about a sixfold increase in population. North America had a sixfold increase in just a single century, between 1850 and 1950. Japan has made the transition in less than a century, more rapidly than any other nation, and yet, despite the speed of the change, has almost tripled from about 35 million in 1868 to nearly 100 million today.

In spite of their increases in population size, the nations of the Western world have had a notable rise in their standards of living. The economic well-being of the people of these nations is higher than it has ever been anywhere. This fact, that standards of living have increased while populations were growing rapidly, has led, it seems clear, to the optimistic view that Malthus was wrong. However, his basic statements were:

1. Population is necessarily limited by the means of subsistence. 2. Population invariably increases, where the means of subsistence increase, unless prevented by some very powerful and obvious checks. 3. These checks, and the checks which repress the superior power of population, and keep its effects on a level with the means of subsistence are all resolvable into moral restraint, vice and misery.

He distinguished between preventive checks, which tended to reduce the birth rate, and positive checks, which raised the death rate. The essential soundness of his position seems clear. What he did not foresee was the possibility that preventive checks could come to be as significant as they are in some nations today.

The Causes of Overpopulation

Because of the revolutions in agriculture and industry, the means of subsistence in the Western world have increased even more rapidly than has the population, and the West has managed thus far to escape the Malthusian devil of overpopulation. The meaning intended here for the term "overpopulation" is that there are more people than can be supported at a reasonable standard of living on the available resources (of all kinds) in the area. The implication is that if the population had not grown so large, the people individually would be better off, and if it continues to grow, living standards will fall still further. It will be worthwhile to examine the routes by which the West has escaped this situation and to evaluate their applicability to those areas of the world that have yet to make the transition.

When such an analysis is made, it becomes obvious that the three-fifths of the world's people who have a low living standard (per capita income usually less than $100 per year), an average length of life in the 30's, a high birth rate, and a low literacy rate cannot hope to escape from overpopulation by following the same sequence of events as the Western world. This statement may seem rather dogmatic and therefore warrants further more detailed consideration and discussion.

The first impact of modern scientific knowledge on a backward agricultural society has always been on the death rate, because public health measures such as sewage disposal, water purification, mosquito control, vaccination, etc., are relatively inexpensive and easy to institute. However, the longer life will not necessarily be a happier one, for countries such as India, China, and Egypt are already densely populated and cannot hope to support even a twofold increase in population at a higher standard of living, let alone a threefold, or sixfold, or tenfold increase. Efforts toward industrialization are beset by the fact that there are few areas (the United States is one) with excess food to exchange for manufactured products, and these areas may not need or want the manufactured goods. Furthermore, markets are not as readily available as they were 150 years ago. If it is argued that the primary need is to increase agricultural production rather than industrial expansion, another dilemma presents itself. This situation can best be clarified by an actual example. It might be expected that a marked rapid increase in the food supply would give the farmers a surplus that could then be exchanged for manufactured goods and for services so that their living standards would rise. This argument, in one form or another, seems to be the one that has led some individuals to view the population problem with equanimity. However, it ignores the demographic effects of an increased food supply in an under-developed country, and therein lies its fallacy. On the Malabar coast of India, rice had been the staple food crop for centuries until research showed that tapioca (cassava) was a more profitable crop for this area. The change to tapioca was put into effect rapidly, and food production was approximately doubled in a few years. In just 12 years, however, the population in this area had also doubled, so that twice as many people now lived on twice as much food at the same bare subsistence level. Therefore, even though various governments have set up five-year plans or other programs designed to increase agricultural production or to encourage the development of industry, such programs may not resolve the problems, even when their goals are achieved, if the demographic factors are not favorable or are ignored in the planning. In fact, the situation may actually become worse than before.

The pressure of the growing population in Europe during the demographic transition was relieved in part by the emigration of large numbers of Europeans to America and to other parts of the world that were then sparsely populated. The safety valve provided by emigration is no longer available, for there are no more large unoccupied habitable areas in the world. Furthermore, the very magnitude of the logistic problems involved makes it clear that the solution for overpopulated areas is not to export their surplus population (even if they were able to decide who was surplus and who was not). In India, for example, a series of favorable crop years between 1931 and 1941 led to an increase of 50 million in her population, an average of 5 million per year. Imagine, if you will, the problems involved merely in transporting 5 million people per year from India to some other part of the world, not to mention the problems of finding housing and jobs for them in their new environment. The United States, at the peak of its all-out effort in World War II, transported and supported overseas only about 8 million men. Clearly, the relocation of millions of people, the numbers about which we must think, would be impossible, especially for those nations whose resources are already strained by overpopulation. Hence, this solution holds little promise for the present problems even if undeveloped lands were available. A further complication should also be pointed out to indicate another aspect of the problems created by migration. Existence of the bitter racial tensions that have developed between white and Negro in South Africa is probably familiar to readers. Less well known, perhaps, is the fact that

South Africa also has a fairly large and rapidly growing population of immigrants from India. This emigration has had no noticeable effect on the rate of growth of the Indian population. However, the migrants took their low living standards and high birth rates with them to South Africa, thereby arousing the resentment of both black and white, and the troubles of South Africa are now being compounded by a three-way racial tension. In a sense the problem has been transplanted rather than solved.

The Regulation of Man's Increasing Numbers

The final possible solution to the problems of the three-fifths of the people who live in either the first or the second stages of the demographic transition is to reduce the birth rate in step with the reduction in the death rate so that numbers remain stabilized. This solution seems to be the one with the greatest chance of success, yet it is by far the most difficult to put into effect.

The situation in these areas is distinctly different from that in Europe two centuries ago. Death rates not only can be but have been brought down drastically in a very short period by the application of modern scientific knowledge in backward areas, and the decrease has been much more rapid than it ever was in Western Europe. Consequently, the potential explosive increase in population size that exists in these areas is far beyond what ever occurred in Europe. It is also possible to increase production in agriculture and industry in these areas, although more time and effort are required than is needed to reduce the death rate. However, a reduction in the birth rate takes much longer and is much more difficult to achieve than is the control of deaths or an increase in productivity. In the past, birth rates have started to fall only after standards of living have been raised. The highest birth rates are associated throughout the world with high levels of poverty and ignorance. If the historical sequence of events is followed in the underdeveloped countries today, the outcome would appear to be different from that in the Western nations. The reproductive potential is so great that population increases, before they can raise living standards to the point where birth rates might be expected to decline, will absorb any increase in production. As a consequence, more and more people will be supported at a bare subsistence level. The contrast between the nations that have made the demographic transition and those that have not will become even more stark, and the explosive possibilities of such a situation on the international scene can hardly be minimized. The conclusion seems inescapable, therefore, that countries today that have high birth and death rates and that wish to better the lot of their people and their positions as nations must direct their efforts toward bringing birth rates under control.

Only if the population growth can be held down can increased production be used to improve living conditions. In the absence of checks on growth, natural increase rather than living standards responds to economic development. The mere development of underdeveloped countries has never been shown capable in itself of raising living standards. Self-generated development is usually slow because of the difficulty in amassing sufficient capital and resources to speed the process. As a result, the population increase rapidly absorbs the gains as they are made, and as the population grows, the problem of making the demographic transition becomes increasingly difficult. External aid on a massive scale has been suggested as a possible solution. However, outside aid, whether in the form of capital, equipment, or technical aid or training, is equally unlikely to be effective if unaccompanied by some means of limiting the increase in population. The experience of the British in India and Egypt and of the United States in Puerto Rico point up some of the problems involved. In the decades of rule by the British in both India and Egypt, during which the gross national product of the countries undoubtedly increased, population growth more than kept pace so that today living standards in these countries are probably lower than they were 50 or more years ago. The United States has poured over a billion dollars in aid into Puerto Rico since assuming control in 1898—the greatest effort ever made to put a backward nation on its feet through outside assistance. The most obvious result of this aid has been an increase in population from about a million to more than two and a quarter million. The death rate per 1000 declined gradually from 31.4 in 1899 to below 10 per 1000 in recent years while the birth rate, which was over 40 per 1000 in 1899, remained high until about 1947 when a slow decline set in. The actual natural increase is still about 60,000 per year. Emigration to the United States has served as a safety valve, for in recent years annual net emigration has almost equaled the natural increase, thus stabilizing the population size. Some progress toward raising the standard of living has been made since about 1945. However, unemployment is still common, and housing and schools are still inadequate. Thus after 60 years of generous aid, limited results are finally forthcoming, but Puerto Rico has occupied such a uniquely favorable position that the picture can hardly be considered encouraging with respect to what might be done for other less well-situated areas. Only after 40 years did signs of progress appear, and Puerto Rico's problems are by no means solved yet. What then can the prospects be for the much larger underdeveloped nations that can find no place to export their surplus population and cannot hope to receive outside aid on the same scale as was used in Puerto Rico?

The answer clearly is that the primary task in the development of the have-not nations of the world is the reduction of the birth rate along with the death rate so that population explosions are not detonated across the surface of the earth. Reduction in the birth rate must accompany the agricultural, industrial, and medical revolutions, and not lag behind. The pattern of the past will somehow have to be broken. To do so will not be easy, for it represents a major effort in educating peoples who are illiterate, poverty stricken, and hunger ridden, and usually not particularly interested in this type of education. The task may be further hampered by religious, ethical, or moral scruples and by legal or political barriers to the dissemination of such information. It may involve educating not only the common people but their leaders, for before the solution can be attempted, the problem itself must be clearly recognized and generally understood. Since fertility has customarily been admired in most societies in the past, a major shift in attitude will be required of many peoples. The freedom to have children must certainly be ranked with the Four Freedoms or any other of the basic human rights. In fact, it might well be argued that the right to reproduce is the most fundamental of all human rights. Therefore, any program designed to reduce the birth rate must, if it is to be in accord with democratic principles, somehow be based on the voluntary cooperation of each couple rather than enforced by decree.

The Roman Catholic Church is often pictured as being opposed to control of the birth rate; this is, in fact, not so, for the Church approves of such control in principle but is opposed to certain of the methods, whch are considered "unnatural." It is to be hoped that other religions and other cultures will also approve in principle and that effective methods for control will be found that are acceptable to the great majority of the peoples of the world. Much research still needs to be done in this area, but present results indicate that simple, inexpensive, and effective methods may soon be available.

Lest those nations not now troubled by overpopulation or likely to be in the foreseeable future stand aside and regard the problem as not being a matter of concern to them, the genesis of World War II should be recalled. In essence, three nations, each nearing completion of the demographic transition, attempted to relieve their growing population pressure by expansion. Germany sought *Lebensraum* to the east in Poland and the Ukraine, Italy expanded into North Africa, while Japan overran China and many of the Pacific islands. The instability and dissatisfaction generated in overpopulated areas will continue to be a threat to world peace, for human dignity, human rights, and human life have little value or meaning in these areas. Therefore, overpopulated areas should be a matter of concern to all, and steps must be taken to raise living standards through agricultural and economic development. However, unless population increase is controlled, all such efforts seem destined to failure. The most hopeful development in recent years is that the governments of Japan and India, two nations beset by the problems of more people than resources with which to support them, have officially recognized the problem and have taken steps to aid their people in limiting the size of their families. The experience gained in these countries and their degree of success will be of great interest and significance to the rest of the world in its search for a better and a happier life for all mankind.

Another solution to the problem of overpopulation is suggested in a passage written by Hendrik Willem van Loon nearly thirty years ago.

Fig. 35-3. One possible solution to the population problem. (With permission from Van Loon's Geography.)

It sounds incredible, but nevertheless it is true. If everybody in this world of ours were six feet tall and a foot and a half wide and a foot thick (and that is making people a little bigger than they usually are), then the whole of the human race (and according to the latest available statistics there are now nearly 2,000,000,000 descendants of the original *Homo sapiens* and his wife) could be packed into a box measuring half a mile in each direction. That, as I just said, sounds incredible, but if you don't believe me, figure it out for yourself and you will find it to be correct.

If we transported that box to the Grand Canyon of Arizona and balanced it neatly on the low stone wall that keeps people from breaking their necks when stunned by the incredible beauty of that silent witness of the forces of Eternity, and then called little Noodle, the dachshund, and told him (the tiny beast is very intelligent and loves to oblige) to give the unwieldy contraption a slight push with his soft brown nose, there would be a moment of crunching and ripping as the wooden planks loosened stones and shrubs and trees on their downward path, and then a low and even softer bumpity-bumpity-bump and a sudden splash when the outer edges struck the banks of the Colorado River.

Then silence and oblivion.

The human sardines in their mortuary chest would soon be forgotten.

The Canyon would go on battling wind and air and sun and rain as it has done since it was created.

The world would continue to run its even course through the uncharted heavens.

The astronomers on distant and nearby planets would have noticed nothing out of the ordinary.

A century from now, a little mound, densely covered with vegetable matter, would perhaps indicate where humanity lay buried.

And that would be all.

Let us hope that it never comes to this. However, if perchance one starry-eyed young couple were somehow overlooked and if they then doubled their numbers every 25 years for just 32 generations, in 800 years they would have over 4 billion living descendants. Such, as Malthus might say, is the power of population.

SUGGESTED READING

Darwin, C. G., 1960. "Can man control his numbers?" *Evolution after Darwin,* Vol. 2, *The evolution of man,* Sol Tax, ed. Chicago: University of Chicago Press.

Malthus, T. R., 1798. *Essay on population,* 1st ed. Ann Arbor Paperbacks (1959). 4th ed., 1807.

Population bulletin. Washington, D. C.: Population Reference Bureau.

Van Loon, H. W., 1932. *Van Loon's Geography.* New York: Simon and Schuster.

World population and resources, 1955. Fairlawn, N. J.: Essential Books.

CHAPTER 36

Man's Future

Predictions are so often wrong, even about such relatively simple matters as horse races or football games, that the effort to make them hardly seems worthwhile. However, forecasts continue to be made, perhaps for the prognosticator's occasional satisfaction in being right, more probably as a guide in determining a course of action. Since the question of man's future is extremely complex, anyone embarking on this sort of crystal-gazing expedition should go well equipped with a supply of conditional clauses.

Man's Future as a Species

One basis for predicting the future is to examine the past. The first conclusion to be drawn from the past is that more than 99 percent of all animal species have become extinct. Some of them disappeared in the process of evolving into something different, but most of them came to a complete dead end; extinction was final and irrevocable. Since there is really no reason to suppose that man has a tighter grip on immortality than any other species, the chances seem quite good that the ultimate fate of *Homo sapiens,* like that of Neanderthal man, will be extinction. After all, men like ourselves did not become common on the face of the earth until less than 50,000 years ago, a mere drop in the bucket of time.

From quite another point of view, the evolutionary line that has given rise to man has persisted for millions and millions of years, and it might therefore be expected, on the basis of its previous success, to persist a while longer. In this event, however, in view of the rapid rate of evolution in the Hominidae during the past million years, *Homo sapiens* can be expected to continue to evolve, eventually into an hominid population sufficiently different from *Homo sapiens* to be recognized as a new species. In either case, man as we know him today seems unlikely to persist indefinitely. This you may regard as fortunate or unfortunate, depending upon your point of view. Although we may prefer to think that man in some form will continue to exist, the realization that we are not immune from complete extinction may lead eventually to a greater maturity in political and social thought than is generally in evidence now.

As we discussed earlier, the human beings now living on the earth form a single polymorphic, polytypic species, *Homo sapiens*. The advent of more efficient transportation and the resulting greater ease of movement and contact among human groups have led to a breakdown in genetic isolates and an increase in gene flow among different human populations. Although this tendency has not resulted in the obliteration of racial differences, there can be little question that hybridization is a greater factor in human evolution now than at any time in the past. Furthermore, this situation seems likely to continue.

Man's Future Numbers

Another fairly safe prediction is that the human population will continue to increase in numbers in the near future. Even safer is the prediction that this increase in population size cannot continue unchecked indefinitely. Sooner or later death rates will equal birth rates, and population growth will cease. The significant question is whether the death rates will rise to match high birth rates, which would signalize a painful, tragic decline in standards of living, or whether they will equilibrate at a low level. Birth and death rates may seem to be crude indices of civilization, culture, or standards of living; nevertheless, they are at present very sensitive indicators of the status of a society. Man's future to a large extent will depend upon how successfully the human population adjusts to the available resources. Very few people accept a bare subsistence level as an adequate way of life, but if population expansion continues, this is the status that all mankind will eventually reach. Before they do, however, bitter and devastating conflicts seem inevitable. Since human population growth has been due to the dramatic reduction in the death rate, it is clear that generally acceptable means of controlling birth rates are essential if the population explosion is to be controlled before it leads to disaster.

Homo sapiens is a dominant species because of the superior intelligence of its members. This mental ability made possible the development of culture; and cultural evolution, as distinct from biological evolution, has added a new dimension to the process of evolutionary change. It seems safe to predict that cultural progress will continue. One need only mention progress since the turn of the century in such fields as physics, aeronautics, genetics, and medicine, to emphasize what tremendous strides have been made. The end to this advance is not yet in sight. However, cultural evolution has not superceded biological evolution but has supplemented it. Biological evolution will continue in man, under the influence of the same evolutionary forces that have affected man as well as other species in the past. Modern medical discoveries have not eliminated the operation of selection in human populations; rather, the selection pressures have been modified or changed. The factors affecting reproductive fitness in modern society may be different from those operating in a primitive society, but there is no reason to suppose that selection has ceased to function altogether.

Man's Genetic Future

It seems probable that the human "load of mutations," the frequency of deleterious genes in the human population, will continue to increase in the near future. Because of their effects on mutation rates, the advent of the atomic age and the widespread use of mutagenic ionizing radiations in industry and in medical practice will be responsible in part for this increase. To the extent that medicine is successful in counteracting the harmful effects of deleterious genes so that affected individuals survive and reproduce, the frequencies of such genes will increase. It is not yet possible to predict just how serious the effects of these trends may be, but it hardly seems likely that they will be favorable. Rather, there will be a somewhat greater percentage of persons who by medical or other environmental manipulations must counteract the harmful effects of their genes.

The question has been raised as to whether current trends are not leading to a dissipation of the favorable genotypes of the past and to an increase in the frequency of deleterious or unfavorable genes in human populations. This question is a very fundamental one, for even though cultural or environmental remedies can to some extent compensate for genetic deficiencies, there must be a point beyond which such measures are inadequate. If too great a proportion of the population were to pass that point, any modern society would collapse. Lest you feel that this picture is an exaggeration, consider what would happen if a group of chimpanzees were made responsible for running a large city. No matter how carefully they were trained for their jobs from birth onward, chaos would result, for the tasks would be beyond the capacity of their genotypes even if they were all exceptionally able chimpanzees. Concern about the possible genetic deterioration of man has been expressed because so many factors at present seem to be favoring an increase in frequency of harmful genes in human populations. In addition to the increased load of mutations mentioned above, differential fertility in many countries leads to a disproportionate number of children being born to the parents least able to give them a favorable home environment and least likely to endow them with a favorable genotype. In the United States, for example, one sixth of the women are now bringing one half of the children of the next generation into families with only one tenth of the national income. Since a laissez-faire policy seems likely to lead to a loss in genetic value, a number of eugenic programs have been proposed, aimed at the genetic betterment of mankind. Because of the radical nature of some of these proposals, especially by early proponents, and because the Nazi pogroms were carried out under the guise of a eugenics program, the term "eugenics" has come to have rather sinister connotations. The current arguments for the need for eugenic measures are based on the evidence that the net effect of many human activities is at present leading to a deterioration of the human gene pool. It is argued that we cannot afford to let this deterioration continue unchecked but must apply our present knowledge to human genetic improvement just as, through conscious effort, we have improved domesticated species of plants and animals. Two types of programs have been suggested: positive eugenic measures to increase the frequency of favorable genes and gene combinations, and negative eugenic measures to reduce the frequency of deleterious genes. All of these measures merit thoughtful consideration, but they also require careful scrutiny because of the risks inherent in any program of deliberate interference with human reproduction.

Eugenics

The great difficulty with any positive eugenics program is that decisions must be made as to which traits are to be favored. These decisions will be based on value judgments, for they cannot be made in any scientific manner. Therefore, the primary question becomes, whose set of values shall prevail, for it is unlikely that there would be any universal agreement sufficiently specific to permit setting up an effective program. Any program put into effect without universal acceptance would represent an unwarranted infringement on human rights. Furthermore, it may even be an error to assume that human evolution should be guided toward any single goal or set of values. The genetic problems involved in breeding a new type of corn or hog are relatively simple. The measure of success is in the increased economic value of the product, but this is not the way we measure men.

At present, negative eugenics seems more likely to be accepted because it is generally agreed that traits such as hereditary blindness, deafness, or similar severe afflictions are undesirable. For this reason it is possible through genetic counseling to convey to the persons concerned sufficient understanding of the hereditary risks involved so that they can make informed decisions concerning their own reproduction. Institutionalization of mentally defective or psychotic persons is a eugenic measure, since they do not ordinarily reproduce while institutionalized. The usefulness of negative eugenics has sometimes been questioned on the grounds that its effect in reducing the frequency of recessive genes is so slight. However, from a humanitarian standpoint any action that averts the birth of a single afflicted person must be regarded as beneficial.

The effectiveness of negative eugenics could be greatly enhanced if we had means to detect heterozygous carriers of deleterious recessive genes. Some traits can now be detected in heterozygotes, and it seems probable that as more refined techniques are discovered, additional information of this sort will become available. A quick reduction in the incidence of individuals affected by harmful dominant genes is already possible; detection of heterozygous carriers would make it possible to reduce still further the incidence of persons afflicted with recessive hereditary diseases.

The success of such a program would depend upon the voluntary cooperation of a well-informed people and would have to be based on the universal desire of parents to have normal, healthy children. Any approach involving coercion could not be justified in a society that even pretended to be free.

It may be argued that a program of such limited objectives is not adequate in the face of such threats to man's heritage as an increased load of mutations or differential fertility. However, we know very little about the magnitude or even the direction of the selection pressures operative in man at the present time. For example, it is well known that the average life span of married men is longer than that of bachelors, a statistic frequently cited as evidence for the beneficial effects of a life of wedded bliss. If one were to weigh all of the variables involved, one might conclude that the bachelors, rather than the married men, had every right to expect a longer life span. An alternative explanation for this fact is that women tend to marry the healthier men and that a selective process of considerable genetic significance, rather than an environmental effect, is responsible for the difference in life span. A careful study would be necessary to determine which of these alternatives is correct.

Another bit of data of possible significance is the fact that in the United States, on the average, only about 90 percent of all women past reproductive age have ever married. Furthermore, among such married women about 15 to 20 percent have never had any children. Thus, the total reproductive burden is being carried by only three quarters of the women in any generation. There is no evidence whatever that there are any genetic differences between women who marry and those who do not, or between married women who have children and those who do not. However, the proportions involved are so great that if any genetic differentials are involved, they could be of considerable importance. Research to test these possibilities has yet to be carried out. Until these and other possibilities for positive selection pressure have been explored, the extent of the genetic deterioration of the human gene pool cannot be estimated with any degree of confidence. The great and obvious need is for more research, not just in medical genetics, but in all aspects of human genetics.

Where actions affecting human reproduction are already being taken, it is clear that some attention should be paid to their eugenic implications. Artificial insemination, for example, is being done on an ever-wider scale, and here the responsibility for serious consideration of the genotype of the donor is clear. Furthermore, persons with a corrected or ameliorated genetic condition should certainly be made aware of the genetic risks involved in their reproduction and of their responsibility to future generations. The point is that as other medical, biological, and genetic techniques are discovered, they will unquestionably be used, and they will also undoubtedly affect the course of human evolution. The problem is to insure that these discoveries are used with wisdom and understanding so that man's genetic heritage, certainly his most precious possession, is not needlessly frittered away.

So much for man's future; what about future man himself? If still here, he will probably be somewhat different from us physically. If past trends continue, his head may well be larger than ours, with the face and teeth still further reduced. His personality may be such that we would consider him a genius, or perhaps a dolt, a criminal, or a crackpot, or even quite normal. Whether we would like him or not is of little consequence, for we shall never have to try to get along with him.

SUGGESTED READING

Haldane, J. B. S., 1949. "Human evolution: past and future," *Genetics, paleontology and evolution.* G. L. Jepsen, E. Mayr, and G. G. Simpson, eds. Princeton, N. J.: Princeton University Press.

Muller, H. J., 1960. "The guidance of human evolution," *Evolution after Darwin,* Vol. 2, *The evolution of man,* Sol Tax, ed. Chicago: University of Chicago Press.

Osborn, F., 1951. *Preface to eugenics.* New York: Harper.

Reed, S. C., 1955. *Counseling in medical genetics.* Philadelphia: Saunders.

APPENDIX *A*

From Charles Darwin's
Voyage of the Beagle

APPENDIX *B*

From Thomas Malthus'
*Essay on the Principle
of Population* 4TH EDITION

APPENDIX *A*

Chapter XVII—
Galapagos Archipelago

September 15th.—This archipelago consists of ten principal islands, of which five exceed the others in size. They are situated under the Equator, and between five and six hundred miles westward of the coast of America. They are all formed of volcanic rocks; a few fragments of granite curiously glazed and altered by the heat, can hardly be considered as an exception. Some of the craters, surmounting the larger islands, are of immense size, and they rise to a height of between three and four thousand feet. Their flanks are studded by innumerable smaller orifices. I scarcely hesitate to affirm, that there must be in the whole archipelago at least two thousand craters. These consist either of lava and scoriae, or of finely-stratified, sandstone-like tuff. Most of the latter are beautifully symmetrical; they owe their origin to eruptions of volcanic mud without any lava: it is a remarkable circumstance that every one of the twenty-eight tuff-craters which were examined, had their southern sides either much lower than the other sides, or quite broken down and removed. As all these craters apparently have been formed when standing in the sea, and as the waves from the trade wind and the swell from the open Pacific here unite their forces on the southern coasts of all the islands, this singular uniformity in the broken state of the craters, composed of the soft and yielding tuff, is easily explained.

From Charles Darwin, 1887. *Journal of researches into the natural history and geology of the countries visited during the voyage of* H.M.S. Beagle *round the world*. New ed. New York: D. Appleton and Company. Pages 372-73, 377-81, 393-98.

Considering that these islands are placed directly under the equator, the climate is far from being excessively hot; this seems chiefly caused by the singularly low temperature of the surrounding water, brought here by the great southern Polar current. Excepting during one short season, very little rain falls, and even then it is irregular; but the clouds generally hang low. Hence, whilst the lower parts of the islands are very sterile, the upper parts, at a height of a thousand feet and upwards, possess a damp climate and a tolerably luxuriant vegetation. This is especially the case on the windward sides of the islands, which first receive and condense the moisture from the atmosphere. . . .

The natural history of these islands is eminently curious, and well deserves attention. Most of the organic productions are aboriginal creations, found nowhere else; there is even a difference between the inhabitants of the different islands; yet all show a marked relationship with those of America, though separated from that continent by an open space of ocean, between 500 and 600 miles in width. The archipelago is a little world within itself, or rather a satellite attached to America, whence it has derived a few stray colonists, and has received the general character of its indigenous productions. Considering the small size of these islands, we feel the more astonished at the number of their aboriginal beings, and at their confined range. Seeing every height crowned with its crater, and the boundaries of most of the lava-streams still distinct, we are led to believe that within a period, geologically recent, the unbroken ocean was here spread out. Hence, both in space and time, we seem to be brought somewhat near to that great fact—that mystery of mysteries—the first appearance of new beings on this earth.

Of terrestrial mammals, there is only one which must be considered as indigenous, namely, a mouse (Mus Galapagoensis), and this is confined, as far as I could ascertain, to Chatham island, the most easterly island of the group. It belongs, as I am informed by Mr. Waterhouse, to a division of the family of mice characteristic of America. At James island, there is a rat sufficiently distinct from the common kind to have been named and described by Mr. Waterhouse; but as it belongs to the old-world division of the family, and as this island has been frequented by ships for the last hundred and fifty years, I can hardly doubt that this rat is merely a variety, produced by the new and peculiar climate, food, and soil, to which it has been subjected. Although no one has a right to speculate without distinct facts, yet even with respect to the Chatham island mouse, it should be borne in mind, that it may possibly be an American species imported here; for I have seen, in a most unfrequented part of the Pampas, a native mouse living in the roof of a newly-built hovel, and therefore its transportation in a vessel is not improbable; analogous facts have been observed by Dr. Richardson in North America.

Of land-birds I obtained twenty-six kinds, all peculiar to the group and found nowhere else, with the exception of one lark-like finch from North America (Dolichonyx oryzivorus), which ranges on that continent as far north as 54°, and generally frequents marshes. The other twenty-five birds consist, firstly, of a hawk, curiously intermediate in structure between a Buzzard and the American group of carrion-feeding Polybori; and with these latter birds it agrees most closely in every habit and even tone of voice. Secondly, there are two owls, representing the short-eared and white barn-owls of Europe. Thirdly, a wren, three tyrant fly-catchers (two of them species of Pyrocephalus, one or both of which would be ranked by some ornithologists as only varieties), and a dove— all analogous to, but distinct from, American species. Fourthly, a swallow, which though differing from the Progne purpurea of both Americas, only in being rather duller coloured, smaller, and slenderer, is considered by Mr. Gould as specifically distinct. Fifthly, there are three species of mocking-thrush—a form highly characteristic of America. The remaining land-birds form a most singular group of finches, related to each other in the structure of their beaks, short tails, form of body, and plumage: there are thirteen species, which Mr. Gould has divided into four sub-groups. All these species are peculiar to this archipelago; and so is the whole group, with the exception of one species of the sub-group Cactornis, lately brought from Bow island, in the Low Archipelago. Of Cactornis, the two species may be often seen climbing about the flowers of the great cactus-trees; but all the other species of this group of finches, mingled together in flocks, feed on the dry and sterile ground of the lower districts. The males of all, or certainly of the greater number, are jet black; and the females (with perhaps one or two exceptions) are brown. The most curious fact is the perfect gradation in the size of the beaks in the different species of Geospiza, from one as large as that of a hawfinch to that of a chaffinch, and (if Mr. Gould is right in including his sub-group, Certhidea, in the main group), even to that of a warbler. The largest beak in the genus Geospiza is shown in Fig. 1, and the smallest in Fig. 3; but instead of there being only one intermediate species, with a beak of the size shown in Fig. 2, there are no less than six species with insensibly graduated beaks. The beak of the sub-group Certhidea, is shown in Fig. 4. [Refer to text Fig. 31-4.] The beak of Cactornis is somewhat like that of a starling; and that of the fourth sub-group, Camarhynchus, is slightly parrot-shaped. Seeing this gradation and diversity of structure in one small, intimately related group of birds, one might really fancy that from an original paucity of birds in this archipelago, one species had been taken and modified for different ends. In a like manner it might be fancied that a bird originally a buzzard, had been induced here to undertake the office of the carrion-feeding Polybori of the American continent.

Of waders and water-birds I was able to get only eleven kinds, and of these only three (including a rail confined to the damp summits of the islands) are new species. Considering the wandering habits of the gulls, I was surprised to find that the species inhabiting these islands is peculiar, but allied to one from the southern parts of South America. The far greater peculiarity of the land-birds, namely, twenty-five out of twenty-six being new species or at least new races, compared with the waders and web-footed birds, is in accordance with the greater range which these latter orders have in all parts of the world. We shall hereafter see this law of aquatic forms, whether marine or fresh-water, being less peculiar at any given point of the earth's surface than the terrestrial forms of the same classes, strikingly illustrated in the shells, and in a lesser degree in the insects of this archipelago.

Two of the waders are rather smaller than the same species brought from other places: the swallow is also smaller, though it is doubtful whether or not it is distinct from its analogue. The two owls, the two tyrant fly-catchers (Pyrocephalus) and the dove, are also smaller than the analogous but distinct species, to which they are most nearly related; on the other hand, the gull is rather larger. The two owls, the swallow, all three species of mocking-thrush, the dove in its separate colours though not in its whole plumage, the Totanus, and the gull, are likewise duskier coloured than their analogous species; and in the case of the mocking-thrush and Totanus, than any other species of the two genera. With the exception of a wren with a fine yellow breast, and of a tyrant fly-catcher with a scarlet tuft and breast, none of the birds are brilliantly coloured, as might have been expected in an equatorial district. Hence it would appear probable, that the same causes which here make the immigrants of some species smaller, make most of the peculiar Galapageian species also smaller, as well as very generally more dusky coloured. All the plants have a wretched, weedy appearance, and I did not see one beautiful flower. The insects, again, are small sized and dull coloured, and, as Mr. Waterhouse informs me, there is nothing in their general appearance which would have led him to imagine that they had come from under the equator. The birds, plants, and insects have a desert character, and are not more brilliantly coloured than those from southern Patagonia; we may, therefore, conclude that the usual gaudy colouring of the intertropical productions, is not related either to the heat or light of those zones, but to some other cause, perhaps to the conditions of existence being generally favourable to life.

. . . Dr. Hooker informs me that the Flora has an undoubted Western American character; nor can he detect in it any affinity with that of the Pacific. If, therefore, we except the eighteen marine, the one fresh-water, and one land-shell, which have apparently come here as colonists from the central islands of the Pacific, and likewise the one distinct Pacific species of the Galapageian group of finches, we see that this archipelago, though standing in the Pacific Ocean, is zoologically part of America.

If this character were owing merely to immigrants from America, there would be little remarkable in it; but we see that a vast majority of all the land animals, and that more than half of the flowering plants, are aboriginal productions. It was most striking to be surrounded by new birds, new reptiles, new shells, new insects, new plants, and yet by innumerable trifling details of structure, and even by the tones of voice and plumage of the birds, to have the temperate plains of Patagonia, or the hot dry deserts of Northern Chile, vividly brought before my eyes. Why, on these small points of land, which within a late geological period must have been covered by the ocean, which are formed of basaltic lava, and therefore differ in geological character from the American continent, and which are placed under a peculiar climate,—why were their aboriginal inhabitants, associated, I may add, in different proportions both in kind and number from those on the continent, and therefore acting on each other in a different manner—why were they created on American types of organization? It is probable that the islands of the Cape de Verd group resemble, in all their physical conditions, far more closely the Galapagos Islands than these latter physically resemble the coast of America; yet the aboriginal inhabitants of the two groups are totally unlike; those of the Cape de Verd Islands bearing the impress of Africa, as the inhabitants of the Galapagos Archipelago are stamped with that of America.

I have not as yet noticed by far the most remarkable feature in the natural history of this archipelago; it is, that the different islands to a considerable extent are inhabited by a different set of beings. My attention was first called to this fact by the Vice-Governor, Mr. Lawson, declaring that the tortoises differed from the different islands, and that he could with certainty tell from which island any one was brought. I did not for some time pay sufficient attention to this statement, and I had already partially mingled together the collections from two of the islands. I never dreamed that islands, about fifty or sixty miles apart, and most of them in sight of each other, formed of precisely the same rocks, placed under a quite similar climate, rising to a nearly equal height, would have been differently tenanted; but we shall soon see that this is the case. It is the fate of most voyagers, no sooner to discover what is most interesting in any locality, than they are hurried from it; but I ought, perhaps, to be thankful that I obtained sufficient materials to establish this most remarkable fact in the distribution of organic beings.

The inhabitants, as I have said, state that they can distinguish the tortoises from the different islands; and that they differ not only in size but in other characters. Captain Porter has described those from Charles and from the nearest island to it, namely, Hood Island, as having their shells in front thick and turned up like a Spanish saddle, whilst the tortoises from James Island are rounder, blacker, and have a better taste when cooked. M. Bibron, moreover, informs me that he has seen what he considers two distinct species of tortoise from the Galapagos, but he does not know from which islands. The specimens that I brought from three islands were young ones; and probably owing to this cause, neither Mr. Gray nor myself could find in them any specific differences. I have remarked that the marine Amblyrhynchus was larger at Albemarle Island than elsewhere; and M. Bibron informs me that he has seen two distinct aquatic species of this genus; so that the different islands probably have their representative species or races of the Amblyrhynchus, as well as of the tortoise. My attention was first thoroughly aroused, by comparing together the numerous specimens, shot by myself and several other parties on board, of the mocking-thrushes, when, to my astonishment, I discovered that all those from Charles Island belonged to one species (Mimus trifasciatus); all from Albemarle Island to M. parvulus; and all from James and Chatham Islands (between which two other islands are situated, as connecting links) belonged to M. melanotis. These two latter species are closely allied, and would by some ornithologists be considered as only well-marked races or varieties; but the Mimus trifasciatus is very distinct. Unfortunately most of the specimens of the finch tribe were mingled together; but I have strong reasons to suspect that some of the species of the sub-group Geospiza are confined to separate islands. If the different islands have their representatives of Geospiza, it may help to explain the singularly large number of the species of this sub-group in this one small archipelago, and as a probable consequence of their numbers, the perfectly graduated series in the size of their beaks. Two species of the sub-group Cactornis, and two of Camarhynchus, were procured in the archipelago; and of the numerous specimens of these two sub-groups shot by four collectors at James Island, all were found to belong to one species of each; whereas the numerous specimens shot either on Chatham or Charles Island (for the two sets were mingled together) all belonged to the two other species: hence we may feel almost sure that these islands possess their representative species of these two sub-groups. In land-shells this law of distribution does not appear to hold good. In my very small collection of insects, Mr. Waterhouse remarks, that of those which were ticketed with their locality, not one was common to any two of the islands.

If we now turn to the Flora, we shall find the aboriginal plants of the different islands wonderfully different. I give all the following results on the high authority of my friend Dr. J. Hooker. I may premise that I indiscriminately collected everything in flower on the different islands, and fortunately kept my collections separate. Too much confidence, however, must not be placed in the proportional results, as the small collections brought home by some other naturalists, though in some respects confirming the results, plainly show that much remains to be done in the botany of this group: the Leguminosae, moreover, have as yet been only approximately worked out. [See table on next page, Ed.]

Hence we have the truly wonderful fact, that in James Island, of the thirty-eight Galapageian plants, or those found in no other part of the world, thirty are exclusively confined to this one island; and in Albemarle Island, of the twenty-six aboriginal Galapageian plants, twenty-two are confined to this one island, that is, only four are at present known to grow in the other islands of the archipelago; and so on, as shown in the table [below], with the plants from Chatham and Charles Islands. This fact will, perhaps, be rendered even more striking, by giving a few illustrations:—thus, Scalesia, a remarkable arborescent genus of the Compositae, is confined to the archipelago: it has six species; one

Name of Island	Total No. of Species	No. of Species found in other parts of the world	No. of Species confined to the Galapagos Archipelago	No. confined to the one Island	No. of Species confined to the Galapagos Archipelago, but found on more than the one Island
James Island	71	33	38	30	8
Albemarle Island	46	18	26	22	4
Chatham Island	32	16	16	12	4
Charles Island	68	39 (or 29, if the probably imported plants be subtracted)	29	21	8

from Chatham, one from Albemarle, one from Charles Island, two from James Island, and the sixth from one of the three latter islands, but it is not known from which: not one of these six species grows on any two islands. Again, Euphorbia, a mundane or widely distributed genus, has here eight species, of which seven are confined to the archipelago, and not one found on any two islands: Acalypha and Borreria, both mundane genera, have respectively six and seven species, none of which have the same species on two islands, with the exception of one Borreria, which does occur on two islands. The species of the Compositae are particularly local; and Dr. Hooker has furnished me with several other most striking illustrations of the difference of the species on the different islands. He remarks that this law of distribution holds good both with those genera confined to the archipelago, and those distributed in other quarters of the world: in like manner we have seen that the different islands have their proper species of the mundane genus of tortoise, and of the widely distributed American genus of the mocking-thrush, as well as of two of the Galapageian subgroups of finches, and almost certainly of the Galapageian genus Amblyrhynchus.

The distribution of the tenants of this archipelago would not be nearly so wonderful, if, for instance, one island had a mocking-thrush, and a second island some other quite distinct genus;—if one island had its genus of lizard, and a second island another distinct genus, or none whatever;—or if the different islands were inhabited, not by representative species of the same genera of plants, but by totally different genera, as does to a certain extent hold good; for, to give one instance, a large berry-bearing tree at James Island has no representative species in Charles Island. But it is the circumstance, that several of the islands possess their own species of the tortoise, mocking-thrush, finches, and numerous plants, these species having the same general habits, occupying analogous situations, and obviously filling the same place in the natural economy of this archipelago, that strikes me with wonder. It may be suspected that some of these representative species, at least in the case of the tortoise and of some of the birds, may hereafter prove to be only well-marked races; but this would be of equally great interest to the philosophical naturalist. I have said that most of the islands are in sight of each other: I may specify that Charles Island is fifty miles from the nearest part of Chatham Island, and thirty-three miles from the nearest part of Albemarle Island. Chatham Island is sixty miles from the nearest part of James Island, but there are two intermediate islands between them which were not visited by me. James Island is only ten miles from the nearest part of Albemarle Island, but the two points where the collections were made are thirty-two miles apart. I must repeat, that neither the nature of the soil, nor height of the land, nor the climate, nor the general character of the associated beings, and therefore their action one on another, can differ much in the different islands. If there be any sensible difference in their climates, it must be between the windward group (namely Charles and Chatham Islands), and that to leeward; but there seems to be no corresponding difference in the productions of these two halves of the archipelago.

The only light which I can throw on this remarkable difference in the inhabitants of the different islands, is, that very strong currents of the sea running in a westerly and W.N.W. direction must separate, as far as transportal by the sea is concerned, the southern islands from the northern ones; and between these northern islands a strong N.W. current was observed, which must effectually separate James and Albemarle Islands. As the archipelago is free to a most remarkable degree from gales of wind, neither the birds, insects, nor lighter seeds, would be blown from island to island. And lastly, the profound depth of the ocean between the islands, and their apparently recent (in a geological sense) volcanic origin, render it highly unlikely that they were ever united; and this, probably, is a far more important consideration than any other, with respect to the geographical distribution of their inhabitants. Reviewing the facts here given, one is astonished at the amount of creative force, if such an expression may be used, displayed on these small, barren, and rocky islands; and still more so, at its diverse yet analogous action on points so near each other. I have said that the Galapagos Archipelago might be called a satellite attached to America, but it should rather be called a group of satellites, physically similar, organically distinct, yet intimately related to each other, and all related in a marked, though much lesser degree, to the great American continent.

An Essay on the Principle
of Population, Book I

**Of the Checks to Population in the Less Civilized
Parts of the World and in Past Times**

Chapter 1 — STATEMENT OF THE SUBJECT.
RATIOS OF THE INCREASE OF POPULATION
AND FOOD

In an inquiry concerning the improvement of society, the mode of conducting the subject which naturally presents itself, is

1. To investigate the causes that have hitherto impeded the progress of mankind towards happiness; and

2. To examine the probability of the total or partial removal of these causes in future.

To enter fully into this question, and to enumerate all the causes that have hitherto influenced human improvement, would be much beyond the power of an individual. The principle object of the present essay is to examine the effects of one great cause intimately united with the very nature of man; which,

From T. R. Malthus, 1807. *An essay on the principle of population.* Fourth ed. London: J. Johnson in St. Paul's Churchyard. Chapters 1 and 2.

though it has been constantly and powerfully operating since the commencement of society, has been little noticed by the writers who have treated this subject. The facts which establish the existence of this cause have, indeed, been repeatedly stated and acknowledged; but its natural and necessary effects have been almost totally overlooked; though probably among these effects may be reckoned a very considerable portion of that vice and misery, and of that unequal distribution of the bounties of nature, which it has been the unceasing object of the enlightened philanthropist in all ages to correct.

The cause to which I allude, is the constant tendency in all animated life to increase beyond the nourishment prepared for it.

It is observed by Dr. Franklin, that there is no bound to the prolific nature of plants or animals, but what is made by their crowding and interfering with each others means of subsistence. Were the face of the earth, he says, vacant of other plants, it might be gradually sowed and overspread with one kind only, as for instance with fennel: and were it empty of other inhabitants, it might in a few ages be replenished from one nation only, as for instance with Englishmen.

This is incontrovertibly true. Through the animal and vegetable kingdoms Nature has scattered the seeds of life abroad with the most profuse and liberal hand; but has been comparatively sparing in the room and the nourishment necessary to rear them. The germs of existence contained in this earth, if they could freely develope themselves, would fill millions of worlds in the course of a few thousand years. Necessity, that imperious all-pervading law of nature, restrains them within the prescribed bounds. The race of plants and the race of animals shrink under this great restrictive law; and man cannot by any efforts of reason escape from it.

In plants and irrational animals, the view of the subject is simple. They are all impelled by a powerful instinct to the increase of their species; and this instinct is interrupted by no doubts about providing for their offspring. Wherever therefore there is liberty, the power of increase is exerted; and the superabundant effects are repressed afterwards by want of room and nourishment.

The effects of this check on man are more complicated. Impelled to the increase of his species by an equally powerful instinct, reason interrupts his career, and asks him whether he may not bring beings into the world, for whom he cannot provide the means of support. If he attend to this natural suggestion, the restriction too frequently produces vice. If he hear it not, the human race will be constantly endeavoring to increase beyond the means of subsistence. But as by that law of our nature which makes food necessary to the life of man, population can never actually increase beyond the lowest nourishment capable of supporting it, a strong check on population, from the difficulty of acquiring food, must be constantly in operation. This difficulty must fall somewhere, and must necessarily be severely felt in some or other of the various forms of misery, or the fear of misery, by a large portion of mankind.

That population has this constant tendency to increase beyond the means of subsistence, and that it is kept to its necessary level by these causes, will sufficiently appear from a review of the different states of society in which man has existed. But before we proceed to this review, the subject will perhaps be seen in a clearer light, if we endeavour to ascertain, what would be the natural increase of population, if left to exert itself with perfect freedom; and what might be expected to be the rate of increase in the productions of the earth, under the most favourable circumstances of human industry.

It will be allowed, that no country has hitherto been known, where the manners were so pure and simple, and the means of subsistence so abundant, that no check whatever has existed to early marriages from the difficulty of providing for a family, and that no waste of the human species has been occasioned by vicious customs, by towns, by unhealthy occupations, or too severe labour. Consequently in no state that we have yet known, has the power of population been left to exert itself with perfect freedom.

Whether the law of marriage be instituted, or not, the dictate of nature and virtue seems to be an early attachment to one woman; and where there were no impediments of any kind in the way of an union to which such an attachment would lead, and no causes of depopulation afterwards, the increase of the human species would be evidently much greater than any increase which has been hitherto known.

In the northern states of America, where the means of subsistence have been more ample, the manners of the people more pure, and the checks to early marriages fewer, than in any of the modern states of Europe, the population has been found to double itself, for above a century and a half successively, in less than in each period of twenty-five years. Yet even during these periods, in some of the towns, the deaths exceeded the births, a circumstance which clearly proves that in those parts of the country which supplied this deficiency, the increase must have been much more rapid than the general average.

In the back settlements, where the sole employment is agriculture, and vicious customs and unwholesome occupations are little known, the population has been found to double itself in fifteen years. Even this extraordinary rate of increase is probably short of the utmost power of population. Very severe labour is requisite to clear a fresh country; such situations are not in general considered as particularly healthy; and the inhabitants are probably occasionally subject to the incursions of the Indians, which may destroy some lives, or at any rate diminish the fruits of their industry.

According to a table of Euler, calculated on a mortality of 1 in 36, if the births be to the deaths in the proportion of 3 to 1, the period of doubling will be only $12\frac{4}{5}$ years. And this proportion is not only a possible supposition, but has actually occurred for short periods in more countries than one.

Sir William Petty supposes a doubling possible in so short a time as ten years.

But to be perfectly sure that we are far within the truth, we will take the slowest of these rates of increase, a rate, in which all concurring testimonies agree, and which has been repeatedly ascertained to be from procreation only.

It may safely be pronounced, therefore, that population, when un-checked, goes on doubling itself every twenty-five years, or increases in a geo-metrical ratio.

The rate according to which the productions of the earth may be sup-posed to increase, it will not be so easy to determine. Of this, however, we may be perfectly certain, that the ratio of their increase must be totally of a different nature from the ratio of the increase of population. A thousand millions are just as easily doubled every twenty-five years by the power of population as a thou-sand. But the food to support the increase from the greater number will by no means be obtained with the same facility. Man is necessarily confined in room. When acre has been added to acre till all the fertile land is occupied, the yearly increase of food must depend upon the melioration of the land already in pos-session. This is a stream, which from the nature of all soils, instead of increasing, must be gradually diminishing. But population, could it be supplied with food, would go on with unexhausted vigour; and the increase of one period would furnish the power of a greater increase the next, and this without any limit.

From the accounts we have of China and Japan, it may be fairly doubted, whether the best directed efforts of human industry could double the produce of these countries even once in any number of years. There are many parts of the globe, indeed, hitherto uncultivated, and almost unoccupied; but the right of exterminating, or driving into a corner where they must starve, even the inhabitants of these thinly populated regions, will be questioned in a moral view. The process of improving their minds and directing their industry would neces-sarily be slow; and during this time, as population would regularly keep pace with the increasing produce, it would rarely happen that a great degree of knowl-edge and industry would have to operate at once upon rich unappropriated soil. Even where this might take place, as it does sometimes in new colonies, a geometrical ratio increases with such extraordinary rapidity, that the advantage could not last long. If America continue increasing, which she certainly will do, though not with the same rapidity as formerly, the Indians will be driven further and further back into the country, till the whole race is ultimately exterminated.

These observations are, in a degree, applicable to all the parts of the earth, where the soil is imperfectly cultivated. To exterminate the inhabitants of the greatest part of Asia and Africa, is a thought that could not be admitted for a moment. To civilize and direct the industry of the various tribes of Tartars and Negroes, would certainly be a work of considerable time, and of variable and uncertain success.

Europe is by no means so fully peopled as it might be. In Europe there is the fairest chance that human industry may receive its best direction. The science of agriculture has been much studied in England and Scotland; and there is still a great portion of uncultivated land in these countries. Let us consider, at what rate the produce of this island might be supposed to increase under circumstances the most favourable to improvement.

If it be allowed, that by the best possible policy, and great encouragements to agriculture, the average produce of the island could be doubled in the first twenty-five years, it will be allowing probably a greater increase than could with reason be expected.

In the next twenty-five years, it is impossible to suppose that the produce could be quadrupled. It would be contrary to all our knowledge of the properties of land. The improvement of the barren parts would be a work of time and labour; and it must be evident to those who have the slightest acquaintance with agricultural subjects, that in proportion as cultivation extended, the additions that could yearly be made to the former average produce must be gradually and regularly diminishing. That we may be the better able to compare the increase of population and food, let us make a supposition, which, without pretending to accuracy, is clearly more favourable to the power of production in the earth, than any experience we have had of its qualities will warrant.

Let us suppose that the yearly additions which might be made to the former average produce, instead of decreasing, which they certainly would do, were to remain the same; and that the produce of this island might be increased every twenty-five years, by a quantity equal to what it at present produces. The most enthusiastic speculator cannot suppose a greater increase than this. In a few centuries it would make every acre of land in the island like a garden.

If this supposition be applied to the whole earth, and if it be allowed that the subsistence for man which the earth affords, might be increased every twenty-five years by a quantity equal to what it at present produces, this will be supposing a rate of increase much greater than we can imagine that any possible exertions of mankind could make it.

It may be fairly pronounced therefore, that, considering the present average state of the earth, the means of subsistence, under circumstances the most favourable to human industry, could not possibly be made to increase faster than in an arithmetical ratio.

The necessary effects of these two different rates of increase, when brought together, will be very striking. Let us call the population of this island eleven millions; and suppose the present produce equal to the easy support of such a number. In the first twenty-five years the population would be twenty-two millions, and the food being also doubled, the means of subsistence would be equal to this increase. In the next twenty-five years, the population would be forty-four millions, and the means of subsistence only equal to the support of thirty-three millions. In the next period the population would be eighty-eight millions, and the means of subsistence just equal to the support of half of that number. And at the conclusion of the first century, the population would be a hundred and seventy-six millions, and the means of subsistence only equal to the support of fifty-five millions, leaving a population of a hundred and twenty-one millions totally unprovided for.

Taking the whole earth instead of this island, emigration would of course be excluded; and supposing the present population equal to a thousand millions, the human species would increase as the numbers 1,2,4,8,16,32,64,128, 256, and subsistence as 1,2,3,4,5,6,7,8,9. In two centuries the population would be to the means of subsistence as 256 to 9; in three centuries as 4096 to 13, and in two thousand years the difference would be almost incalculable.

In this supposition no limits whatever are placed to the produce of the earth. It may increase for ever, and be greater than any assignable quantity; yet still the power of population being in every period so much superior, the increase of the human species can only be kept down to the level of the means of subsistence by the constant operation of the strong law of necessity acting as a check upon the greater power.

Chapter 2 — OF THE GENERAL CHECKS TO POPULATION, AND THE MODE OF THEIR OPERATION

The ultimate check to population appears then to be a want of food arising necessarily from the different ratios according to which population and food increase. But this ultimate check is never the immediate check, except in cases of actual famine.

The immediate check may be stated to consist in all those customs, and all those diseases which seem to be generated by a scarcity of the means of subsistence; and all those causes, independent of this scarcity, whether of a moral or physical nature, which tend prematurely to weaken and destroy the human frame.

These checks to population, which are constantly operating with more or less force in every society, and keep down the number to the level of the means of subsistence, may be classed under two general heads, the preventive, and the positive checks.

The preventive check, as far as it is voluntary, is peculiar to man, and arises from that distinctive superiority in his reasoning faculties, which enables him to calculate distant consequences. The checks to the indefinite increase of plants and irrational animals are all either positive, or, if preventive, involuntary. But man cannot look around him, and see the distress which frequently presses upon those who have large families; he cannot contemplate his present possessions or earnings, which he now nearly consumes himself, and calculate the amount of each share, when with very little addition they must be divided, perhaps, among seven or eight, without feeling a doubt, whether if he follow the bent of his inclinations, he may be able to support the offspring which he will probably bring into the world. In a state of equality, if such can exist, this would be a simple question. In the present state of society other considerations occur. Will he not lower his rank in life, and be obliged to give up in great measure his former habits? Does any mode of employment present itself by which he may reasonably hope to maintain a family? Will he not at any rate subject himself to greater difficulties, and more severe labour than in his single state? Will he not be unable to transmit to his children the same advantages of education and improvement that he had himself possessed? Does he even feel secure that, should he have a large family, his utmost exertions can save them from rags and squalid poverty, and their consequent degradation in the community? And may he not be reduced to the grating necessity of forfeiting his independence, and of being obliged to the sparing hand of charity for support?

These considerations are calculated to prevent, and certainly do prevent, a great number of persons in all civilized nations from pursuing the dictate of nature in an early attachment to one woman.

If this restraint do not produce vice, it is undoubtedly the least evil that can arise from the principle of population. Considered as a restraint on a strong natural inclination, it must be allowed to produce a certain degree of temporary unhappiness; but evidently slight, compared with the evils which result from any of the other checks to population; and merely of the same nature as many other sacrifices of temporary to permanent gratification, which it is the business of a moral agent continually to make.

When this restraint produces vice, the evils which follow are but too conspicuous. A promiscuous intercourse to such a degree as to prevent the birth of children seems to lower in the most marked manner the dignity of human nature. It cannot be without its effect on men, and nothing can be more obvious than its tendency to degrade the female character, and to destroy all its most amiable and distinguishing characteristics. Add to which, that among those unfortunate females with which all great towns abound, more real distress and aggravated misery are perhaps to be found, than in any other department of human life.

When a general corruption of morals with regard to the sex pervades all the classes of society, its effects must necessarily be, to poison the springs of domestic happiness, to weaken conjugal and parental affection, and to lessen the united exertions and ardour of parents in the care and education of their children; effects which cannot take place without a decided diminution of the general happiness and virtue of the society; particularly as the necessity of art in the accomplishment and conduct of intrigues, and in the concealment of their consequences, necessarily leads to many other vices.

The positive checks to population are extremely various, and include every cause, whether arising from vice or misery, which in any degree contributes to shorten the natural duration of human life. Under this head therefore may be enumerated all unwholesome occupations, severe labour and exposure to the seasons, extreme poverty, bad nursing of children, great towns, excesses of all kinds, the whole train of common diseases and epidemics, wars, plagues, and famine.

On examining these obstacles to the increase of population which I have classed under the heads of preventive and positive checks, it will appear that they are all resolvable into moral restraint, vice, and misery.

Of the preventive checks, the restraint from marriage which is not followed by irregular gratifications may properly be termed moral restraint. Promiscuous intercourse, unnatural passions, violations of the marriage bed, and improper arts to conceal the consequences of irregular connexions, are preventive checks that clearly come under the head of vice.

Of the positive checks, those which appear to arise unavoidably from the laws of nature may be called exclusively misery; and those which we obviously bring upon ourselves, such as wars, excesses, and many others which it would be in our power to avoid, are of a mixed nature. They are brought upon us by vice, and their consequences are misery.

The sum of all these preventive and positive checks taken together forms the immediate check to population; and it is evident that in every country where the whole of the procreative power cannot be called into action, the preventive and the positive checks must vary inversely as each other; that is, in countries either naturally unhealthy, or subject to a great mortality, from whatever cause it may arise, the preventive check will prevail very little. In those countries, on the contrary, which are naturally healthy, and where the preventive check is found to prevail with considerable force, the positive check will prevail very little, or the mortality be very small.

In every country some of these checks are, with more or less force, in constant operation; yet notwithstanding their general prevalence, there are few states in which there is not a constant effort in the population to increase beyond the means of subsistence. This constant effort as constantly tends to subject the lower classes of society to distress, and to prevent any great permanent melioration of their condition.

These effects, in the present state of society, seem to be produced in the following manner. We will suppose the means of subsistence in any country just equal to the easy support of its inhabitants. The constant effort towards population, which is found to act even in the most vicious societies, increases the number of people before the means of subsistence are increased. The food therefore which before supported eleven millions, must now be divided among eleven millions and a half. The poor consequently must live much worse, and many of them be reduced to severe distress. The number of labourers also being above the proportion of work in the market, the price of labour must tend to fall, while the price of provisions would at the same time tend to rise. The labourer therefore must do more work, to earn the same as he did before. During this season of distress the discouragements to marriage, and the difficulty of rearing a family are so great, that population is nearly at a stand. In the mean time, the cheapness of labour, the plenty of labourers, and the necessity of an increased industry among them, encourage cultivators to employ more labour upon their land, to turn up fresh soil, and to manure and improve more completely what is already in tillage; till ultimately the means of subsistence may become in the same proportion to the population, as at the period from which we set out. The situation of the labourer being then again tolerably comfortable, the restraints to population are in some degree loosened; and, after a short period, the same retrograde and progressive movements, with respect to happiness, are repeated.

This sort of oscillation will not probably be obvious to common view; and it may be difficult even for the most attentive observer to calculate its periods. Yet that in the generality of old states, some such vibration does exist, though in a much less marked, and in a much more irregular manner, than I have described it, no reflecting man who considers the subject deeply can well doubt.

One principal reason why this oscillation has been less remarked, and less decidedly confirmed by experience than might naturally be expected, is, that the histories of mankind which we possess are, in general, histories only of the higher classes. We have not many accounts, that can be depended on, of the manners and customs of that part of mankind, where these retrograde and progressive movements chiefly take place. A satisfactory history of this kind, of one people and of one period, would require the constant and minute attention of many observing minds in local and general remarks on the state of the lower class of society, and the causes that influenced it; and to draw accurate inferences upon this subject, a succession of such historians for some centuries would be necessary. This branch of statistical knowledge has of late years been attended to in some countries, and we may promise ourselves a clearer insight into the internal structure of human society from the progress of these inquiries. But the science may be said yet to be in its infancy, and many of the objects, on which it would be desirable to have information, have either been omitted or not stated with sufficient accuracy. Among these perhaps may be reckoned, the proportion of the number of adults to the number of marriages; the extent to which vicious customs have prevailed in consequence of the restraints upon matrimony; the comparative mortality among the children of the most distressed part of the community, and of those who live rather more at their ease; the variations in the real price of labour; the observable differences in the state of the lower classes of society with respect to ease and happiness, at different times during a certain period; and very accurate registers of births, deaths, and marriages, which are of the utmost importance in this subject.

A faithful history, including such particulars, would tend greatly to elucidate the manner in which the constant check upon population acts; and would probably prove the existence of the retrograde and progressive movements that have been mentioned; though the times of their vibration must necessarily be rendered irregular from the operation of many interrupting causes; such as, the introduction of or failure of certain manufactures, a greater or less prevalent spirit of agricultural enterprise; years of plenty, or years of scarcity; wars, sickly seasons, poor laws, emigration, and other causes of a similar nature.

A circumstance which has perhaps more than any other contributed to conceal this oscillation from common view is, the difference between the nominal and real price of labour. It very rarely happens that the nominal price of labour universally falls; but we well know that it frequently remains the same, while the nominal price of provisions has been gradually rising. This is, in effect, a real fall in the price of labour; and, during this period, the condition of the lower classes of the community must be gradually growing worse. But the farmers and capitalists are growing rich from the real cheapness of labour. Their increasing capitals enable them to employ a greater number of men; and, as the population had probably suffered some check from the greater difficulty of supporting a family, the demand for labour, after a certain period, would be great in proportion to the supply, and its price would of course rise, if left to find its natural level; and thus the wages of labour, and consequently the condition of the lower classes of society, might have progressive and retrograde movements, though the price of labour might never nominally fall.

In savage life, where there is no regular price of labour, it is little to be doubted that similar oscillations take place. When population has increased nearly to the utmost limits of the food, all the preventive and the positive checks will naturally operate with increased force. Vicious habits with respect to the sex will be more general, the exposing of children more frequent, and both the probability and fatality of wars and epidemics will be considerably greater; and these causes will probably continue their operation till the population is sunk below the level of the food; and then the return to comparative plenty will again produce an increase, and, after a certain period, its further progress will again be checked by the same causes.

But without attempting to establish these progressive and retrograde movements in different countries, which would evidently require more minute histories than we possess, and which the progress of civilization naturally tends to counteract, the following propositions are intended to be proved:

1. Population is necessarily limited by the means of subsistence.

2. Population invariably increases, where the means of subsistence increase, unless prevented by some very powerful and obvious checks.

3. These checks, and the checks which repress the superior power of population, and keep its effects on a level with the means of subsistence, are all resolvable into moral restraint, vice, and misery.

The first of these propositions scarcely needs illustration. The second and third will be sufficiently established by a review of the immediate checks to population in the past and present state of society. . . .

Glossary

Acentric—lacking a centromere.

Adaptation—adjustment to environmental conditions by an organism or a population so that it becomes more fit for existence under the prevailing conditions.

Adaptive radiation—the evolution from a common ancestry of morphologically and ecologically divergent types.

Allele—one of a pair or series of alternative forms of a gene, occupying the same locus in homologous chromosomes.

Allesthetic—traits that assume adaptive significance via the sense organs and nervous system of other organisms.

Allopatric—individuals or populations spatially isolated from one another.

Allopolyploid—an organism with more than two sets of chromosomes derived from two or more species by hybridization. At meiosis, synapsis is primarily between homologous chromosomes of like origin.

Ammonites—an extinct group of mollusks related to the living chambered nautilus.

Amphiploid—an allopolyploid.

Analogous—similar in function but different in structure and origin.

Anaphase—the stage in nuclear division during which the daughter chromosomes separate and move from the equatorial plate to the poles of the spindle. It follows metaphase and precedes telophase.

Aneuploid—having a chromosome number that is not an exact multiple of the basic haploid number; heteroploid.

Angiosperm—the flowering plants: a class having seeds enclosed in an ovary.

Anther—the pollen-bearing part of the stamen.

Anthocyanin—any of a class of soluble glucoside pigments of flowers and plants; range in color from red through violet to blue.

Apomixis—asexual reproduction in which the outward appearance of sexual reproduction is retained but no fertilization occurs.

Asexual—any mode of reproduction not involving fertilization, conjugation, or genetic recombination. Progeny have the same genotype as the parent.

Autopolyploid—an organism having more than two homologous sets of chromosomes in its somatic cells and derived from a single parent species.

Autosome—chromosomes other than the sex chromosomes, ordinarily found in equal numbers in both males and females.

Back-cross—the mating of a hybrid to one of the parental types used to produce the hybrid.

Back mutation—the mutation of a mutant gene back to its original state.

Balanced lethals—lethal genes so closely linked that crossing over is rare, the genes remain in repulsion, both homozygotes die, and only the heterozygote survives.

Balanced polymorphism—two or more distinct types of individuals coexisting in the same breeding population, actively maintained by selection.

Chiasma—a visible change in pairing affecting two out of the four chromatids in a tetrad or bivalent in the first meiotic prophase. The point of apparent exchange of partners is the chiasma.

Chromatids—half chromosomes resulting from longitudinal duplication of a chromosome, observable during prophase and metaphase and becoming daughter chromosomes at anaphase.

Chromosome—nucleoprotein bodies in the nucleus, usually constant in number for any given species, and bearing the genes in linear order.

Cline—a geographical gradient in phenotypic traits.

Clone—all the individuals descended from a single individual by asexual reproduction.

Coelom—the body cavity of most higher Metazoa; lined by a distinct epithelium.

Coincidence—the ratio of observed double crossovers to expected double crossovers calculated on the basis of independent occurrence. This ratio is used as a measure of interference in crossing over.

Crossing over—the exchange of corresponding segments between the chromatids of homologous chromosomes. The result is a recombination of genes between two homologous groups of linked genes.

Cytology—the study of the structure, physiology, development, reproduction, and life history of cells.

Deficiency—the absence or deletion of a segment of a chromosome.

Deletion—a deficiency, especially in which an internal chromosomal segment is missing.

Demographic transition—the change from a high birth rate—high death rate society to one with a low birth rate and a low death rate.

Deuterostomia—animal groups in which the blastopore becomes the anus and the mouth is formed *de novo*.

Differential reproduction—reproduction in which different types do not contribute to the next generation in proportion to their numbers.

Diploid—having two sets of chromosomes. Somatic cells of higher plants and animals derived from the fertilized egg are ordinarily diploid in contrast to the haploid gametes.

DNA—deoxyribonucleic acid, the hereditary material in the majority of species.

Dominant—an inherited trait expressed in the phenotype, regardless of whether the gene controlling it is in the heterozygous or the homozygous condition. Thus the dominant trait from one parent is expressed in a hybrid but the recessive trait, though transmitted, is not expressed. Also a group of animals or plants that is pre-eminent in a given region or at a given time.

Doubling dose—the dose, usually of radiation, sufficient to cause a number of mutations equal to that occurring spontaneously.

Duplication—the occurrence of a chromosome segment more than once in the same chromosome or haploid genome.

Dysgenic—tending to be harmful to the hereditary qualities of a species.

Ecological niche—the place occupied by a species in the community structure of which it is a part.

Ecotype—an ecological race whose genotype is adapted to a particular restricted habitat as the result of natural selection. Many plant species have distinct ecotypes on the sea coast, in the desert, or in the mountains.

Effective size of population—the number of individuals in a local breeding population that actually contribute genes to the next generation.

Embryo sac—the mature female gametophyte in higher plants.

Endosperm—the nutritive tissue, typically triploid, arising from double fertilization by the second male nucleus of two of the eight nuclei of the embryo sac.

Enzyme—protein catalyst in living organisms, typically formed from a protein part (apoenzyme) conferring specificity and a nonprotein part (coenzyme) necessary for activity.

Epigamic—promoting the union of gametes.

Epistasis—the suppression of the expression of a gene or genes by other genes not allelic to the genes suppressed. Similar to dominance but involving the interaction of nonallelic genes. Sometimes used to refer to all nonallelic interactions.

Ethology—the study of animal behavior.

Euploid—an exact multiple of the haploid chromosome number.

Eutheria—the placental mammals.

Fertilization—the fusion of gametes to form a zygote.

Finalism—the concept that the world is directed toward a definite purposive goal.

Fitness—the number of offspring left by an individual as compared with the average of the population of which it is a member or compared to individuals of different genotypes.

Flame bulb—a cup-shaped mass of protoplasm bearing a tuft of cilia projecting into the cavity of the cup, found at the closed inner end of a protonephridium.

Founder principle—the concept that, when a small population invades a new area, evolutionary divergence may be hastened not only because of the new and probably different selection pressures but also because, due to sampling, the gene pool of this small group may differ in significant ways from that of the parental population.

Gamete—a sex cell.

Gametogenesis—the formation of gametes.

Gametophyte—the gamete-forming haploid generation in higher plants.

Gene—a Mendelian factor or unit of inheritance that occupies a fixed chromosomal locus, is transmitted in the germ cells, and, interacting with other genes, the cytoplasm, and the environment, controls the development of a character.

Gene flow—the spread of genes from one breeding population to others as the result of migration.

Gene frequency—the proportion between one particular type of allele and the total of all alleles at this locus in a breeding population.

Gene pool—the sum total of the genes in a given breeding population.

Genetic drift—changes in gene frequency in small breeding populations due to random fluctuations.

Genetic isolate—a breeding population not exchanging genes with any other group.

Genetic system—the way in which the genetic material is organized and transmitted from one generation to the next.

Genome—the chromosome complement of a gamete; also, of a zygote.

Genotype—the entire genetic constitution of an organism.

Gynandromorph—an individual with both male and female sectors; a sexual chimaera.

Haploid—having only a single set of chromosomes.

Hardy-Weinberg law—in a large random mating population in the absence of mutation and selection, gene frequencies remain constant.

Hermaphrodite—an individual with functional ovaries and testes.

Heterogametic—producing unlike gametes, especially with regard to the sex chromosomes. Where the male is XY, he is heterogametic.

Heteromorphic—having more than one form.

Heteroploid—having a chromosome number that is not an exact multiple of the basic haploid number; aneuploid.

Heterosis—hybrid vigor.

Heterozygous—having different alleles at one or more loci.

Hexaploid—having six haploid sets of chromosomes.

Homeostasis—a dynamic equilibrium in a biological system.

Homologous—1. similarity of structure due to similar hereditary and developmental origin; 2. chromosomes in which the same gene loci occur in the same sequence.

Homozygous—having any specified gene or genes present in double dose so that the organism breeds true at these particular gene loci.

Inbred—the result of matings between relatives.

Incompatibility—the inability of pollen to fertilize due to failure of the pollen tube to grow normally in the style.

Independent assortment—segregation of one factor pair occurring independently of the segregation of other factor pairs.

Industrial melanism—the appearance of dark or melanistic forms of a species in industrial regions.

Interference—the effect by which the occurrence of one cross-over reduces the probability of another occurring in its vicinity.

Interphase—the "resting" stage, used especially in referring to the phase between the two meiotic divisions.

Intersex—an individual with traits intermediate between those of males and females.

Introgressive hybridization—the addition of genes from one species to the gene pool of another species through hybridization and back-crossing.

Inversion—rotation of a chromosome segment through 180 degrees so that the linear order of the genes is reversed relative to the rest of the chromosome.

Isoalleles—alleles so similar in their effects that special techniques are needed to distinguish between them.

Isolating mechanism—any intrinsic factor that prevents or reduces interbreeding between two populations.

Isomorphic—having similar form.

Lamarckism—usually, the theory of the inheritance of acquired characteristics.

Lethal—a gene or genotype that, when expressed, is fatal to its bearer.

Linkage—the association of genes in inheritance due to their being on the same chromosome. Genes borne on homologous chromosomes belong to the same linkage group.

Locus (pl., loci)—the position of a gene on a chromosome.

Materialism—any theory that considers the nature of the universe to be sufficiently explained by the existence and nature of matter.

Mean—the sum of a group of observations divided by the number in the group.

Mechanist—one who regards the phenomena of nature as the effects of merely mechanical forces.

Megaspore—the larger of the two kinds of haploid spores produced by heterosporous plants. In seed plants the megaspore gives rise to the embryo sac, the female gametophyte.

Meiosis—the reduction divisions during which the chromosome number is reduced from diploid to haploid; two nuclear divisions during which the chromosomes divide only once.

Mendel's laws—segregation and independent assortment.

Metabolism—the sum total of the chemical processes in living cells by which energy is provided, new materials assimilated or synthesized, and wastes removed.

Metamorphosis—a more or less abrupt change in the form of an animal after the embryonic period.

Metanephridia—nephridia (excretory organs) with open inner ends.

Metaphase—the stage of nuclear division during which the chromosomes lie in the equatorial plane of the spindle; after prophase and prior to anaphase.

Microspore—the smaller of the two kinds of haploid spores produced by heterosporous plants. In seed plants the microspore gives rise to the pollen grain, the male gametophyte.

Mitosis—the process by which the nucleus is divided into two daughter nuclei, each with a chromosome complement similar to that of the original nucleus.

Modifying factor—a gene that affects the expression of another nonallelic gene. Often without other known effects.

Monohybrid—a cross involving parents that differ with respect to a single specific gene.

Monosomic—a diploid with one chromosome missing from the chromosome complement.

Multiple alleles—a series of more than two alternative forms of a gene at a single locus.

Multiple factors—two or more pairs of factors with a similar or complementary cumulative effect on a single trait.

Mutagenic—capable of inducing mutations.

Mutation—in the broad sense, any sudden change in the hereditary material, including both "point" or gene mutations and chromosomal rearrangements. In the narrow sense, point mutations only.

Mutation pressure—the continued recurrent production of a gene by mutation, tending to increase its frequency.

Mutation rate—the frequency with which a particular mutation occurs. Also the frequency of all mutations in a given population.

Mutation rate gene—a gene that influences the mutation rate of genes at other loci.

Nephridium—an excretory tubule.

Normal curve—a symmetrical bell-shaped curve often approximated when frequency distributions are plotted from observations on biological materials.

Octoploid—a polyploid with eight haploid sets of chromosomes.

Oöcyte—primary: egg mother cell giving rise by the first meiotic division to the secondary oöcyte and the first polar body. The secondary oöcyte at the second meiotic division gives rise to the ovum and to a second polar body.

Oögonium—a cell giving rise to primary oöcytes by mitosis.

Orthogenesis—evolution more or less continuously in a single direction over a long span of time. Often used with vitalistic implications.

Orthoselection—natural selection acting continuously in the same direction over long periods of time. Often used in place of orthogenesis to avoid implication of vitalism.

Overdominance—the superiority of the heterozygote over both types of homozygotes.

Paracentric—an inversion that does not include the centromere, but is entirely within one arm of the chromosome.

Parthenogenesis—the development of a new individual from a germ cell (usually female) without fertilization. May be either haploid or diploid.

Pericentric—an inversion that includes the centromere; hence both chromosome arms are involved.

Phenocopy—environmentally induced nonhereditary phenotypic imitations of the effects of mutant genes.

Phenotype—the sum total of the observable or measurable characteristics of an organism without reference to its genetic nature.

Photosynthesis—the synthetic metabolism carried on by the chlorophyll-bearing tissues in plants.

Phyletic evolution—evolution by a related group of species within a broad adaptive zone, carried on at moderate rates and without marked change of adaptive type.

Phylogeny—the evolutionary history of a taxonomic group.

Pistil—in flowers, the female portion—the ovary, style, and stigma, collectively.

Pleiotropic—a single gene influencing more than one character.

Polar body—in oögenesis, the smaller cells produced during meiosis that do not develop into functional egg cells.

Polygene—originally associated with a particular theory of quantitative inheritance but now frequently used as a synonym for multiple factor.

Polymorphic—two or more recognizably different sorts of individuals within a single breeding population.

Polyploid—an organism with more than two haploid sets of chromosomes.

Polysaccharide—a molecule formed by the condensation of a number of simple sugar molecules—for example, starch, cellulose.

Polytypic—generally, a species composed of several geographic races or subspecies.

Position effect—change in the effect of a gene due to a change in its position with respect to other genes in the genotype as the result of chromosomal rearrangement.

Preadaptation—a characteristic that enables an organism to be adapted to environmental conditions to which it has not yet been exposed.

Preformation—the concept that the individual is present in miniature in the embryo and that development to adulthood involves growth but not differentiation.

Prophase—the first stage of nuclear division.

Protonephridia—nephridia with closed inner ends.

Protostomia—those animal groups in which the blastopore becomes the mouth.

Pseudoalleles—very closely linked genes, usually affecting the same trait, and showing a mutant phenotype rather than the wild type when in repulsion in heterozygotes.

Pseudocoelom—a body cavity not lined with epithelial cells.

Quantum evolution—relatively rapid evolution involving a major adaptive shift.

Race—a subspecies or a geographical subdivision of a species. A geographically defined group of breeding populations that differs from other similar groups in the frequency of one or more genetically determined traits.

Random mating—the situation when any individual of one sex has an equal probability of mating with any individual of the opposite sex.

Recapitulation—the theory that ontogeny recapitulates phylogeny; that is, that the development of the individual passes through phases resembling the adult forms of its successive ancestors.

Recessive—an inherited trait only expressed in the phenotype when the allele controlling it is in the homozygous condition. Thus a recessive trait is not expressed in a hybrid.

Reciprocal cross—a second cross similar to the first but with the sexes of the parents interchanged.

Repeat—a duplication.

Reproductive isolation—inherent blocks to crosses between members of different breeding populations.

Roentgen (r)—the unit of measurement of dosage for ionizing radiation. Equal to the amount of radiation that in air at STP will produce 2.1×10^9 ion pairs per cubic centimeter or in tissue approximately two ionizations per cubic micron.

Saprophyte—any organism living on dead or decaying organic material.

Segmental allopolyploid—an allopolyploid in which some chromosome segments from the parent species are still homologous.

Segregation—the separation of maternal from paternal chromosomes at meiosis and hence the basis for Mendel's first law.

Semilethal—a gene or genotype that, when expressed, reduces the viability of its bearers to less than half of that of the "normal" or standard type.

Serology—the study through antigen-antibody reactions of the nature and specificity of antigenic materials from different sources.

Sex chromosomes—chromosomes that are particularly involved in sex determination.

Sex reversal—a change in the sexual character of an individual from male to female or vice versa.

Sexual—a mode of reproduction normally involving of fusion of gametes and genetic recombination.

Sexual isolation—reproductive isolation due to a tendency toward homogamic mating.

Sexual selection—selection based on male competition or female choice and responsible for sexual dimorphism.

Solenocyte—a long tubular cell with a flagellum at the base of the tube that extends into the tube and forms the closed end of a protonephridial tubule.

Somatic—referring to the body tissues, as contrasted with the germinal tissues that give rise to the germ cells.

Speciation—the process by which new species are formed. In the restricted sense, the splitting of one species into a number of different contemporaneous species.

Spermatid—the haploid cell that results from meiosis and develops into a functional spermatozoan without further nuclear division.

Spermatocyte—primary: a sperm mother cell giving rise by the first meiotic division to two secondary spermatocytes. The secondary spermatocytes at the second meiotic division give rise to four haploid spermatids.

Spermatogonium—a cell giving rise to primary spermatocytes by mitosis.

Spontaneous generation—the direct formation of living organisms from nonliving matter.

Sporophyte—the spore-forming diploid generation in higher plants.

Stamen—in flowers, the male portion—the anther containing the pollen plus the filament or stalk.

Standard deviation—the square root of the sum of the deviations from the mean squared and divided by one less than the number of observations. A measure of the variability of a population of individuals.

Standard error—the standard deviation divided by the square root of the number of observations. A measure of the variation of a population of means.

Subspecies—*see* Race.

Subvital—a gene or genotype that, when expressed, reduces the viability of its bearers significantly below that of the "normal" or standard type but has a viability at least half as great.

Supervital—a gene or genotype that, when expressed, is significantly more viable than the "normal" or standard type.

Sympatric—coexisting in the same area, with the implication that crossing is at least possible.

Synapsis—the pairing of homologous chromosomes of maternal and paternal origin during the first meiotic prophase. Also observed occasionally in somatic cells—for example, salivary gland chromosomes in *Drosophila*.

Systematics—taxonomy. The classification of organisms.

Systemic mutation—mutations of major effect presumed to give rise to new species or higher categories at a single step.

Teleology—the concept that evolution is purposeful and is directed toward some definite goal.

Telophase—the last phase of nuclear division, following anaphase, during which the daughter nuclei are formed and separate cells are formed.

Test cross—a cross between a presumed heterozygote and a recessive homozygote.

Tetraploid—a polyploid with four haploid sets of chromosomes.

Transduction—genetic recombination in bacteria mediated by bacteriophage.

Transformation—genetic recombination in bacteria brought about by the addition of DNA from a different strain to the culture.

Transient polymorphism—temporary polymorphism observed while one adaptive type is replacing another.

Translocation—change in position of a chromosome segment to another part of the same chromosome or to a different chromosome. Reciprocal—the exchange of segments between two chromosomes.

Triploid—a polyploid with three haploid sets of chromosomes.

Trisomic—an organism, otherwise diploid, that has three chromosomes of one type.

Variance—the mean squared deviation from the mean. The square of the standard deviation.

Vitalism—the concept that living organisms are animated by a vital principle or force distinct from physical forces.

Wild type—the customary phenotype. Also the most frequent allele in wild populations.

Zygote—the cell produced at fertilization by the union of gametes. Also the individual derived from this cell.

Index

Index

411